Introduction
to
Ecological
Biochemistry

Introduction to Ecological Biochemistry

J. B. HARBORNE

Department of Botany
The University of Reading, Reading, England

1977

ACADEMIC PRESS

London · New York · San Francisco

A Subsidiary of Harcourt Brace Jovanovich, Publishers

ACADEMIC PRESS INC. (LONDON) LTD.
24–28 Oval Road,
London NW1

United States Edition published by
ACADEMIC PRESS INC.
111 Fifth Avenue
New York, New York 10003

Library of Congress Catalog Card Number: 77-76679
ISBN: 0-12-324670-9

PRINTED IN GREAT BRITAIN
AT THE SPOTTISWOODE BALLANTYNE PRESS
BY WILLIAM CLOWES AND SONS LIMITED
LONDON, COLCHESTER AND BECCLES

PREFACE

The last decade has witnessed the growth of a new interdisciplinary subject, variously termed ecological biochemistry, chemical ecology or phytochemical ecology, which is concerned with the biochemistry of plant and animal interactions. Its development has been due in no small measure to the increasingly successful identifications of organic molecules in microquantities, following the application of modern chemical techniques to biological systems. It has also been due to the awareness of ecologists that chemical substances—and particularly secondary metabolites such as alkaloids, flavonoids and terpenoids—have a significant role in the complex interactions occurring between animal and animal, animal and plant or plant and plant in the natural environment. A further stimulation has been the possible applications of such new information in the control of insect pests and of microbial diseases in crop plants and in the conservation of natural communities. The present text is intended as an introduction to these new developments in biochemistry that have so enormously expanded our knowledge of plant and animal ecology.

Much has been written in symposia proceedings on plant-animal interactions and some of the present material has been adapted from such works. Two publications which have been drawn on extensively are "Chemical Ecology" (1972) edited by the late E. Sondheimer and J. B. Simeone and "Phytochemical Ecology" (1972) edited by the author. Two other valuable books which should be consulted by all interested in the topics discussed here are "Insect-Plant Relationships" (1973) edited by H. F. van Emden and "Co-evolution of Animals and Plants" (1975) edited by L. E. Gilbert and P. H. Raven. The choice of selection of examples to illustrate various interactions has been difficult and many interesting studies have had to be omitted for reasons of space. Other topics such as the biochemistry of plant parasitism have been omitted because present knowledge is still fragmentary. However, no doubt, a more coherent story will be available in this and other areas of present research by the time a new edition may be called for.

The present text is based on a course taught by the author over a number of years. It has been planned so that it is suitable for second or third year University teaching in departments of botany, biochemistry and biological sciences. Because of its interdisciplinary content, it should be an especially useful course in those Universities which offer combined Honours degrees in Botany and Zoology. It is also hoped that the book will be of more general value as a simple introduction to a new subject area.

The author is grateful to Dr Miriam Rothschild for her introductory Foreword. By her own pioneering experiments with aposematic insects and equally her encouragement of other scientists, Dr Rothschild has contributed more than anyone else to this new subject and this book owes much to her example. The author is also particularly indebted to Professor Tony Swain for his many valuable comments on the first draft of this book. Other colleagues have helped in many matters, including Drs Roy Snaydon and Christine Williams and Mrs Audrey Wooldridge. Finally, he is grateful to the staff of Academic Press for their interest and encouragement and for organizing such rapid publication.

July, 1977   *Jeffrey B. Harborne*
Plant Science Laboratories
The University of Reading

FOREWORD

Science, says François Jacob, attempts to confront the possible with the actual, and by so doing must inevitably renounce a unified world concept. Jeffrey Harborne puts this to rights in one corner of the biological and biochemical fields, and that is perhaps the main reason why one is so wholeheartedly delighted with his book. We have all been waiting impatiently for a synthesis fusing plant/insect relationships with their ecological biochemistry, but in addition to the welcome unification of the underlying theme, the subject matter is presented with felicitous directness and simplicity. We are given a masterly *überblick*, so that with a sigh of appreciation and relief we know for the first time not only where we are, but also the lines along which we should now proceed. Although the complicated and tangled subject matter is presented in a straightforward fashion, with perspicacious sifting and appraisal of the evidence, without frills and in a logical and scientific manner, there is still a romantic undertone which reveals the author as a fine and enthusiastic naturalist as well as a laboratory investigator.

Curiously enough, one of the first attempts to link the fields of entomology and plant chemistry in the modern sense was initiated by field naturalists (British Empire builders in fact)—their imagination fired by the evolutionary implications of the theory of warning coloration and mimicry among butterflies. It was their infectious enthusiasm and ebullient writing, now often dismissed as "anecdotal", which first encouraged me to investigate the chemistry of Lepidoptera/plant relationships. The observations of C. F. M. Swynnerton were particularly enthralling and it was tragic that the vast piles of notes he had accumulated by virtue of his drive and tireless energy, could not be satisfactorily decoded when he died suddenly in the prime of life. In 1915 he published an account of feeding experiments (in Africa) with butterflies as prey and woodhoopoes, hornbills and babblers as predators, which showed without doubt that Danaids, unlike their mimics, were toxic species. He also demonstrated unequivocally that taste and odour, as well as the chemical ingredients producing emesis in his captive birds, were deterrent qualities possessed by these butterflies. His description of the manner in which a parent bird, who had swallowed the nauseating insect, tried to dissuade its young from eating it was wholly delightful and telling. We are awaiting further research into bird vision and behaviour in this field.

Simultaneously, E. B. Poulton, who encouraged Swynnerton in his experimentation and astute observations, and had an encyclopaedic knowledge of the field, came to the conclusion after evaluating the theories of Haase, Wallace, Müller, Meldola and Slater that these authors' speculations were justified: aposematic butterflies and moths, the larvae of which feed on poisonous plants, can derive protective toxins from their foliage and serve as models for innocuous species. He began to agitate for chemical proof of these theories. It was necessary, perhaps, that such proof should be provided by a combined biochemist and botanist, but no such individual materialized until 50 years later when T. Reichstein, whose knowledge of the chemistry of Asclepiad and Aristolochic plants was enormous, turned his attention to the Danaids and Papilios which fed upon them. In the meantime, however, Jane van Z. Brower had made a great step forward, with an impeccable series of laboratory experiments proving that mimicry really worked. Further important observations of hers (later emphasized and elaborated in a series of joint papers with Lincoln Brower) were that mimics as well as models are somewhat distasteful to predators, and that the disagreeable experience produced by the plant toxins stored by a butterfly model leave a lasting impression on the predators. However it was T. Reichstein's matchless and trustworthy chemistry which suddenly floodlit the scene and linked the herbivores and their host plants in a biochemical synthesis.

In a sense this scene had already been set by Gottfried Frankel's intuitive interpretation of the protective role of secondary plant substances, which in turn inspired Ehrlich and Raven to produce their memorable paper on the co-evolution of plants and butterflies. The field naturalists who provided the basic observations which made their synthesis possible, in particular Sevastopulo, van Someren and Carcasson, must not be forgotten. It is a curious facet of modern science that these authors actually experienced difficulty in publishing their invaluable lists of food-plant records. Also all of those interested in Danaid ecological chemistry were fortunate in having to hand the knowledge accumulated and published by F. A. Urquhart on the general biology, life-style and migrating habits of the Monarch.

We are now entering on a period when undreamed of subtle adjustments between plant and insect become apparent—thus the ovipositing female Monarch selects for preference those species of *Asclepias* as food plants, from which the larvae can best assimilate and store the toxic secondary plant substances; the mimics of certain Danaids not only resemble the models in appearance but secrete chemicals which mimic the cardioactivity of cardenolides.

Reichstein's identification of ten cardiac glycosides in both *D. plexippus* and its food plant seemed to be the spark which ignited a small conflagration, for up to 1966 there was really relatively little interest in the co-evolution of plant and insect biochemistry. Such an explosion of interest—*embarras de richesse*—leaves the scene in some sort of confusion, and we can now be grateful to Jeffrey Harborne for drawing the scattered pieces of the jigsaw together, thereby achieving a synthesis, richly flavoured with his own original ideas and lucid interpretations.

One of the most stimulating aspects of this book is the many doors he deliberately leaves ajar. It is all too easy when reviewing an intricate field to give a student new to the area the feeling that everything is now known about the subject. This book has exactly the reverse effect on the reader: a dozen new ideas spring to mind at the end of each chapter. Although grateful for an integrated and unified survey, particularly because of its intricacies and scattered literature, one is stimulated to take the next step forward and push hard against the nearest door.

Ashton Wold   Miriam Rothschild
Peterborough, England
July, 1977

CONTENTS

1. The Plant and Its Biochemical Adaptation to the Environment

2. Biochemistry of Plant Pollination

3. Plant Toxins and Their Effects on Animals

4. Hormonal Interactions Between Plants and Animals

5. Insect Feeding Preferences

1 | The Plant and Its Biochemical Adaptation to the Environment

I. INTRODUCTION

The marriage between such diverse disciplines as ecology and biochemistry may seem at first a curious alliance. Ecology is largely observational, is concerned with interactions between living organisms in their natural habitats and is carried out in the field. By contrast, biochemistry is experimental, is concerned with interactions at the molecular level and is carried out at the laboratory bench. Nevertheless, these two distinctive disciplines have cross-fertilized in recent years with astonishing success and a whole new area of scientific endeavour has opened up as a result. Ecological biochemistry is only one of a variety of phrases that have been employed to describe these exciting developments.

1

To the ecologist, knowledge of biochemistry has illuminated to a remarkable degree the complex interactions and co-evolutionary adaptations that occur between plant and plant, plant and animal and animal and animal. It has led to the realization, for example, that plants are functionally interdependent with respect to their animal herbivores and form what are termed "plant defense guilds" (Atsatt and O'Dowd, 1976). Similarly, to the biochemist, studies in ecology have provided for the first time a rational and satisfying explanation for at least a part of the enormous proliferation of secondary metabolism that is observed in plants. Much of the purpose of the synthesis of complex molecules of terpenoids, alkaloids and phenolics lies in their use as defense agents in the plant's fight for survival against animal depredation.

The aim, therefore, of the present text is to provide an account for the student reader of the explosive development in ecological biochemistry that has occurred in the last decade. The various chapters deal in turn with the plant and its interactions with animals and with other plants, while animal–animal interactions are considered in some detail in Chapter 7. It should be emphasized at this point that the biochemistry of many interactions has been deliberately simplified here in order to present a coherent story. It must be recognized that a given interaction between a plant host species and its animal predator species can be very subtle and complex and certain aspects of such an interaction may require many years of study before all is revealed.

The term plant is generally used throughout this book to refer to higher plants and mainly to angiosperms, gymnosperms and ferns. Fungi, bacteria and viruses will usually be referred to as micro-organisms; other groups of plants will rarely be mentioned—i.e. algae, mosses and liverworts—largely because their ecological biochemistry has not yet been studied in much detail.

The selection of animals mentioned in this text is restricted to those taxa that have been studied experimentally and is certainly very unrepresentative of the Animal Kingdom as a whole. This is because plant–animal interactions in terms of feeding and defense have largely centred on the insect kingdom and only more recently have biochemical aspects of mammalian ecology been explored to any extent.

The emphasis here on the plant is due, at least in part, to the fact that plants are richer than animals in their biochemical diversity. Although secondary metabolism occurs in animals (Luckner, 1972), nevertheless, over four-fifths of all presently known natural products are of plant origin (Robinson, 1975; Swain, 1974). Some idea of the range of secondary compounds found in plants can be obtained from Table 1.1, which lists some of the major classes, together with an indication of numbers of known compounds, distribution patterns and biological activities. Many of these substances will be mentioned in more detail in subsequent chapters. The richness in secondary chemistry in plants is at least partly explicable in the simple fact that plants are rooted in the soil and cannot move; they cannot respond to the environment in ways open to animals.

Table 1.1 Major classes of secondary plant compounds involved in plant–animal interactions

Class	Approx. number of structures	Distribution	Physiological activity
NITROGEN COMPOUNDS			
Alkaloids	5,500	Widely in angiosperms, especially in root, leaf and fruit	Many toxic and bitter-tasting
Amines	100	Widely in angiosperms, often in flowers	Many repellent smelling; some hallucinogenic
Amino acids (non-protein)	400	Especially in seeds of legumes but relatively widespread	Many toxic
Cyanogenic glycosides	30	Sporadic, especially in fruit and leaf	Poisonous (as HCN)
Glucosinolates	75	Cruciferae and ten other families	Acrid and bitter (as isothio-cyanates)
TERPENOIDS			
Monoterpenes	1,000	Widely, in essential oils	Pleasant smells
Sesquiterpene lactones	600	Mainly in Compositae, but increasingly in other angiosperms	Some bitter and toxic, also allergenic
Diterpenoids	1,000	Widely, especially in latex and plant resins	Some toxic
Saponins	500	In over 70 plant families	Haemolyse blood cells
Limonoids	100	Mainly in Rutaceae, Meliaceae and Simaroubaceae	Bitter tasting
Cucurbaticins	50	Mainly in Cucurbitaceae	Bitter tasting and toxic
Cardenolides	150	Especially common in Apocynaceae, Asclepiadaceae and Scrophulariaceae	Toxic and bitter
Carotenoids	350	Universal in leaf, often in flower and fruit	Coloured
PHENOLICS			
Simple phenols	200	Universal in leaf, often in other tissues as well	Anti-microbial
Flavonoids	1,000	Universal in angiosperms, gymnosperms and ferns	Often coloured
Quinones	500	Widely, especially Rhamnaceae	Coloured
OTHER			
Polyacetylenes	650	Mainly in Compositae and Umbelliferae	Some toxic

In this first chapter, attention is focused on biochemical adaptation. In its widest sense, this topic continues in later chapters, but here, it is taken in the narrower sense as adaptation to the physical environment. Attention is deliberately restricted to the plant kingdom, where information on biochemical adaptation is only of recent origin. Much is known about biochemical adaptation in animals and the subject is well documented in textbooks on comparative biochemistry (e.g. Baldwin, 1937; Florkin and Mason, 1960–1964). A useful reference to recent developments in the subject of biochemical adaptation of animals to environmental change is that of Smellie and Pennock (1976).

Adaptation represents the flexibility of a living organism to fit into a changing environment, at the same time improving its chances of survival and ultimately of reproducing itself. The extensive diversity of life forms on this Planet (i.e. several million species) and their presence in every type of habitat are witness to the view that living organisms indeed are morphologically and anatomically adapted to their environments. Such ideas are fundamental to the Darwinian view of nature and have been supported by much experimentation during the last century. Ideas of physiological and biochemical adaptation came later, during the 1920s and 1930s, with the experimental development of these two subjects. It is only, however, very recently that biochemical aspects have been developed sufficiently with plants to warrant their separate consideration, as in this present chapter.

Adaptation is generally considered as occurring on an extensive time-scale, involving many generations, but it can also take place during the lifetime of an individual, when it is sometimes termed acclimatization. The term adaptation is used here largely in the evolutionary sense. Biochemical adaptation is particularly closely connected to physiological adaptation and indeed it is sometimes difficult to distinguish the two. Physiological adaptation in plants will be considered here where appropriate; for a comprehensive account, see Levitt (1972).

Biochemical adaptation can operate at different levels in metabolism. It may affect the enzymes and produce amino acid substitutions in the primary sequence of protein or else alter the balance of isozymes. It may affect intermediary metabolism; an example in the case of the carbon pathway in photosynthesis is mentioned later. Finally, it may affect secondary metabolism; this is especially true of the plant's adaptation to animal feeding.

The environmental factors that plants are subject to can be broadly divided into five types:

(1) *Climatic factors.* These include temperature, light intensity, daylength, moisture and seasonal effects.
(2) *Edaphic factors.* All plants, except epiphytes and parasites, obtain their mineral nutrition through the soil. The soil is also the source of symbiotic

microbes, e.g. those required by legumes and other nitrogen-fixing plant species. Through contact with the soil, plants may have to cope with toxic heavy metals or with excess salinity. Equally, they may be subject to biochemical stress due to mineral deficiency in the soil.

(3) *Unnatural pollutants*. These are distributed through the upper atmosphere (ozone, industrial gases, gasoline fumes) or through the environment (organic pesticides) and may be potentially toxic to many plants.

(4) *Animals*. Although there is an element of symbiosis in animal feeding, herbivores are primarily hostile to plants, since they depend on them for their very existence. Many different defense adaptations are known in plants. An element of symbiosis is also present in the case of those animals which visit plants for the purpose of pollination (see Chapter 2).

(5) *Competition from other plants*. This can be either competition between different higher plants or between different forms of plant life, e.g. higher plants and micro-organisms.

In this chapter, we are concerned only with the first three factors: the climate, the soil, and unnatural pollutants. Biochemical adaptation to animal predation and biochemical interactions between plants will be the subject matter of later chapters in this book.

II. THE BIOCHEMICAL BASES OF ADAPTATION TO CLIMATE

A. General

Anatomical and morphological adaptation of plants to different climatic factors is well known and indeed its study is a major part of the science of plant ecology. Everyone is familiar with the ways that desert cacti and succulents are adapted to their parched habitats and are able to reduce moisture loss under the scorching desert sun. This is done by extending the area of soil for water uptake, by reduction of water loss through the leaf or by increased water storage in the tissues. Situations where biochemical features are involved in climatic adaptation are less often considered or discussed. Nevertheless, there is a growing awareness of the need to explore biochemical aspects, from the practical viewpoint.

In recent years, there has been much study of the hormonal control, through the sesquiterpenoid abscisic acid, of moisture loss from plants by stomatal closure. There is practical incentive here in the need to develop drought-resistant crop varieties for growing in marginal desert areas of the world. In Israel, for example, plant scientists are working on the development of agricultural crops which will grow successfully in areas of the Negev desert. Conversely, plants may have to adapt to excess moisture and something is now known of the adaptation of intermediary metabolism to the flooding of plant roots. Also, plants growing in frost conditions undergo biochemical changes in their sap constituents. Perhaps the most dramatic example of long term bio-chemical adaptation to climate discovered in recent years is of the special photosynthetic pathway that tropical plants appear to have developed in response to hot and arid conditions. All these topics will be discussed in more detail in the following sections.

B. Photosynthesis in Tropical Plants

It has been apparent since the experiments of Warburg (1920) on O_2 inhibition of photosynthesis that temperate plants, when subjected to high temperatures (as on a hot summer's day), do not show the expected increase in photo-synthetic rate with temperature that theoretically should occur. Their efficiency in incorporating atmospheric CO_2 into respiratory sugar is limited by carbon loss from the well-known Calvin carbon cycle via phosphoglyceric acid and glycollate (see Fig. 1.1) so that a proportion of the CO_2 originally absorbed by the plant is lost by "photorespiration" at the leaf surface. Such losses in CO_2 conversion to sugar, due to O_2 inhibition, are not too serious since high temperatures are relatively infrequent in temperate latitudes. Such losses could, however, be much more considerable in plants growing in the tropics.

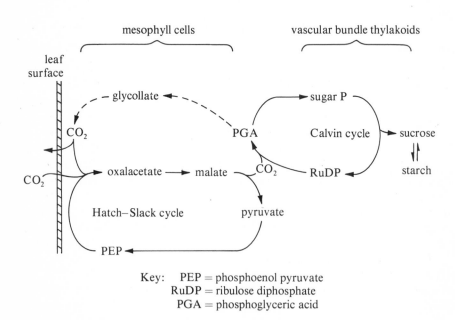

Key: PEP = phosphoenol pyruvate
RuDP = ribulose diphosphate
PGA = phosphoglyceric acid

Fig. 1.1 The Hatch–Slack modification of the carbon pathway of photosynthesis

Evidence that tropical plants such as sugar-cane are able to resist inhibition by high partial pressures of O_2 and are able to photosynthesize efficiently in hot climates has only become available very recently. These new discoveries have shown that such plants differ biochemically from temperate species (Hatch and Slack, 1970; Bjorkman and Berry, 1973). When leaves of sugar-cane are exposed to $^{14}CO_2$ for a few seconds, the first compounds labelled are not those of the Calvin cycle but are C_4 acids. Such plants have a modified pathway of carbon, which includes a new cyclic system, called the Hatch–Slack pathway, which transports CO_2 from the leaf surface to the Calvin cycle (Coombs, 1971). Plants with this so-called Hatch–Slack pathway in effect collect the CO_2 which would otherwise be lost by "photorespiration" and "drive it back" into the Calvin cycle to be converted to sucrose (Fig. 1.1). Such tropical plants are called C_4 plants (after the four-carbon acids involved in the Hatch–Slack pathway) to distinguish them from the more usual C_3 plants which only have the simple Calvin cycle.

This modification in biochemistry is correlated with anatomical differences; plants with the C_4 pathway have special mesophyll cells, in which the pathway is located, beside the bundle sheath cells, where the Calvin cycle operates. The anatomical differentiation of C_4 plants was recognized long before their distinctive biochemistry was elucidated, the anatomical features of such tropical species being described as the Kranz syndrome. Besides recognizing C_4 plants by anatomical observations, it is possible to identify them by determining the relative uptakes of $^{13}CO_2$ and $^{12}CO_2$ by these plants. This ratio is measured in the carbon fixed by the plant as sucrose and can even be determined in dead tissue, i.e. in herbarium specimens. The relative $^{13}C/^{12}C$ ratio in C_4 plants is between -9 and -18, while in C_3 plants it lies between -21 and -38.

The Hatch–Slack pathway was first recognized in sugar-cane, *Saccharum officinale,* a member of the grass family, Gramineae. Subsequent investigations have shown that the majority of tropical and subtropical grasses in the subfamilies Eragrastoideae, Panicoideae and Arundinoideae have this pathway (Brown, 1975). The ability to achieve optimal photosynthesis under tropical conditions is by no means restricted to grasses and at least ten other families with tropical members contain it. They include the Cyperaceae, Compositae, Euphorbiaceae, Zygophyllaceae and several families of the Centrospermae. In Cyperaceae, the distribution of C_4 plants is correlated with taxonomy; the character occurs exclusively in the tribes Cypereae and Fimbristylideae of the Cyperoideae (Raynal, 1973). In general, plants with the C_4 pathway are exclusively herbaceous and it is fairly clear that it is an advanced evolutionary condition compared to C_3 plants.

An outline of the path of carbon in plants which are adapted to tropical climates is shown in Fig. 1.1. Essentially, the purpose of the Hatch–Slack

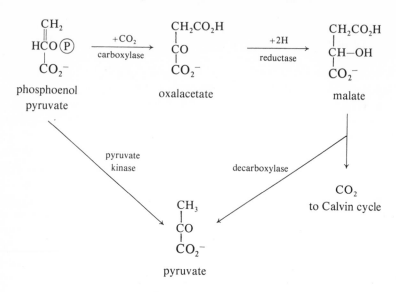

Fig. 1.2 Chemistry of the C_4 pathway

pathway is to transport CO_2 from the outside surface of the leaf to the actual site of photosynthesis in the inner chloroplast. The CO_2 is first combined with phosphoenol pyruvate (PEP) (Fig. 1.2) to give oxalacetate which is then reduced to malate, which in turn is decarboxylated to pyruvate. The CO_2 released at this stage enters the Calvin cycle by combining with ribulose-diphosphate to give phosphoglyceric acid, the first C_3 organic compound of the Calvin pathway. Most of the enzymes required in the C_4 pathway are already present in all plant species, the only really distinctive enzyme being pyruvate kinase which regenerates PEP from pyruvate to complete the cycle (Fig. 1.2). However, there is evidence that other forms (or isozymes) of the enzymes common to both C_3 and C_4 plants are required to make the C_4 pathway function most efficiently. Equally important for the success of C_4 plants is the rearrangement of the cells and membranes which allow the translocation of C_4 acids and of pyruvate between the two types of cells.

One final point may be made about C_4 plants: it is possible that adaptation to retain photosynthetic efficiency in the tropics may have additional benefit in providing resistance to herbivores. There is at least some circumstantial evidence that herbivores, and particularly grasshoppers, avoid eating C_4 plants if given a free choice between both C_3 and C_4 plants (Caswell *et al.*, 1973). The reason for this may be simply due to the anatomical modifications reflected in The Kranz syndrome. Thus, the starch in C_4 plants is located further away from the leaf surface and hence is less accessible to feeders. The bundle sheaths of C_4 plants also seem to be relatively tough and in grasses at least lignin content seems to be much higher in C_4 than in C_3 plants. Finally, there is evidence that the availability of nitrogen in C_4 plants is less than that in C_3 plants.

C. Adaptation to Freezing

Many plants and animals have the ability to resist and survive the below zero temperatures which they may be subjected to during winter months in northern temperate and arctic regions of the world. In insects, there is evidence that freezing tolerance is achieved fairly simply by the synthesis of glycerol (see Fig. 1.3), which acts as an anti-freeze, exactly as ethylene glycol, $CH_2OH—CH_2OH$, does in water-cooled car engines. In higher plants, adaptation to freezing conditions seems to be more complex than this (Levitt, 1972). There is little doubt however that freezing tolerance is correlated with an increase of sugar content in the cell sap. Experiments show also that the ability to withstand frost can be achieved artificially by infiltrating plants with sugars.

The sugars identified in frost-resistant plants vary from plant to plant. They are often the three common sugars—glucose, fructose and sucrose—with or without oligosaccharides such as raffinose. Polyhydric alcohols such as mannitol, sorbitol and glycerol (see Fig. 1.3) which presumably could act directly as anti-freeze agents, are less frequently reported. However, all three have been found in significant amount (up to 40% total sugars) in plants such as gardenia, apple, mountain ash and pomegranate (Sakai, 1960; see also Sakai, 1961; Sakai and Yoshida, 1968).

Whether sugars play a crucial role in resistance to freezing in plants is not yet clear. They appear to be involved in freezing tolerance in at least two ways. First, by their osmotic effect, they decrease the amount of ice formed in the vacuole. Secondly, by their metabolic effect, by being converted in the protoplasm to other constituents, they have an additional protective role.

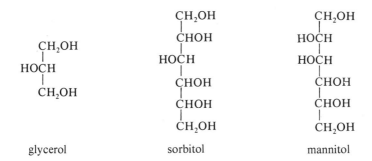

Fig. 1.3 Structures of polyhydric alcohols

Whether these changes involve conversion of common sugars to polyhydric alcohols or whether more complex biochemistry is involved is not yet known.

D. Adaptation to Flooding

A number of plant species are able to grow in areas, e.g. in the flat plains of glaciated river valleys, where their root systems are subjected to flooding. Indeed, some plants may spend up to half the year with their roots and lower stems immersed in water; the rest of the year the conditions are distinctly drier. Thus, they may have to regularly re-adapt their metabolism to wet and dry conditions at six monthly intervals during the life-cycle. Species where this happens include the flag iris, *Iris pseudacorus* and the soft rush, *Juncus effusus*. The ability to tolerate flooding may even vary within species: both tolerant and non-tolerant races of groundsel, *Senecio vulgaris*, can be distinguished.

Such plants may have to modify the respiratory pathway in their root systems to survive the change from aerobic to semi-anaerobic conditions as a result of flooding. That such adaptation occurs has been demonstrated by Crawford and his co-workers (1967, 1968, 1970) who have found that under anaerobic conditions, there is a significant accumulation of several metabolites, usually only present as trace constituents. Thus, roots of *Iris pseudacorus* during winter flooding contain exceptionally high levels of shikimic acid, but only trace amounts occur in summer when the roots are aerobic. Roots of the rush *Juncus effusus,* similarly accumulate malate during flooding, one possible reason for this accumulation being the absence from the roots of malic enzyme, which normally converts malate to pyruvate. A third product, glycerol, accumulates in roots of the alder, *Alnus incana,* during flooding (Crawford, 1972); five-fold increases in concentration occur within 8 days of the onset of flooding.

In plants which lack the ability to tolerate flooding (e.g. *Senecio squalidus*) anaerobic breakdown of sugar leads to the production of phosphoenol pyruvate, which in turn increases acetaldehyde accumulation in the roots (Fig. 1.4). Increased levels of alcohol dehydrogenase are induced and this leads to the accumulation of ethanol, which is highly toxic to plant life, and kills the plant. It is clear that in an adapted plant, such as *Iris*, the phosphoenol pyruvate is shunted into shikimic acid, which is also formed directly from sugar via erythrose 4-phosphate (Fig. 1.4); no accumulation of alcohol is then possible. Similarly in another tolerant plant like *Juncus effusus*, excess pyruvate is channelled to malate instead of going to alcohol. Thirdly, in *Alnus,* the glycolytic pathway is interrupted and glycerol is formed at the expense of pyruvate. When this happens, the plant actually shows a gain in net ATP, due to regeneration of ATP from ADP during the conversion of glycerol 1-phosphate to glycerol.

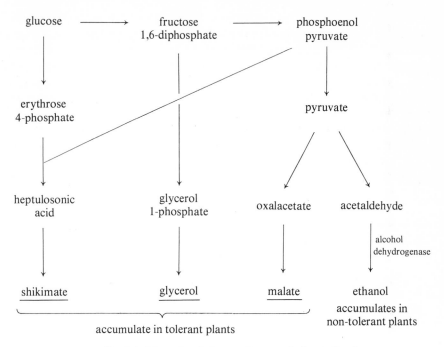

Fig. 1.4 Adaptations in intermediary metabolism to flooding

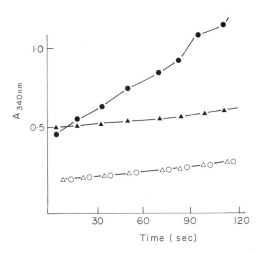

Fig. 1.5 Reduction of NAD to NADH due to alcohol dehydrogenase activity in root extracts of flooded and unflooded *Zea mays* (●, ▲) and *Leavenworthia uniflora* (○, △)

A simple but elegant demonstration that metabolic adaptation to flooding occurs in a particular plant species has been provided by Baskin and Baskin (1976). They compared the umbellifer *Leavenworthia uniflora* which is a winter annual, restricted to shallow, limestone soils which are waterlogged from autumn to the spring, with maize which is intolerant to flooding. They measured alcohol dehydrogenase levels by means of the UV absorption at 340 nm which increases when the enzyme cofactor NAD is converted to NADH (Fig. 1.5). Flooding in *Zea mays* caused a large increase in alcohol dehydrogenase content of the roots but similar flooding in *Leavenworthia* did not increase enzyme levels appreciably.

In summary then, the failure of flood tolerant plants to develop high levels of alcohol dehydrogenase as a consequence of anaerobis contributes to their homeostatic survival under conditions of a high water table; this ineffectiveness is expressed in the accumulation of intermediary metabolites such as glycerol, malate or shikimate which are not hostile, like ethanol, to the plant system.

E. Adaptation to Drought

Plants which grow in areas of low rainfall often tolerate drought and are termed xerophytes. Such plants of desert or high plateau areas of the world adapt to drought by morphological or anatomical means. For example, cacti have thick waxy coatings and their pincushion shape helps to minimize water loss by evaporation.

Plants which resist drought have been broadly divided into two groups: those which conserve water and those which have an increased ability to absorb water (Levitt, 1972). The latter mechanism is largely physiological, while the former has a biochemical element. Thus, one way of conserving water is to reduce the time when the leaf stomata are open or to only open the stomata at night time. The hormone abscisic acid causes stomatal closure and there is circumstantial evidence that drought resistant plants contain larger amounts of this important hormone. In addition, it has been found that the content of abscisic acid can increase as much as forty-fold within 4 hr of wilting in wheat plants; the level continues to rise in such osmotically-stressed plants for at least 48 hr after wilting induction (Wright and Hiron, 1969; Milborrow and Noddle, 1970).

The effect of abscisic acid is reversible and the hormone drops to normal low levels when the water supply is replenished. There is evidence that the abscisic acid produced during wilting is not subsequently degraded but instead is stored in inactive form in the leaf and presumably becomes available to the plant if another period of water stress is imposed on it. In the control of stomatal closure, abscisic acid can be replaced by at least three related oxygenated sesquiterpenes (Fig. 1.6). In particular, phaseic acid and *trans-*

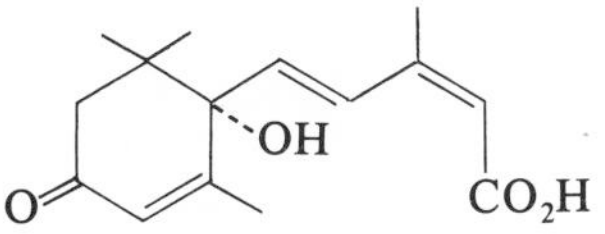

abscisic acid

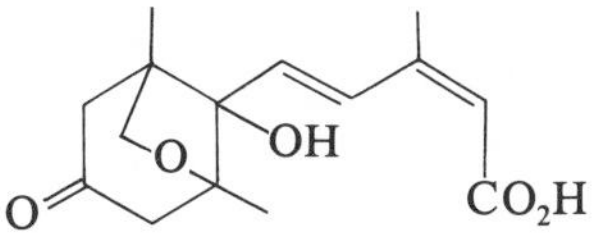

phaseic acid

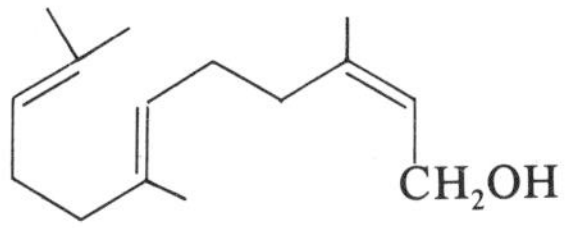

trans-farnesol

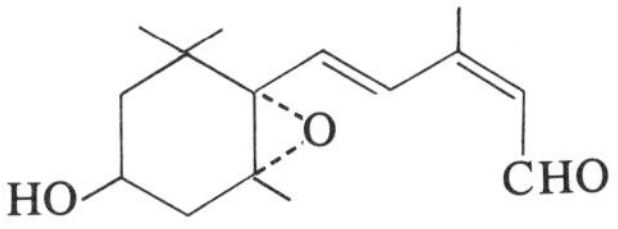

xanthoxin

Fig. 1.6 Sesquiterpenoids capable of initiating stomatal closure in plants

farnesol have been shown to produce stomatal closure in *Vitis vinifera* and *Sorghum* respectively (Loveys and Kriedemann, 1974; Wellburn *et al.*, 1974). The exogenous application of abscisic acid to plant leaves should theoretically have practical benefits in reducing transpiration and hence the amount of water needed by a given crop. Unfortunately, it would be very expensive in that relatively large amounts of hormone are needed to be effective and in view of the rapid turnover of this substance when applied externally to crop plants.

Another set of biochemical observations on water-stressed plants indicates that proline accumulates during adaptation. Indeed, a comparison of drought resistant and susceptible varieties within a species has shown consistently higher levels of proline in the former than in the latter. Production of increased proline levels is so regular in barley that it is possible to use proline concentration for scoring varieties for their ability to resist drought (Singh *et al.*, 1972). The proline increase is usually such that about 30% of the free amino acid pool is made up of this imino acid. In actual figures, an increase to 1·2 mg/g dry wt has been recorded in water-stressed Bermuda grass, *Cynodon dactylon*. The increase in proline could be simply a symptom of some more fundamental adaptation to water stress. It is also possible that proline itself, because of its special osmotic properties, is able to contribute directly to the retention of water in the plant and hence to drought resistance (see also the role of proline in halophyte adaptation, p. 18).

III. BIOCHEMICAL ADAPTATION TO THE SOIL

A. Selenium Toxicity

Selenium is an element in the same group six of the periodic table as sulphur but unlike sulphur it is not usually essential to plants. Because of its close similarity in properties to sulphur, it can substitute for sulphur in biochemical systems. It is this ability to exchange with sulphur and become incorporated into amino acids and further into protein, as selenoprotein, which is the basis of its toxic properties. In any quantity selenium is thus highly toxic to all living organisms.

Selenium occurs mainly in soils in bound form so that it is not normally a hazard to plant life. There are, however, areas of the world where unusually high levels of soluble selenium are present in the soil and are taken up by plants. These include pasture lands in central Asia, Australia and North America. The effects of these high levels of selenium are revealed in toxic symptoms in grazing animals. The toxicity is expressed in both acute and chronic forms and continued ingestion leads to death. One of the symptoms of toxicity in sheep is the falling out of the woolcoat, with the production of bald patches. Human fatalities have also been recorded. However, it was not until the 1930s that serious attempts were made to investigate this phenomenon. The cause of the toxicity was traced to the ability of certain plants to adapt to selenium by accumulation of the element and it was ingestion of these plants which caused the death of cattle and sheep (Rosenfeld and Beath, 1964).

Many of the plants which have adapted to high levels of available selenium in the soil belong to the legume genus *Astragalus* and most work has been done with these plants. Of the some 500 species of *Astragalus* in the North American flora, some 25 species have adapted to selenium and are called selenium-accumulators, as distinct from non-adapted plants which avoid such areas and are called non-accumulators. The ability of accumulators such as *A. bisulcatus* and *A. pectinatus* to sequester selenium is remarkable; such plants have as much as 5,000 ppm selenium, compared to non-accumulators which have less than 5 ppm. The dangerous nature of these plants to other life forms can be realized from experiments in which toxic symptoms have been recorded in *Trifolium* plants treated with 5 ppm and in grazing animals fed on a diet containing as little as 1 ppm selenium (Shrift, 1969, 1972).

The question now arises—how have these plants been able to absorb so much selenium without any damage to themselves? The answer appears to lie in the ability of accumulators to separate inorganic sulphur (as sulphate) from inorganic selenium (as selenate or selenite) as they enter the plant and to channel the selenium into the synthesis of non-protein amino acid analogues (Fig. 1.7). These amino acids are structurally different from the two standard protein sulphur amino acids, cysteine and methionine, and are not therefore incorporated into protein synthesis. The plant then presumably sequesters them in the vacuole of the leaf and they are perfectly harmless to the plant but, of course, intensely harmful to any unsuspecting grazing animals.

By contrast, the absorption of soluble selenium from the soil into non-adapted plants follows a parallel but fatal pathway, shown in Fig. 1.7, whereby

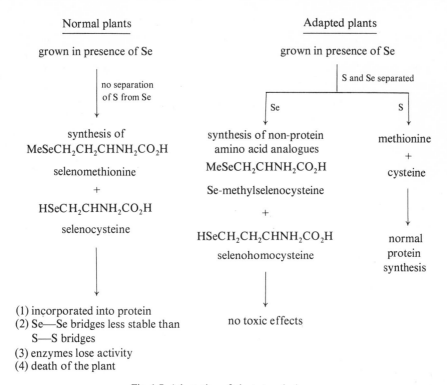

Fig. 1.7 Adaptation of plants to selenium

protein amino acids are synthesized in which sulphur is directly replaced by selenium. While selenocysteine and selenomethionine may possibly be harmful as such, the greatest damage must occur after they are mistaken for sulphur amino acids and are incorporated into enzymic protein. Evidence of incorporation of selenium amino acid into protein has not yet been conclusively demonstrated in plants, but it has been found in the bacterium *Escherichia coli*, grown in the presence of selenomethionine, that as many as 150 methionine residues of the enzyme β-galactosidase can be replaced by the seleno analogue. This large selenoprotein is more unstable than the normal enzyme, probably because the S—S bonds used to hold the polypeptide chains of the protein together are replaced by the more labile Se—Se bonds. Other properties of the seleno-β-galactosidase are also affected and it is not induced as rapidly as the normal enzyme. There is evidence that selenoproteins are ineffective catalysts and their accumulation causes disruption of the metabolic activity of the cell.

The non-protein selenium-containing amino acids synthesized by accumulator *Astragalus* include the two shown in Fig. 1.7 but several others are also found particularly Se-methylcysteine sulphoxide, γ-glutamyl-Se-methyl-cysteine and its sulphoxide. These various acids are found not only in the leaf, but also in the seed and surveys of *Astragalus* for accumulators and non-accumulators can be carried out on the seed amino acids, as well as on those of the leaf (Dunnill and Fowden, 1967). It is possible that accumulator species actually thrive on the presence of selenium salts in the soil. In laboratory experiments with accumulators, it is possible to demonstrate stimulation of growth by adding selenate to the soil. This behaviour is similar to that of some halophytes which grow better in the presence of NaCl than in its absence (see p. 18).

B. Heavy Metal Toxicity

One of the most striking examples of the ability of plants to be selected for and adapt to high concentrations of toxic metals in soils is provided by the way in which grasses such as fine bent *Agrostis tenuis* and Sheep's fescue *Festuca ovina* have rapidly colonized waste tips from heavy metal mining. Some strains of *A. tenuis,* for example, will grow successfully on soils containing as much as 1% lead. Genetic aspects of this phenomenon have been studied among the plant communities in mining areas of North Wales by Bradshaw and his associates (e.g. Gregory and Bradshaw, 1965; Smith and Bradshaw, 1970). Populations tolerant to lead and other heavy metals develop rapidly and it is possible to examine these plants in order to determine the biochemical basis of this tolerance. While the precise mechanism of adaptation is not yet known, there are some clues about the processes involved.

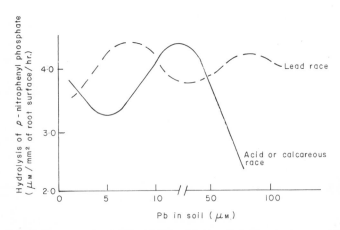

Fig. 1.8 Activities of acid phosphatases in roots of *Agrostis tenuis*

The first point where the ability to deal with toxic amounts of heavy metals is important is at the root surface. That biochemical changes occur here has been demonstrated by Woolhouse (1970), who examined the activities of acid phosphatases present on the roots of *Agrostis tenuis*. His experiments (Fig. 1.8) show that the root surface enzymes are adapted to the high metal concentrations and can function in spite of the high toxic metal content of their environment. Presumably several different forms (or isozymes) of acid phosphatase occur on the root surface and particular forms are selected for by the environment.

The actual mechanism by which the toxic metal is sequestered, assuming it penetrates into the plant, is not entirely clear. One possibility is that specific proteins of the cell wall are able to chelate the different heavy metals and thus deactivate them. This is supported by the differential uptake of radioactive metal observed in roots of tolerant populations of *Agrostis tenuis* and subsequent accumulation of label in the cell wall fraction (Turner and Marshall, 1972).

Plant populations that have become adapted to other heavy metals besides lead are known; thus, there can be tolerance to copper, tin, zinc and nickel. In the case of resistance to copper in *Silene cucubalus*, Schiller (1974) has shown that tolerant races have a greater membrane resistance to the metal and are able to reduce the uptake of copper, if it is supplied in ionic form. On zinc contaminated soils, most plant species develop tolerant races by selection. *Typha latifolia* is unusual in having a built-in resistance to uptake of zinc; clones from zinc soils and normal soils grew equally well when subjected to high zinc levels in pot culture (McNaughton *et al.,* 1974). No cross-tolerance has yet been found, i.e. a strain adapted to lead will be killed if grown in the presence of traces of copper and so on. The ability of certain plants such as those mentioned above to adapt to one or other of these heavy metals has been turned to advantage by man in prospecting for new mine-fields. The use of indicator plants for showing where valuable mineral deposits are present under the soil is now an accepted part of mining techniques. For example, the plant *Eriogonum ovalifolium* is an indicator for silver deposits in Montana, while certain *Astragalus* species are indicators for uranium in Colorado.

C. Adaptation to Salinity

Plants which grow in saline habitats, in salt marshes, salt deserts or on the sea coast, are termed "halophytes". That they have adapted to such conditions of high salinity in the soil is clear when attempts are made to grow nonhalophytes, or glycophytes as they are called, in the presence of increasing amounts of sodium chloride (NaCl). The normal requirement in higher plants for Na in the soil is very low (a few ppm) and toxic symptoms develop quite quickly as soon as this is raised; amounts as low as 0·1% NaCl can be damaging to relatively sensitive glycophytes such as tomatoes, peas and beans. By contrast, true halophytes are resistant to high concentrations of NaCl; indeed presence of 1–2% NaCl may be needed by these plants to stimulate growth. Some halophytes can withstand up to 20% NaCl in the soil, although the levels in most saline soils are lower than this, between 2 and 6% (Levitt, 1972).

Among typical coastal halophytes are such plants as sea thrift, *Armeria maritima* and sea plantain *Plantago maritima* of temperate floras and the mangroves (e.g. *Avicennia*) and sea-grasses (e.g. *Zannichellia*) of tropical coastlines. Desert halophytes include many *Atriplex* species, e.g. *A. halimus* and *A. spongiosa,* and *Suaeda fruticosa*. The definition of a halophyte is not always clear cut and such plants are not necessarily restricted to growing in saline habitats. With glycophytes, there is a degree of variation in response to NaCl stress, some species (e.g. tomatoes, peas) being particularly sensitive and others (e.g. many grasses) being more resistant. Detailed accounts of the ecology and general biology of halophytes are contained in the books of Reimold and Queen (1974) and of Waisel (1972).

Adaptation is by one of three procedures: accumulation of NaCl within the vacuole (*Salicornia* has a 10% NaCl solution in its tissues); resistance to the entry of NaCl into the cell; and dilution of NaCl after its entry into the plant. Biochemical differences, especially in enzyme levels, have been recorded between halophytes and glycophytes but, in fact, none of these differences seems to be associated with the adaptation process. Thus, enzymes of halophytes are not, *in vitro*, more tolerant of high salt concentrations than those of glycophytes. Furthermore, although it is possible to demonstrate stimulation of activity of certain enzymes, e.g. malate dehydrogenase, by adding NaCl (up to 50 mM), such stimulation occurs with enzymes extracted from both halophytes and glycophytes (Flowers *et al.,* 1976). One particular symptom of excess NaCl in the broad bean *Vicia faba* is the accumulation of the diamine putrescine (Strogonov, 1964). This can, however, be explained as an effect of excess Na on limiting the absorption of K by the cell, since K deficiency in a number of plants including the broad bean also causes putrescine to accumulate (Smith, 1965).

Recently, two critical biochemical features of halophytes have been discovered: accumulation of two nitrogen compounds, the protein imino acid proline and the quaternary nitrogen compound, betaine. In the case of proline, concentrations found can be up to ten times the "normal" level present in the free amino acid pool of glycophytes (Stewart and Lee, 1974). In the extreme case of the halophyte *Triglochin maritima*, free proline accumulates in such amount that it represents 10–20% of the shoot dry weight. Other halophytes in which high levels have been found are *Aster tripolium* and *Armeria maritima*. It should be noted, however, that a few halophytes, notably *Plantago maritima*, do not show enhanced proline levels.

The importance of the above observations on proline content has been reinforced by the induction of high levels of this acid in glycophytes by subjecting them artificially with high salt levels (see results with tomatoes in Table 1.2). Indeed, increased levels of proline can be induced in both halophytes and glycophytes by growing them under non-saline conditions and then moving them gradually into increasing salinity. That proline is truly an adaptive response to salinity is suggested by the observation of Stewart and Lee (1974) that inland populations of *Armeria* have a relatively normal proline content (1·4 μmol/g fr. wt) while nearby coastal populations reach a concentration of 26 μmol/g fr. wt.

How such high levels of proline actually provide the basis of resistance to salt accumulation is not known precisely but proline does have valuable osmotic properties so that its presence may enable such plants to withstand the high osmotic forces their cells would otherwise be subjected. This accumulation of proline in halophytes seems to be related to the enhanced levels of proline found in drought resistant plants (see p. 13). Clearly, there may be a common mechanism in adaptation to saline habitats and to extremes of dry climates.

Evidence that the accumulation of aliphatic quaternary ammonium compounds provides plants with relief from NaCl stress has been obtained by Wyn Jones and his collaborators (see e.g. Storey and Wyn Jones, 1977). Most attention has been given to choline, $Me_3N^+CH_2CH_2OH$, and the related acid betaine, $Me_3N^+CH_2CO_2^-$. Both are widespread in plants but while choline has a recognized function as a constituent of membrane lipid, no similar role has been ascribed to betaine. Measurements of the concentration of betaine in plants representing a spectrum of salt sensitivities have shown that increasing the salt stress produces large increases in betaine, without affecting choline levels (Table 1.2). Increases in betaine levels are often accompanied by increases in proline, but there are some exceptions. Thus, while proline levels increase dramatically in the salt-sensitive tomato, the betaine levels are not similarly affected (Table 1.2). Conversely, in the case of the two halophytes chosen for study by Storey and Wyn Jones (1975), betaine levels are significantly raised by high salt concentrations but proline levels do not change.

These data (Table 1.2) indicate that in some ways betaine may be more important than proline in the adjustment of halophytes to NaCl stress. However, as with proline accumulation, there are some halophytes which do not show betaine accumulation. One must therefore assume that there is more than one biochemical mechanism for adaptation to salinity. However, the actual role of betaine in providing osmotic adjustment may well be similar to that of proline. Indeed, a close correlation has been observed between the osmotic pressure of shoots and their betaine content, both when values were compared in a single plant grown at various salinities and when different plant species were compared under similar growth conditions (Wyn Jones *et al.,*

Table 1.2 Betaine and proline levels in plant shoots grown under low and high salt conditions

		mg/100 g fr. wt			
		BETAINE		PROLINE	
		Low	High	Low	High
Plant type	Plant	salt	salt	salt	salt
Salt sensitive					
glycophyte	Tomato	2	2	6·9	72
Salt resistant	Barley "Arimar"	32	158	0·8	22
glycophyte	*Chloris gayana*	25	106	0·6	48
halophyte	*Atriplex spongiosa*	177	246	1·3	2·0
	Suaeda monoica	385	462	5·7	3·7

Data from Storey and Wyn Jones (1975). Similar changes were also noted in root levels. Low salt conditions refer to standard Hoagland's solution, high salt conditions to growth in the presence of from 100 to 500 mM NaCl.

1976). The protective role of both these nitrogen compounds is further emphasized by the fact that neither betaine nor proline has any inhibitory effect on enzyme activities in halophytes, even when present in high concentration.

In summary then, recent experiments with halophytes suggest that many, perhaps the majority, are able to adapt biochemically to NaCl stress by accumulating in the cell vacuole one or more neutral aliphatic compounds, which exert a protective effect on osmotic regulation. Two substances especially implicated are proline and betaine but it is possible that other simple nitrogenous substances may have a role in some instances; accumulation of polyols such as glycerol or mannitol might also achieve the same end in other cases. Considering the enormous range of higher plants that are able to establish themselves in saline environments, a variety of responses might well be anticipated.

Plants growing in or near the sea or in salt marshes are subjected to influx of other ions besides sodium and chloride and it is conceivable that adaptation to other inorganic salts present in brackish waters may be necessary for survival of plants in such habitats. One such ion present in sea-water in some quantity is inorganic sulphate; one possible route for inactivation or storage is through conjugation with naturally occurring phenolic compounds, and particularly with flavonoids. A large number, over 50, of such conjugates, have recently been discovered in plants (Harborne, 1977) and remarkably enough, they occur principally in plants which are subject to water stress, but especially in halophytes.

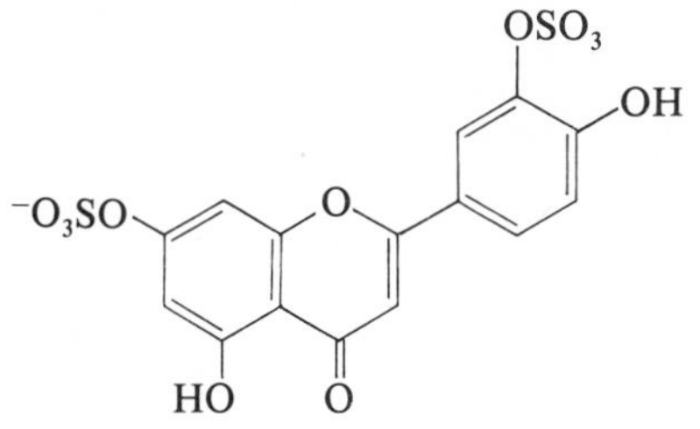

luteolin 7,3'-disulphate
present in *Zostera*

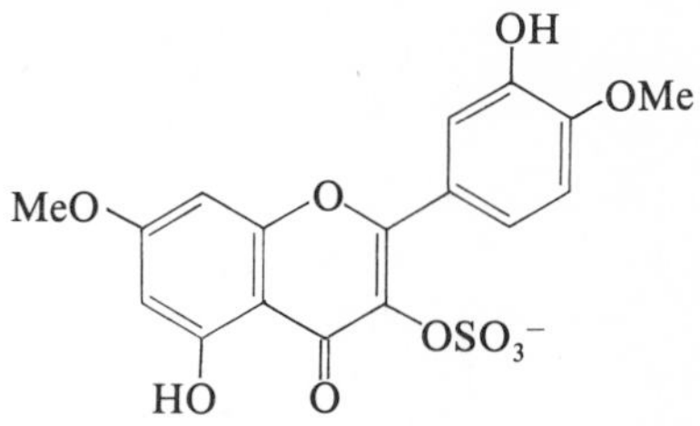

tamarixetin 3-sulphate
present in *Tamarix*

Fig. 1.9 Structures of two flavonoid sulphates found in halophytes

Flavonoid sulphates (for typical structures, see Fig. 1.9) have been identified in such land halophytes as *Suaeda maritima, Armeria maritima, Limonium vulgare, Nypa fruticans* and species of *Atriplex, Frankenia* and *Tamarix*. They also occur abundantly in sea-grasses such as *Thalassia, Zannichellia* and *Zostera*. Just as with proline or betaine accumulation, there are some halophytes (e.g. *Plantago maritima*) in which flavonoid sulphates are apparently absent. This presumably means that more than one system of sulphate conjugation occurs. That these organic conjugates of sulphur have a dynamic role in ion relationships is still largely conjectural, but such a role is under active current study.

IV. DETOXIFICATION MECHANISMS

A. General

Besides the many stresses which plants are subjected to in the natural environment, they are also today subjected to stresses which are man-made. These are derived from the pollution of the atmosphere with factory fumes and degraded gasoline exhaust vapours, other escapes of organic matter into the environment and from the deliberate application of a variety of pesticides to plant crops. It is fortunate that plants are able to cope with these stresses and indeed continue to survive in spite of such bombardment. That they can do so is due at least in part to the fact that they have an efficient system for the detoxification of foreign compounds within their cells. This fact has been established by feeding experiments with toxic compounds and it is also apparent in the way that plants can store toxins within their cells in non-toxic bound form (e.g. HCN bound as cyanogenic glycoside).

The key detoxification reaction of organic compounds in plants is glucoside formation, carried out by a glycosyltransferase enzyme in the presence of the energy-rich uridinediphosphateglucose as co-factor. This contrasts with the major detoxification route in animals, which involves conversion to glucuronide, not glucoside, or ethereal sulphate formation (Williams, 1964). The purpose in both plants and animals is the same, to inactivate the toxin and to give it water solubility so that it can be pushed into the cell vacuole in plants or excreted in the urine in animals.

Foreign compounds containing phenolic or nitrogen groups are directly detoxified as glucoside. In other compounds, these functional groups have first to be introduced before conjugation with sugar can occur. Thus, other chemical reactions may take place as part of the detoxification procedure, especially oxidation, decarboxylation, methylation, acylation or esterification. Conjugation with amino acid instead of glucose may also happen occasionally.

B. Detoxification of Phenols

Phenols have been the most widely studied group of compounds from this viewpoint (Towers, 1964). Phenols are highly toxic to both plants and microorganisms. Feeding experiments have shown that they are rapidly glucosylated within a few hours of entry into the plant and the products—the glucosides—are either stored in the vacuole or further metabolized within the plant and broken down eventually to CO_2.

Some examples of the products of glucosylation of phenols are shown in Fig. 1.10. The detoxification of hydroquinone has been especially widely studied (Pridham, 1964) and it has been found that the ability to glucosylate it is universally distributed in all higher plants; only fungi, algae and bacteria lack this capacity. Usually, the monoglucoside, arbutin, which occurs naturally in *Pyrus* leaf, is formed. In some plants and in some tissues, the glucosylation reaction is so well developed that higher glucosides are also produced; in wheat germ, for example, both the diglucoside (gentiobioside) and triglucoside have been identified as metabolites. In compounds which have two adjacent phenolic hydroxyls (e.g. aesculetin), isomeric glucosides may be formed; aesculetin is also methylated to scopoletin in some plants and is recovered as the glucoside scopolin.

Compounds containing both phenolic and carboxyl groups, e.g. *p*-coumaric acid (Fig. 1.10), are mainly detoxified via the glucose ester, i.e. the sugar is attached preferentially to the carboxyl and not to the phenolic group. It is interesting, however, that when cinnamic acid is fed, only small amounts of cinnamyl-glucose are recovered. The main reaction is hydroxylation to *p*-coumaric acid, which is subsequently glucosylated at the carboxyl group so that the main product is *p*-coumarylglucose. In this connection, it may be noted that the growth hormone, indoleacetic acid, when fed to plants is not *N*-glucosylated but is detoxified via the glucose ester. In this case, the aspartic acid conjugate, also joined through the carboxyl group, may be formed.

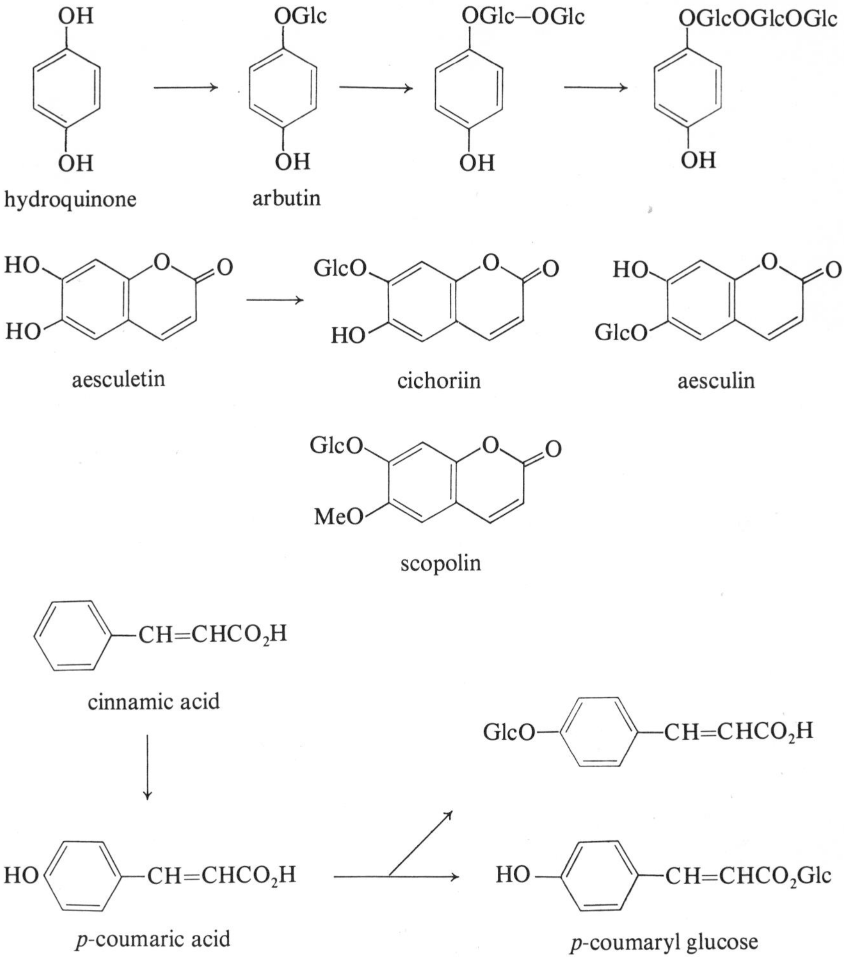

Fig. 1.10 Detoxification products of phenols in plants

Conjugation with this amino acid represents another, but minor, detoxification pathway in plants.

C. Detoxification of Systemic Fungicides

In the last 10 years, systemic fungicides have been developed to control such diseases as powdery mildew on cereals and cucumber. The rationale behind the use of such fungicides is that they should be absorbed by the plant, where they are harmless, and be retained within its tissues to prevent the growth and

Fig. 1.11 Metabolism of ethirimol in Barley

development of the fungal parasite. While earlier types of fungicide were sprayed onto the mature crop, systemic fungicides can be applied as a seed dressing and persist in the plant for a sufficient time to provide resistance during the whole growing season. Such compounds may of course be modified *in vivo*, the detoxification product itself providing much of the resistance to fungal invasion.

One widely used systemic fungicide on barley is ethirimol, a pyrimidine derivative which presumably acts as an antimetabolite in its effectiveness against the fungus. Its metabolism has been studied in barley leaves and it has been shown by tracer experiments to have a half-life *in vivo* of only 3 days. There is some photochemical reaction, but one of the major metabolites is the expected glucoside. However, it is interesting that no simple *N*-glucoside is formed. Instead, the aliphatic side chain of ethirimol is first oxidized to the corresponding alcohol and it is the glucoside of this alcohol, which is the natural metabolite (Fig. 1.11) (Teal, 1973).

D. Detoxification of Herbicides

One final example of the flexibility of plants to handle foreign compounds is taken from the field of practical weed control. Detoxification of herbicides has been widely studied and it appears that the rate and mode of detoxification is often critical to their effectiveness as selective weed killers. Indeed, the selective use of 2,4-dichlorophenoxyacetic acid (2,4-D) to kill weeds among crop plants such as cereals depends on the fact that while the crop can readily metabolize it, the weeds cannot and are killed as a result.

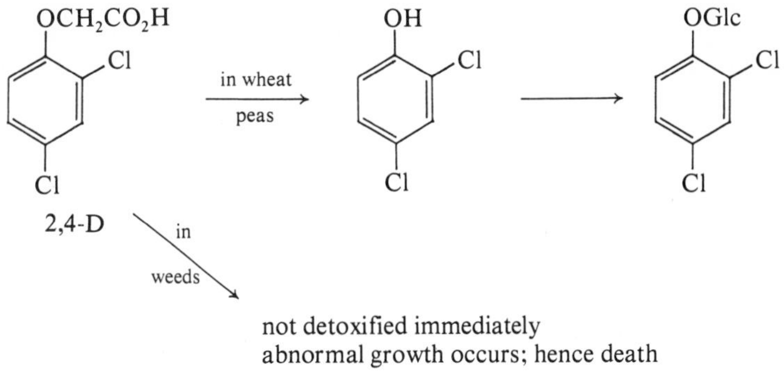

Fig. 1.12 Detoxification and metabolism of 2,4-D in plants

While conjugation at the carboxyl group with glucose or aspartic acid or hydroxylation of the aromatic ring may occur, an important reaction in the detoxification of 2,4-D is oxidation of the side chain (Naylor, 1976). Once this side chain is removed, growth hormone activity is lost, 2,4-dichlorophenol is formed and this is then conjugated with glucose in the normal way (Fig. 1.12). Although the ability to degrade the side chain is widespread in plants, the facility to do it rapidly is limited to a few crop plants. The enzyme machinery is not immediately active in weeds, and it is this variation in *rate* of detoxification which is the key issue. The weed species, unable to detoxify 2,4-D rapidly enough, are killed, not because 2,4-D is toxic as such, but because it is an extremely active auxin. In excess concentration, it causes the plant to grow too fast and it is the upset in growth pattern which causes the death of the plant.

An example of a more unusual pathway of detoxification is the case of the nitrogen-containing herbicide monuron. This compound in the cotton plant is first demethylated, the terminal *N*-methyl group is then oxidized and finally glucosylation occurs (Fig. 1.13). Two complex enzymic changes are needed before the compound can be removed from the system via the glucoside (Frear

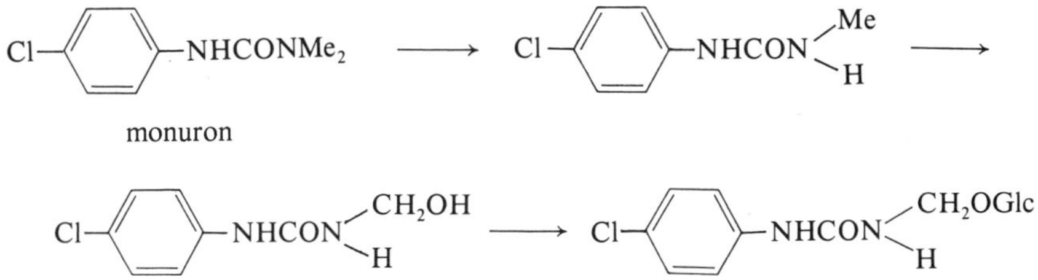

Fig. 1.13 Metabolism of the herbicide monuron in plants

et al., 1972). Further references to the metabolism of herbicides may be found in the reviews of Casida and Lykken (1969), Kearney and Kaufman (1968) and Naylor (1976).

BIBLIOGRAPHY

Books and Review Articles

Atsatt, P. R. and O'Dowd, D. J. (1976). Plant defense guilds. *Science* **193**, 24–29.

Baldwin, J. (1937). "An Introduction to Comparative Biochemistry." University Press, Cambridge.

Bjorkman, O. and Berry, J. (1973). High efficiency photosynthesis. *Scientific American* (October), pp. 80–93.

Casida, J. E. and Lykken, L. (1969). *Ann. Rev. Plant Physiol.* **20**, 607–636.

Florkin, M. and Mason, H. (1960–1964). "Comparative Biochemistry", Vols. 1–8. Academic Press, New York.

Harborne, J. B. (1977). Flavonoid sulphates: a new class of natural product of ecological significance in plants. *Progr. Phytochem.* **4**, 189–208.

Hatch, M. D. and Slack, C. R. (1970). The C_4-dicarboxylic acid pathway of photosynthesis. *Prog. Phytochem.* **2**, 35–106.

Kearney, P. C. and Kaufman, D. E. (1969). "Degradation of Herbicides." Dekker, New York.

Levitt, J. (1972). "Responses of Plants to Environmental Stress." Academic Press, New York.

Luckner, M. (1972). "Secondary Metabolism in Plants and Animals", 404 pp. Chapman & Hall, London.

Naylor, A. W. (1976). Herbicide metabolism in plants. In: Audus L. J. (ed.), "Herbicides," Vol. 1, pp. 397–426. Academic Press, London.

Reimold, R. J. and Queen, W. H. (1974). "Ecology of Halophytes", 605 pp. Academic Press, New York.

Robinson, T. (1975). "The Organic Constituents of Higher Plants", 3rd edn., 347 pp. Cordus Press, N. Amherst, Mass.

Rosenfeld, I. and Beath, O. A. (1964). "Selenium, Geobotany, Biochemistry, Toxicity and Nutrition." Academic Press, New York.

Shrift, A. (1969). Selenium toxicity. *Ann. Rev. Plant Physiol.* **20**, 475–494.

Shrift, A. (1972). Selenium toxicity. In: Harborne, J. B. (ed.), "Phytochemical Ecology", pp. 145–162. Academic Press, London.

Smellie, R. M. S. and Pennock, J. F. (eds.) (1976). "Biochemical Adaptation to Environmental Change", 240 pp. Biochemical Society, London. Symposium vol. no. 41.

Swain, T. (1974). Biochemical evolution in plants. *Comprehensive Biochemistry* **29A**, 125–302.

Strogonov, B. P. (1964). "Physiological Basis of Salt Tolerance of Plants", Poljakoff-Mayber and Mayer, A. M. (ed. & trans.). Monson, Jerusalem.

Towers, G. H. N. (1964). Metabolism of phenolics in higher plants and microorganisms. In: Harborne, J. B. (ed.), "Biochemistry of Phenolic Compounds", pp. 249–294. Academic Press, London.

Waisel, Y. (1972). "Biology of Halophytes", 395 pp. Academic Press, New York.

Williams, R. T. (1964). Metabolism of phenolics in animals. In: Harborne, J. B. (ed.), "Biochemistry of Phenolic Compounds", pp. 205–248. Academic Press, London.
Woolhouse, H. (1970). Environment and enzyme evolution in plants. In: Harborne, J. B. (ed.), "Phytochemical Phylogeny", pp. 207–232. Academic Press, London.

Literature References

Baskin, J. M. and Baskin, C. C. (1976). *J. Chem. Ecol.* **2**, 441–448.
Brown, W. V. (1975). *Amer. J. Bot.* **62**, 395–402.
Caswell, H., Reed, F., Stephenson, S. N. and Werner, P. A. (1973). *Amer. Naturalist* **107**, 465–480.
Coombs, J. (1971). *Proc. R. Soc. Lond. B.* **179**, 221–235.
Crawford, R. M. M. (1967). *Nature (Lond.)* **214**, 427–428.
Crawford, R. M. M. (1972). *Trans. Bot. Soc. Edinburgh* **41**, 309–322.
Crawford, R. M. M. and McManmon, M. (1968). *J. Exp. Bot.* **19**, 435–441.
Dunnill, P. M. and Fowden, L. (1967). *Phytochemistry* **6**, 1659–1663.
Flowers, T. J., Hall, J. L. and Wand, M. E. (1976). *Phytochemistry* **15**, 1231–1234.
Frear, D. S., Swanson, H. R. and Tanaka, F. S. (1969). *Recent Adv. Phytochem.* **5**, 225–246.
Gregory, R. P. G. and Bradshaw, A. D. (1965). *New Phytol.* **64**, 131–143.
Loveys, B. R. and Kriedemann, P. E. (1974). *Aust. J. Plant Physiol.* **1**, 407–415.
McNaughton, S. J., Campbell, R. S., Freyer, R. A., Mylraie, J. E. and Rodland, K. D. (1974). *Ecology* **55**, 168–172.
Milborrow, B. V. and Noddle, R. C. (1970). *Biochem. J.* **119**, 727–734.
Pridham, J. B. (1964). *Phytochemistry* **3**, 493–497.
Raynal, J. (1973). *Adansonia* Ser. 2, **13**, 145–171.
Sakai, A. (1960). *Low Temp. Sci. Ser.* **B18**, 15–22.
Sakai, A. (1961). *Nature (Lond.)* **189**, 416–417.
Sakai, A. and Yoshida, S. (1968). *Cryobiology* **5**, 160–174.
Schiller, W. (1974). *Flora* **163**, 327–341.
Singh, T. N., Aspinall, D. and Paleg, L. G. (1972). *Nature New Biol.* **236**, 188–190.
Smith, R. A. H. and Bradshaw, A. D. (1970). *Nature (Lond.)* **227**, 376–377.
Smith, T. A. (1965). *Phytochemistry* **4**, 599–607.
Stewart, G. R. and Lee, J. A. (1974). *Planta* **120**, 279–289.
Storey, R. and Wyn Jones, R. G. (1975). *Plant Science Letters* **4**, 161–168.
Storey, R. and Wyn Jones, R. G. (1977). *Phytochemistry* **16**, 447–453.
Teal, G. (1973). Ph.D. thesis, Univ. Reading.
Turner, R. G. and Marshall, C. (1972). *New Phytol.* **71**, 671–676.
Tyler, P. D. and Crawford, J. M. M. (1970). *J. Exp. Bot.* **21**, 677–682.
Warburg, O. (1920). *Biochem. Z.* **103**, 188.
Wellburn, A. R., Ogunkanmi, A. B. and Mansfield, T. A. (1974). *Planta* **120**, 255–263.
Wright, S. T. C. and Hiron, R. W. P. (1969). *Nature (Lond.)* **224**, 719–720.
Wyn Jones, R. G., Storey, R., Leigh, R. A., Ahmad, N. and Pollard, A. (1976). In: Morrè, E. (ed.), "Regulation of Cell Membrane Activities in Plants." North Holland Press, Amsterdam (in press).

2 | Biochemistry of Plant Pollination

I. INTRODUCTION

When insects, bats and birds visit flowers to feed on (or collect for future consumption) the nectar and pollen, they usually pollinate the flowers in the process, so that both partners clearly benefit from this mutualistic association. There are three biochemical factors in this interrelationship; scent and colour of the flower and the nutritional value of nectar and pollen. As a pollinating animal approaches a flowering plant, one of the signals it receives is an olfactory one, from the flower scent. Animals live in a world of chemical communication, of pheromones, and they are undoubtedly able to detect the terpenes and other volatiles of flower odour at some distance. As the pollinator arrives near the plant, it also receives a visual signal, in the contrasting colour of the flower against the general green leafy background. As it alights on the flower, it may be drawn to the nectar by visual honey guides on the petal, derived from the differential distribution of pigments within the flower tissue. Finally, as it transfers the pollen from stigma to style, it gains its reward, a nutritional one, based on the sugar and other constituents of nectar and pollen.

In spite of the great amount written on pollination ecology (e.g. Baker and Hurd, 1968; Faegri and van der Pijl, 1971; Proctor and Yeo, 1973), biochemical aspects have rarely been explored in any detail. The present account is an attempt to gather together most of the available information on this ecological topic. The subject of pollination biology is vast, largely because this interaction between plant and animal is such a complex and subtle one and also because almost every group of plants has its own method of attracting pollinators and there are an enormous number of morphological adaptations to the various animal pollinators available to plants. Some brief introduction to the subject is needed here, particularly regarding the range of animal pollinators, the varying roles of animal visitors in relationship to flower pollinating processes and the phenomenon of flower constancy.

To the casual observer in a flower garden in temperate latitudes, the pollination of the flowers would largely appear during daylight hours to be the province of the very active bumble and hive bee, with some help being provided by a few smaller insects. This ignores, of course, the much wider range of active pollinators in tropical habitats: the humming birds, an enormous variety of large tropical butterflies, the wasps and the beetles. In addition, some flowers are only pollinated at night by bats or moths. Finally, there are many smaller fauna, different kinds of flies and fleas which are only apparent as pollinators to the most acute observer. The problem of determining which pollinator or pollinators are active on a particular plant species is difficult, requiring much time-consuming observation by the field naturalist. Some animals may visit flowers for other reasons than pollination; also they may be able to "steal" the nectar, without carrying out the pollination necessary to the plant. Ants, for example, are well known nectar thieves and are often so small that they sneak in and out of blossoms without touching the reproductive organs. They do, however, act as genuine pollinators in some cases. Hickman (1974) has shown that the small self-incompatible annual *Polygonum cascadense* is cross-pollinated by the ant *Formica argentea*.

The need of a plant to attract animals to visit it for purposes of pollination depends quite naturally on its sexual system and floral structure. There are some groups, e.g. the grasses, where pollination is by wind and animal visitations to the inflorescences would be superfluous. However, such angiospermous plant groups are relatively few and the majority of plants clearly require animals to achieve their pollination. This is obvious in plants with single sex flowers, particularly those that are dioecious, i.e. where the male and female flowers are on different plants. It is also obvious in self-incompatible hermaphrodite plants, which account for the majority of angiosperms. Self-incompatibility is essentially a system which ensures out-crossing and hence genetic variability and vigour within a plant population. There are immunological barriers to self-pollination and such plants depend on cross-pollination, i.e. insects travelling from flower to flower and unwittingly transferring pollen from the stigma of one plant to the style of a second, in order to achieve seed set.

The evolution of the sexual system in the angiosperms has generally progressed from self-incompatibility to self-compatibility (see Crowe, 1964). However, even in self-compatible species (e.g. the sweet pea) where the floral morphology is such that self-pollination can occur without animal visitors, it is generally agreed that insects are beneficial in increasing seed set. This may be because pollinators increase the amount of self pollen transferred to the style or because, when cross pollen is available, it grows faster down the style than self pollen. At least, the theory that many self-pollinated species still gain an advantage from animal pollinators explains why many such plants continue to produce large and brightly coloured petals and fragrant flower scents which attract bees and other visitors.

Finally, there is the phenomenon of flower constancy, a factor of great significance in the co-evolution of angiosperms and their animal partners. It represents the fidelity of a pollinator to regularly visit only a limited number of plant species and in extreme cases, only one. Such fidelity is guided by floral morphology, odour and petal colour. Indeed many plants through evolution of their floral parts have deliberately restricted themselves to pollination by one type of vector so that they have what are called "bee-flowers" (with short, wide corollas), "butterfly-flowers" (with medium-length, narrow corollas) or "humming bird-flowers" (with long, narrow corollas). Animals on their part, within the range of plants they are capable of pollinating, become restrictive and dependent on a small number of species and eventually even a single plant. This may be because of a special blossom fragrance, a richness in nectar or some other lure. This mutual co-evolution has many benefits to both plant and animal. In extreme form, it can be seen in the fig genus, *Ficus*, where almost every species has its own species of chalcid wasp to pollinate it. Similarly, one finds examples in the Orchidaceae, where individual species of *Ophrys* depend on a single pollinator, an *Andrena* bee to pollinate it. The case of the bee orchids will be considered in more detail in a later section.

II. ROLE OF FLOWER COLOUR

A. Colour Preferences of Pollinators

Largely due to the work of von Fritsch (1950) and others, much information is available about the colour preferences of bees. They are known to prefer what to us appear as blue and yellow colours. They can also discern differences in absorption in the UV region of the spectrum and are sensitive to the intensely

UV-absorbing flavones and flavonols, which are present as such in practically all white flowers and also occur as co-pigments in cyanic flowers. Although bees are insensitive to red colours, they still visit some red flowered species (e.g. red poppies) guided by the presence of UV-absorbing flavones, which are also present in these blooms.

Hive bees (*Apis mellifera*) are very catholic in the flowers they visit. They do, however, visit some plant families more than others. Families which have many species with typical bee blossoms include the Labiatae, Scrophulariaceae and Leguminosae (Lotoideae); blue and yellow flower colour are common in these groups. Honey bees are also regular pollinators of Compositae, a family in which yellow is the dominant flower colour. Other types of bee are more restricted in their choice of flowers, notably those of the genus *Andrena* which mainly visit orchids such as *Ophrys*.

Hive bees exhibit their colour preferences by visiting blue and yellow blossomed flowers if given a choice of other colours as well. Clearly, when nectar is in short supply, bees will visit flowers with other colours (assuming the nectar is available to them) but such plants are at a selective disadvantage, e.g. in a bad summer when bee activity is limited. The operation of natural selection for bee colour can be seen in blue flowered species (e.g. the bluebell, *Scilla non-scripta*) which give rise to the white mutant forms in natural populations. Such mutants are unable to maintain themselves, seed set and viability being poor, largely because of the lack of insect visitors.

The colour preferences of other pollinators have been less well studied; present available data are collected in Table 2.1. Humming birds are sensitive

Table 2.1 Colour preferences of different pollinators

Animal	Flower colour preferences	Comments
Bats	White or drab colours, e.g. greens and pale purples	Mostly colour-blind
Bees	Yellow and blue intense colours, also white	Can see in UV, but not sensitive to red
Beetles	Dull, cream or greenish	Poor colour sense
Birds	Vivid scarlets, also bicolours (red-yellow)	Sensitive to red
Butterflies (Lepidoptera)	Vivid colours, including reds and purples	—
Moths (Heterocera)	Reds and purples, white or pale pinks	Mostly pollinate at night
Flies	Dull, brown, purple or green	Chequered pattern may be present
Wasps	Browns	—

Data modified from Faegri and van der Pijl (1971).

only to red and their preferences for bright scarlet blooms as in *Hibiscus* is well known. Tropical members of the Bignoniaceae, Gesneriaceae and Labiatae all have characteristic humming bird blossoms with red, orange-red or yellow-red colours. These birds do, on occasion, visit plants with white blooms in special habitats, e.g. in the Hawaiian forests. Some humming birds have brilliant scarlet plumage resembling the colour of the flower they pollinate. This is seen in the flower paraqueet *Loriculus* which feeds from scarlet *Erythrina* blossoms. This is a clear case of protective colouring, since these birds are most vulnerable to predators when hovering by the flower to collect nectar.

The other classes of pollinator (Table 2.1) show less sensitivity to flower colour. While butterflies are actively attracted to brightly coloured blossoms, moths and wasps prefer dull and drab colours. Finally, there are the beetles and bats which are visually colour-blind and they depend mainly on other sorts of signal to draw them to their host plants.

B. Chemical Basis of Flower Colour

Flower colour is largely due to the presence of pigments present in chromoplasts or cell vacuoles of floral tissues. Colours produced by the reflection and refraction of light from cell surfaces, so important in the animal kingdom, are not apparent in plants. Flower pigments have been widely studied, particularly from the genetical viewpoint and much information is now available about them (see e.g. Goodwin, 1976).

The most important group of flower pigments are the flavonoids, since they contribute cyanic colours (orange, red to blue) as well as to yellow and white (Harborne, 1967, 1976). The only other major group are the carotenoids, which provide principally yellow colours, with some oranges and reds. Other classes of much less importance in relation to flower pigmentation are chlorophylls (greens), quinones (occasional reds and yellows), and betalain alkaloids (giving yellow, red and purple colours in Centrospermae). A brief summary of the chemical basis of flower colour is presented in Table 2.2 together with some indication of frequency and importance of the different pigment types.

In the case of cyanic colour, the chemical basis is simple. There are three main pigments, all members of the class of flavonoids known as anthocyanidins: pelargonidin (Pg) (orange-red), cyanidin (Cy) (magenta) and delphinidin (Dp) (mauve). These differ in structure only in the number (one, two or three) of hydroxyl groups in the B-ring (see Fig. 2.1). These three chromophores occur, usually singly or occasionally as mixtures, in angiosperm flowers and provide the whole range of colour from orange, pink, scarlet and red to mauve, purple and blue. Essentially, all pink, scarlet and orange-red flowers contain pelargonidin, all crimson and magenta flowers cyanidin and all mauve and blue flowers delphinidin.

Table 2.2 Chemical basis of flower colour in angiosperms

Colour	Pigments responsible[a]	Examples
White, ivory, cream,	Flavones (e.g. luteolin) and/or flavonols (e.g. quercetin)	95% of white flowered spp.
Yellow	(a) Carotenoid alone	Majority of yellows
	(b) Yellow flavonol alone	*Primula, Gossypium*
	(c) Anthochlor alone	*Linaria, Oxalis, Dahlia*
	(d) Carotenoid + yellow flavonoid	*Coreopsis, Rudbeckia*
Orange	(a) Carotenoid alone	*Calendula, Lilium*
	(b) Pelargonidin + aurone	*Antirrhinum*
Scarlet	(a) Pure pelargonidin	Many, inc. *Salvia*
	(b) Cyanidin + carotenoid	*Tulipa*
Brown	Cyanidin on carotenoid background	*Cheiranthus*, many Orchidaceae
Magenta, crimson	Pure cyanidin	Most reds, inc. *Rosa*
Pink	Pure peonidin	Peony, *Rosa rugosa*
Mauve, violet[b]	Pure delphinidin	Many, inc. *Verbena*
Blue	(a) Cyanidin + copigment/metal	*Centaurea*
	(b) Delphinidin + copigment/metal	Most blues, *Gentiana*
Black (purple black)	Delphinidin at high concn.	Black tulip, pansy
Green	Chlorophylls	*Helleborus*

[a] In the table and elsewhere, anthocyanidins are referred to as pigment chromophores; these pigments actually occur *in vivo* as glycosides (anthocyanins). The nature of the sugar, however, has little effect on colour.

[b] One group of ten families in the Centrospermae differ from all other higher plants in having alkaloidal betalains as their yellow and purple pigmentation.

A rare change in hydroxylation pattern is loss of the 3-hydroxyl. This happens infrequently, but when it does, it causes significant shifts to shorter wavelengths. Two such pigments are known, luteolinidin (3-desoxycyanidin) and apigeninidin (3-desoxypelargonidin) which are orange-yellow and yellow respectively (Fig. 2.1). These compounds occur in the New World Gesneriaceae (see p. 39) but hardly anywhere else.

A number of other chemical factors modify the basic anthocyanidin colours (Table 2.3); this is one of the reasons why such a variety of different shades and hues can be found in flowering plants. One of the modifying factors is methylation of one or more of the free hydroxyl groups in the three basic pigments. Only three methylated pigments are at all common: peonidin, petunidin and malvidin (see Fig. 2.1 for structures). While methylation has

The three common anthocyanidins

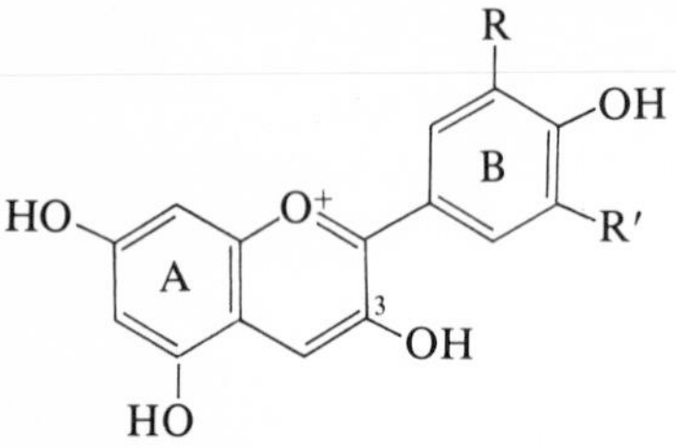

Common methylated pigments

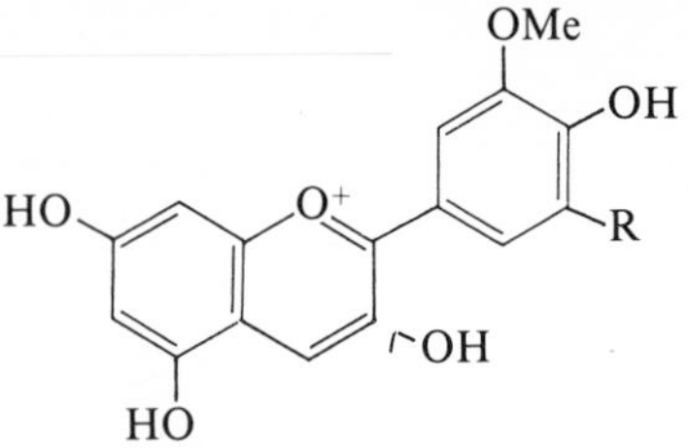

pelargonidin, R = R' = H (510)
cyanidin, R = OH, R' = H (525)
delphinidin, R = R' = OH (535)

peonidin, R = H (523)
petunidin, R = OH (534)
malvidin, R = OMe (532)

Rare 3-desoxyanthocyanidins

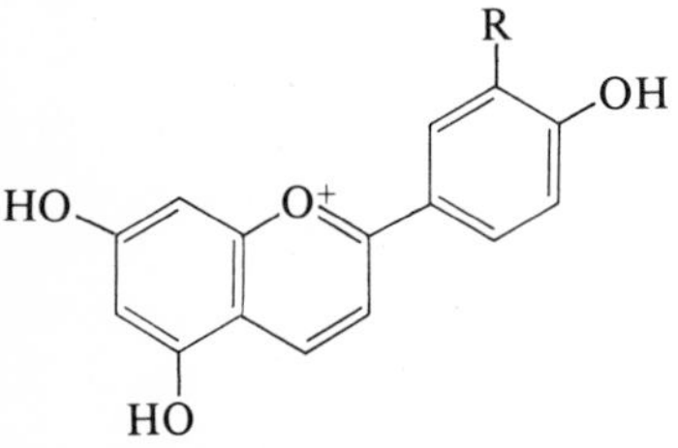

Rare methylated pigments

apigeninidin, R = H (477)
luteolinidin, R = OH (495)

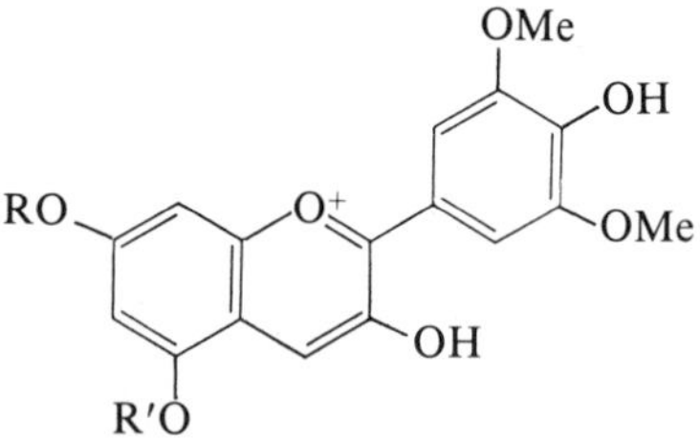

hirsutidin, R = Me, R' = H (530)
capensinidin, R = H, R' = Me (529)

Fig. 2.1 Anthocyanidin chromophores of the angiosperms

Note: All pigments occur naturally with sugars attached (usually to the 3-OH) as anthocyanins. The values in parentheses refer to the visible wavelength maxima (in nm) of the different pigments in methanolic HCl.

only a small reddening effect on colour, it is probably important in improving the stability of the anthocyanidin chromophore; methylated pigments are relatively common in the more highly specialized plant families. All anthocyanidins occur *in vivo* as glycosides (anthocyanins) and have sugars attached to the 3- or 3- and 5-hydroxyl groups. Sugar attachment is probably important (as is methylation) for pigment stability but generally has little effect on flower colour *per se* since glycosylation is the rule rather than the exception.

One of the factors modifying cyanic colour (Table 2.3) needs special mention—presence of flavone and/or flavonol co-pigment. For many years, it was thought that co-pigmentation was a special effect, restricted to plants

Table 2.3 Factors controlling cyanic colour in flowers

1.[a] Hydroxylation pattern of the anthocyanidins (i.e. based on pelargonidin, cyanidin or delphinidin)

2. Pigment concentration

3. Presence of flavone or flavonol co-pigment (may have blueing effect)

4. Presence of chelating metal (blueing effect)

5. Methylation of anthocyanidins (small reddening effect)

6. Presence of other types of pigment (carotenoids have browning effect).

---

[a] In approximate order of importance. There are other minor factors, including pH, physical phenomena, etc.

with blue flowers. The co-pigments were present to form weak complexes with the anthocyanidin, shifting the mauve or purple delphinidin colour to pure shades of blue. Recent research (Asen *et al.,* 1972) has now demonstrated that for the full expression of the colour of all three common anthocyanidins—Pg, Cy and Dp—flavones or flavonols are needed to stabilize the pigment chromophore at the pH of the flower cell sap (around 4·5). This explains why, in fact, *all* cyanic flowers, not just those which are blue, contain both anthocyanidin *and* flavone or flavonol (as glycosides). Then, the blueing effect of flavones in blue flowers is simply due to an increase in the concentration of flavone; i.e. the anthocyanin: flavone ratio is decreased from that in mauve blooms. That this is so has been confirmed by directly comparing the spectra of pigments and co-pigments mixed in the test tube with those given by the pigments in the living flower.

One other chemical feature may be important in providing blue flower colour, the presence of chelating metal. Aluminium, molybdenum, iron and other metal complexes of anthocyanidins have been isolated from blue flowered plants, including *Commelina*, blue cornflower and blue lupin. The complexes are unstable and are broken down in the presence of acid. All such complexes also contain flavone as an integral part of the complex and it is not exactly clear what extra benefit is provided by the metal ion since the blueing is achieved by the flavone alone. However, it may be of importance in providing *in vivo* stability.

There are a variety of ways that yellow colour may be produced in flowers (see Table 2.2). Most are due to carotenoids; almost all yellow and lemon-yellow carotenoid-containing flowers have mainly xanthophylls, such as zeaxanthin and its 5,8-epoxides auroxanthin and flavoxanthin. Deep orange flowers may have large amounts of β-carotene (e.g. the orange fringes of *Narcissus majalis*) or alternatively lycopene (*Calendula*) (for carotenoid structures, see Fig. 2.2). The carotenoids in petals are concentrated in the

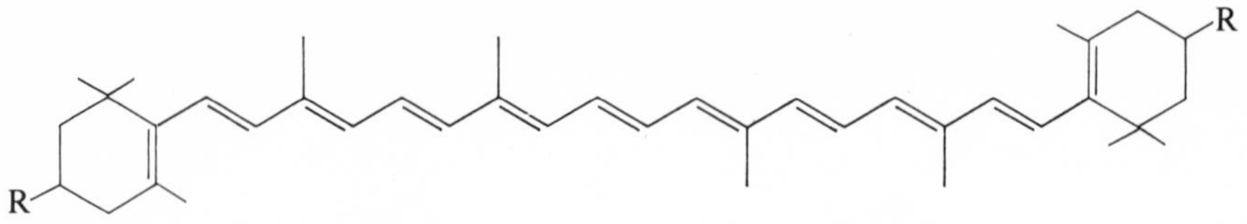

β-carotene, R = H (in daffodils) (451, 482)
zeaxanthin, R = OH (in tulips) (423, 451, 483)

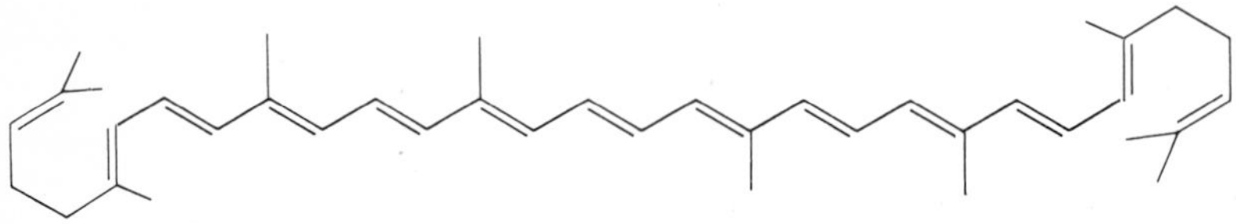

lycopene (in marigolds) (446, 472, 505)

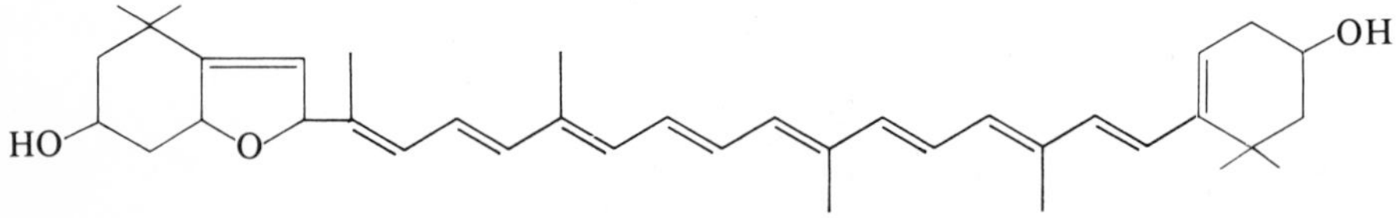

flavoxanthin (in yellow chrysanthemum) (432, 481)

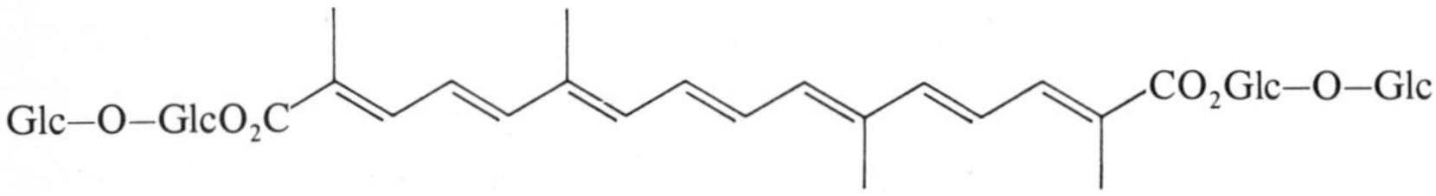

crocein (crocus flowers) (411, 437, 458)

Fig. 2.2 Some carotenoid pigments of yellow flowers
(figures in parentheses = visual maxima measured in EtOH)

chromoplasts and may be present in bound form linked to protein or esterified with fatty acids.

Flavonoids make minor contributions to yellow colour, through three groups of pigment: yellow flavonols, chalcones and aurones (Fig. 2.3). Yellow flavonols such as gossypetin, quercetagetin and their derivatives provide colour in cotton flower, in the primrose and in various composites, e.g. *Chrysanthemum segetum*. Yellow flavonols owe their colours to the presence of an extra hydroxyl (or methoxyl) group in the 6- or 8-position of the aromatic A-ring of their structures. The related flavonols without this feature, e.g. quercetin (Fig. 2.4), are more or less colourless. Chalcones and aurones

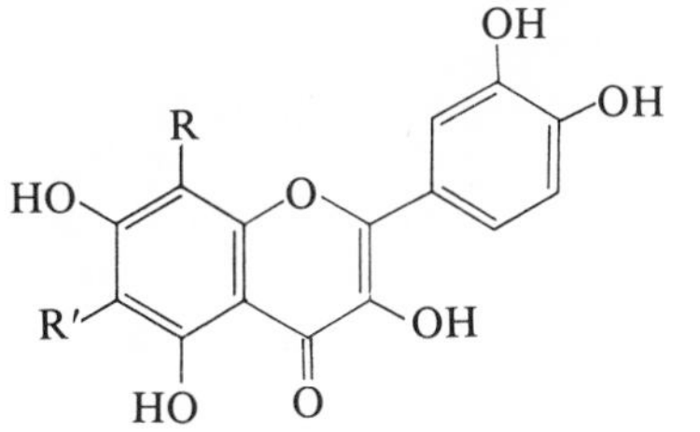

gossypetin, R = OH, R' = H (388)
quercetagetin, R = H, R' = OH (367)

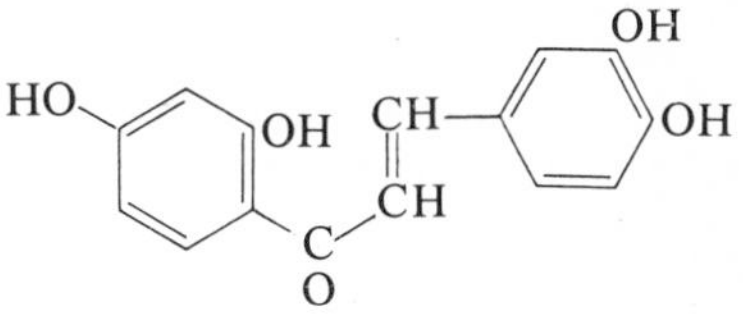

butein, chalcone of *Coreopsis* (382)

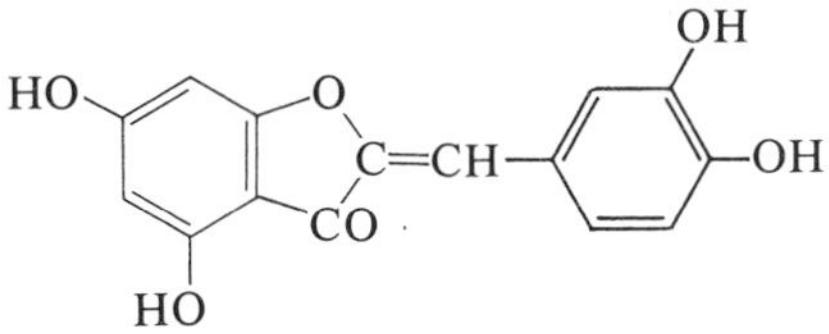

aureusidin, aurone of yellow
Antirrhinum (399)

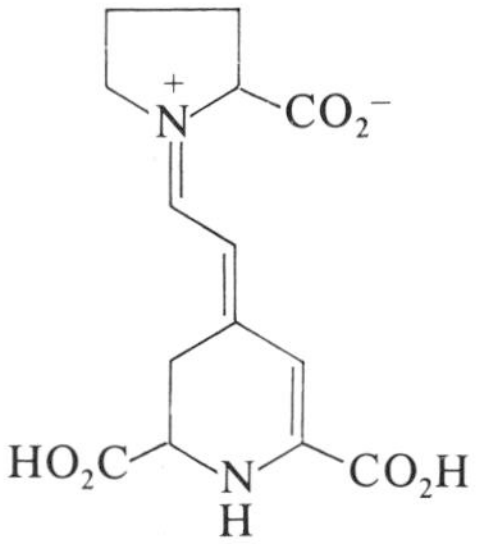

indicaxanthin, betaxanthin
of *Opuntia ficus-indica* (480)

Fig. 2.3 Yellow flavonoid and alkaloid pigments

occur especially frequently in another group of composites including *Coreopsis* and *Dahlia* but do also occur sporadically in nine other plant families. They are distinguished from other types of yellow pigment in that when petals containing them are fumed with ammonia (or the basic smoke of a cigar) there

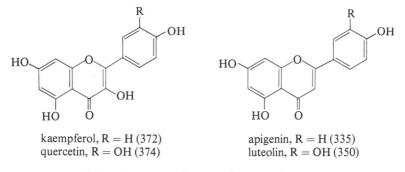

kaempferol, R = H (372)
quercetin, R = OH (374)

apigenin, R = H (335)
luteolin, R = OH (350)

Fig. 2.4 Flavones and flavonols of white petals

is a colour change from yellow to red. Chalcones and aurones often occur together in flower petals and are collectively known as anthochlor pigments.

One other class of water-soluble yellow pigment needs to be mentioned: those based on alkaloids. The well-known base berberine, for example, contributes yellow colour in *Berberis* tissues. One important class of yellow alkaloids are the betaxanthins of the Centrospermae. Within this order, all yellows are given by pigments such as indicaxanthin (Fig. 2.3) a betaxanthin based on the amino acid proline linked to a betalamic acid moiety. Eight other betaxanthins are known in the Centrospermae with different aliphatic amino acids other than proline as part of their structures (Piatelli, 1976).

One final point may be made about yellow colour. Mixtures of two unrelated classes of yellow pigment are not infrequent in petals, especially of carotenoids and yellow flavonoids in members of the Compositae. This seems peculiarly wasteful in terms of biosynthetic potential for plants to produce two classes of compound to carry out the same function. However, the explanation for this apparent profligacy has recently been uncovered in relation to guide marks in petals, as will be discussed in a later section.

Finally, there are the compounds which occur in white flowers. They are scarcely colours to human eyes, appearing as pale cream or ivory in the petal. However, as already mentioned, they are clearly discernible by bees and other insects, which can perceive differences in absorption in the UV range of the spectrum. There are two classes: flavones such as luteolin and apigenin; and flavonols such as kaempferol and quercetin (see Fig. 2.4). There seems to be no particular advantage one over the other, although the flavonols absorb at slightly longer wavelengths (at *c.* 360–380 instead of at 335–350 nm) than the flavones. In fact, flavones are more widely found in the flowers of more advanced plant families than are flavonols.

C. Evolution of Flower Colour

The distribution of cyanic coloration in angiosperms is by no means haphazard. There is a pattern in the relative frequency of delphinidin (Dp), cyanidin (Cy) and pelargonidin (Pg) types. The frequencies vary according to the flora sampled, and there is clear evidence of natural selection for particular colours in different environments, according to the most active pollinators which are present. Analyses of the results of pigment surveys show that selection has worked in two directions, from cyanidin as the basic or more primitive type (see Fig. 2.5). Loss mutations in tropical habitats produce scarlet and orange colours favoured by humming birds; by contrast, gain mutations in temperate climates produce blue colours favoured by bees.

Evidence that cyanidin is the most primitive pigment type is based on a variety of observations. It is the most common type in the ancestors of angiosperms, i.e. the gymnosperms. It is the major pigment of wind pollinated

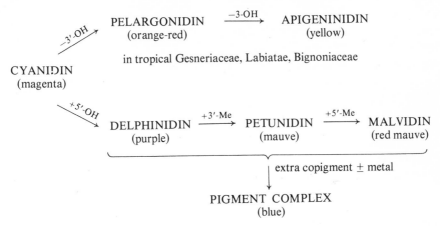

Fig. 2.5 Directions of evolution in cyanic colour in angiosperms

groups such as the grasses, where clearly selection for flower colour will not operate. It is also the most common pigment found in tissues more primitive than the flower, in the leaf.

Evidence that pelargonidin is advanced over Cy is based on its regular occurrence in tropical plants and almost complete absence from temperate floras. The further loss mutation to give the 3-desoxyanthocyanidins luteolinidin and apigeninidin (Fig. 2.5) only appears in very advanced angiosperm families, such as the Gesneriaceae and Bignoniaceae. In the former family, 3-desoxyanthocyanidins are clearly restricted to the tropical American New World species and are completely absent from the Old World taxa in the family. This difference in cyanic pigmentation is also correlated with differences in the type of yellow pigmentation in the two geographical groups (Table 2.4).

Table 2.4 Differences in pigment chemistry of subfamilies of the Gesneriaceae

Subfamily[a]	Presence of desoxyanthocyanin	Presence of yellow pigments		
		Carotenoid	Chalcone	Quinone
New World Gesnerioideae	In 29/36	+	−	−
Old World Cyrtandrioideae	Absent 0/50	−	+	+

[a] Generic coverage 74%; data from Harborne (1967).

Finally, evidence that delphinidin and its derivatives are advanced over cyanidin is drawn from distribution patterns in the angiosperms and especially the frequent presence of Dp in advanced bee families, such as the Scrophulariaceae, Boraginaceae, Hydrophyllaceae and Polemoniaceae.

The situation illustrated in Fig. 2.5 is only an evolutionary trend and clearly there will be some exceptions. The position of Cy itself is to some extent ambiguous since with suitable modifying factors it can under different circumstances provide the basis of scarlet colours (e.g. in *Tulipa*, see Table 2.1) or the basis of blue colours, as in the cornflower, *Centaurea cyanus*. However, if one takes the other two pigment types, Pg and Dp, it seems that humming bird flowers never have delphinidin, bee flowers never have pelargonidin; such cases, if they exist in nature, have yet to be found.

The effects of the evolutionary trends portrayed in Fig. 2.5 can be gauged also, by comparing the frequencies of Pg, Cy and Dp types in various floras. In the Australian flora, the relative frequencies based on analyses of wild plant species, are Dp 63%, Cy 47% and Pg 2%. The remarkable scarcity of Pg types is presumably due at least in part to the infrequency of species with bird pollinating mechanisms in the flowers. Where bird pollination occurs, the mechanism is often distinctive as in brush flowers of the Myrtaceae which have bright red stamens arranged like the bristles of a bottlebrush. On the other hand, the high figure for Dp suggests that pollination by insects attracted to mauve and blue colours must be especially common.

Figures from the contrasting tropical flora of the West Indies are also available. Here a sampling based on both wild and introduced species (and hence not entirely representative of the natural habitat) gave the results of Dp 47%, Cy 70% and Pg 17%. The high figure for Pg and to some extent that of Cy is undoubtedly because bird pollination is a widespread feature in this flora (see van der Pijl, 1961).

The dichotomous nature of evolutionary trends in cyanic colours can also be seen at work in families which have both tropical and temperate members. One of the best examples here is the Polemoniaceae, a family restricted to the New World but present both in northern temperate areas as well as central tropical habitats. The animal pollinators of these plants have been exhaustively studied by Grant and Grant (1965). In their monograph on the family, these authors include two colour plates of typical Polemoniaceae species pollinated by humming birds and by bees respectively. There is a remarkable contrast in colour and flower shape in these plates. The humming bird flowers have long, narrow corollas, either yellow or scarlet. The bee flowers are wide open short corollas, nearly all blue in colour. Analyses of blue flowered Polemoniaceae have confirmed that delphinidin is their major pigment. Similar analysis of one of the humming bird pollinated species (*Ipomopsis*) has shown pelargonidin to be present (Harborne, 1967). Similar differences in flower colour types can be seen by comparing pigment types identified in tropical and temperate members of the Leguminosae and Plumbaginaceae. The results with the Gesneriaceae, where the main geographical difference is Old World/New World, have already been referred to above.

Evolutionary changes in flower colours can also be observed at the species level. Plants may have to switch their flower colours within a generation or two in order to adapt to changes in pollinators. Baker and Hurd (1968) have pointed out the considerable differences in dominant flower colour that can exist between two habitats adjacent to each other. In the northern Californian flora, herbaceous species growing in the open prairie are pollinated by bees and have yellow flowers. Close by in the dark Redwood forest, the plants are pollinated by moths and have white or pale pink flowers. Any species migrating across the border from one habitat to another would have to switch flower colour rapidly in order to adapt to the new environment. Species known to be variable in their flower colour (e.g. members of the *Viola* genus) are presumably in a better position than most to achieve emigration from one contrasting habitat to another in this way.

One way that flower colour may be modified is by hybridization, but this may not always be advantageous. In *Penstemon* for example, there is a red humming bird-pollinated species which will hybridize with a blue carpenter bee-pollinated species when growing sympatrically (see Grant, 1971). The hybrid is purple flowered and attracts yet another pollinator, a wasp. The purple intermediate is presumably pigmented by the same delphinidin as the blue form, but with less co-pigment being present; delphinidin would be expected to be dominant to the cyanidin or pelargonidin present in the red flowering species (Beale, 1941). Such a purple hybrid may not always be fortunate enough as in this case to attract its own pollinator. It clearly could be at a selective disadvantage, since it may not be able to attract either of the pollinators of the parental plants. In other situations, it might then have to revert back quickly to the flower colour of one or other parent. This could clearly be a limiting factor in the success of hybrids in evolving plant populations.

D. Honey Guides

Honey guides or guide marks are part of the pigment patterning in flowers, their object being to guide pollinating insects to the centre, where the sex organs and nectar are present. They are particularly prominent in bee flowers and take a variety of forms. Many are visible to the human eye and may be a colour contrast—a yellow spot on the lip of an otherwise blue flower, as in *Cymbalaria muralis*. They also may take the form of coloured dots or lines on the corolla tube. Recent research has shown that some honey guides in yellow

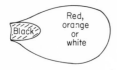

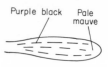

Papaver
superimposition of
cyanidin in high concn.
on background of
cyanidin or pelargonidin

Digitalis
local concentration of
corolla pigment
(cyanidin) in spots

Streptocarpus
local concentration of
corolla pigment (malvidin
based) in lines

Fig. 2.6 Some visible honey guides in cyanic flowers

flowers are invisible to the human eye, but can be detected by insects due to
their intense absorption in the UV; this work has created a new impetus in the
study of honey guides in flowering plants.

Visible honey guides are often produced by the local concentration of
anthocyanin pigmentation in particular areas of the corolla (see Fig. 2.6). This
is true in the foxglove, *Digitalis purpurea,* which has a pink bell-shaped
corolla, pigmented by cyanidin, with a series of concentrated areas of the same
pigment in the inside of the bell drawing the insect to the stigma and style. In
Streptocarpus species, a similar situation exists except that the honey guides
take the form of lines of pigment inside the tubular corolla.

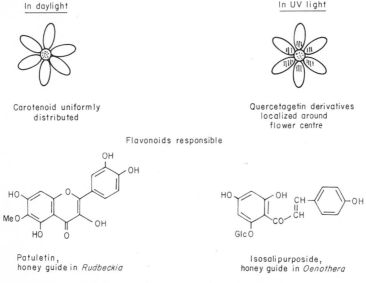

Fig. 2.7 Invisible honey guides in yellow flowers

A slightly different situation holds in the genus *Papaver* where honey guides generally take the form of pigment blotches on the petals (Fig. 2.6). In this case, the pigment in the blotch (cyanidin as the 3-glucoside) is different from that present in the rest of the petal, which is cyanidin as the 3-sophoroside (in *P. rhoeas*) or pelargonidin as the 3-sophoroside (in *P. orientale*).

The first published evidence that honey guides invisible to the human eye occur in flowers was provided by Thompson *et al.* (1972) in a variety of *Rudbeckia hirta* called Black Eyed Susan. In daylight, the petals of this composite are uniformly yellow. However, in UV light, the outer parts of the ray are UV-reflecting and bright, while the inner parts are dark-absorbing (see Fig. 2.7). Chemical analyses reveal that carotenoid pigment is responsible for the UV reflection of the outer ray and also that this lipid pigment is uniformly distributed throughout the ray. In the inner dark absorbing zones of the ray, there is a different kind of pigment. In fact, three water-soluble yellow flavonols are present including especially a derivative of patuletin (see Fig. 2.7).

Thus, in *Rudbeckia,* there is separation of function of the two types of yellow pigment present. The carotenoid provides the general yellow flower colour in the plant, in order to attract the bee from a distance. On the other hand, the water soluble yellow flavonols, differentially present only in the inner ray, act as a UV honey guide, directing the UV-sensitive bee once it has landed on the flower head to the nectar in the centre of the blossom. This explains why many highly-evolved plant species tend to have two types of yellow pigment in the flower; the two types clearly have different functions (see p. 38).

Invisible honey guides can be readily detected in yellow flowering species by looking at flower heads under UV light and then by confirming the result by photography, using an appropriate filter. Such detection can actually be done on plants from herbarium sheets. However, it is also vital to actually identify that both carotenoids and yellow flavonoids are present in the flower and this can only be done on fresh flowers. Herbarium surveys have shown that UV guides probably occur in a number of other yellow flowering composites, particularly those in the same tribe Heliantheae as *Rudbeckia* (Eisner *et al.*, 1973). Pigment analyses, however, still have to be carried out on these plants. Detection of both yellow carotenoid and yellow flavonoid in a flower does not *a priori* mean that UV guides are present. We have found that in another tribe of the Compositae, in the Anthemideae, there are many yellow flowered species with both carotenoid and yellow flavonols (Harborne *et al.,* 1976) but there is no evidence of honey guides in them.

Other types of yellow flavonoid can contribute to honey guides. In *Oenothera* (Onagraceae), Dement and Raven (1974) have shown that the chalcone isosalipurposide is responsible for UV honey guides in these flowers. Similarly, Scogin and Zakar (1976) have found that both chalcones and aurones provide UV absorption patterns in flowers of *Bidens* (Compositae).

These patterns are not universally present but occur in 5 of the 7 sections of the genus; there is also variation in how far along the ray the absorbing pigments extend.

UV honey guides could also be present in white flowers, provided the flavone and flavonol present is differentially distributed within the petal. Horovitz and Cohen (1972) have obtained photographic evidence that honey guides of this type may be present in white flowering members of the Cruciferae. Evidence has also been obtained in white flowering Compositae that the flavone is concentrated only in the epidermal cells of the ray, where their effectiveness in attracting pollinators will obviously be considerably improved (Brehm and Krell, 1975).

III. ROLE OF FLOWER SCENT

A. Types of Scent

The odour or scent of a flower often plays a major role as attractant to pollinating insects in the angiosperms. There is evidence that scent may be a more ancient attractant than flower colour. Thus, many primitive beetle-pollinated flowers lack colour but have strong odours. Bees are especially responsive to flower scents which we would describe as fragrant or "heady" and many bee flowers are scented, e.g. the violet and the rose. Odour is of special importance in night-flying insects and other animals, where visual stimulus is practically absent; bat-pollinated and moth-pollinated flowers are generally strong smelling.

Because of the sensitivity of insects to small concentrations of volatile chemicals, flower odours are probably effective at relatively low concentrations. Many species which do not appear to be strongly scented to human senses may, in fact, produce sufficient odour to attract bees or butterflies. In many species, maximum scent production is co-ordinated with the time when the pollen is ripe and the flower is ready for pollination. Diurnal variations in production also occur so that scent is produced for day-time pollinators at noon, for night-time pollinators at dusk.

Other plant tissues besides the petals give off scents. Indeed, many labiates and other plants have special scent glands on the leaf surfaces which are full of volatile oils. It is not clear in such cases whether leaf odours contribute at all to the attraction of pollinating vectors. Certainly higher animals may be sensitive to leaf odours of the Labiatae—witness the well-known attraction of the domestic cat for the catmint, *Nepeta cataria*.

From the viewpoint of the human observer, flower scents broadly fall into two classes: those that are pleasant, fragrant or fruity; and those that are distinctly unpleasant or aminoid. While we can make such a classification for

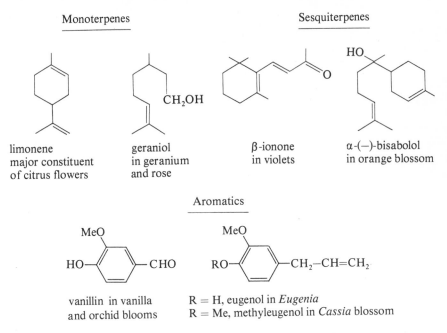

Monoterpenes

Sesquiterpenes

limonene
major constituent
of citrus flowers

geraniol
in geranium
and rose

β-ionone
in violets

α-(−)-bisabolol
in orange blossom

Aromatics

vanillin in vanilla
and orchid blooms

R = H, eugenol in *Eugenia*
R = Me, methyleugenol in *Cassia* blossom

Fig. 2.8 Structures of some major flower scent volatiles

our own benefit, the pollinator concerned is clearly attracted to the scent whatever its particular quality to the human nose. Pleasant odours are generally contained in the "essential oil" fraction of the flower, that part which can be separated by steam distillation or ether extraction and is volatile. Within the essential oils, a range of organic compounds may be present, the majority being mono- or sesqui-terpenes. Volatile aromatic substances may be present, as well as simple aliphatic alcohols, ketones and esters. Typical structures of some flower odoriferous principles are illustrated in Fig. 2.8. In some cases, a major constituent may be responsible for a particular flower scent but more usually, a mixture of components provide the scent. An important factor in scent production is that one component may reinforce the effectiveness of a second and third in producing a characteristic odour.

Flower scents have, of course, been utilized for many years in human society as perfume, particularly by the female to attract the male. While most modern perfumes are synthetic in origin, natural flower scent extracts still have an importance for boosting the effectiveness of synthetic mixtures. Roses are still cultivated in Bulgaria for their scent. Modern research by perfumers has shown that even the simplest flower scent may have many, indeed a hundred or more constituents. In view of this complexity, the way in which many plant species have recognizably different flower scents may readily be appreciated.

Unpleasant aminoid odours in plants have, perhaps not unnaturally, been poorly studied. Our knowledge of the chemistry of highly repulsive and distasteful plant odours is therefore limited. Three typical plants with obnoxious odours are the hogweed, *Heracleum sphondylium*, stinking hellebore *Helleborus foetidus* and the cuckoo pint, *Arum maculatum*. Other examples occur in the families to which these species belong, especially the Umbelliferae and Araceae. Unpleasant smells, in fact, represent a chemical mimicry by which the plant produces the smell of decaying protein or faeces to deceive carrion and dung insects to transfer their attention to the flower heads. Indeed, the chemicals produced are very similar to those given off by carrion or dung.

Major constituents of aminoid plant odours are monoamines, which have unpleasant fishy smells. They are fairly volatile and range from methylamine to hexylamine (Fig. 2.9). Even more offensive to some are the two diamines, putrescine and cadaverine, which as their names imply are characteristic breakdown products of decaying protein. They are known as plant products (see Smith, 1975) but have not been identified as yet in unpleasant flower odours; nevertheless, it is likely that they contribute in some cases. Other unpleasant compounds that may be present are skatole and indole (which have faecal odours) and odd-chain aliphatic organic acids, such as isobutyric acid with its rancid smell.

The floral allurement by which plants use such smells as a trap for insects has been investigated in some detail (see Faegri and van der Pijl, 1971). In *Arum nigrum* and *A. maculatum* for example, the bright purple spathe opens

Monoamines

CH_3NH_2	methylamine
$CH_3CH_2NH_2$	ethylamine
$CH_3(CH_2)_2NH_2$	propylamine
$CH_3(CH_2)_3NH_2$	butylamine
$CH_3(CH_2)_4NH_2$	amylamine
$CH_3(CH_2)_5NH_2$	hexylamine

Diamines

$NH_2-(CH_2)_4-NH_2$	putrescine
$NH_2-(CH_2)_5-NH_2$	cadaverine

Indoles

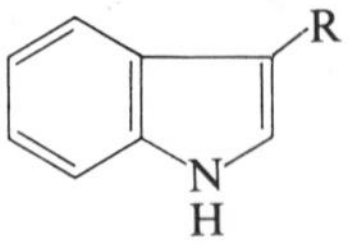

R = H, indole
R = Me, skatole

Fig. 2.9 Unpleasant amines in plant odours

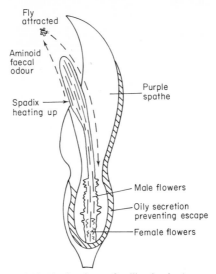

Fig. 2.10 Biochemistry of pollination in *Arum*

overnight to reveal the spadix in which respiration is unusually rapid and temperatures of 30°C have been measured (Fig. 2.10). The heat thus generated in the spadix aids the volatilization of the amine in the objectionable odours which are then released. Dung beetles and flies attracted by the amines alight on the spadix, fall into the bottom of the flower, where they are trapped. The insects cannot escape because of the slippery surface of the inner spathe and are kept prisoner for 24 h, during which time they transfer pollen to the receptive styles; rapid anatomical changes then occur (including wrinkling of the spathe surface) and the insect is eventually released. The generation of heat in the spadix is a truly remarkable feature of these plants and it must increase the effectiveness of the faecal odours. The rapid respiration that occurs uses up a quantity of starch in the process but presumably this is offset in terms of metabolic efficiency by the fact that only small amounts of nitrogen compounds are needed in the scent.

In *Arum*, it is important that the insect escapes so that it can carry pollen from one plant to another, for purposes of cross-pollination, and the scent is only a bait put out by the plant to achieve this end. Certain other plants, as is well known, trap insects for food and flies so caught are not allowed to escape. It is interesting that scent is occasionally used as a lure in these circumstances. Thus *Sarracenia flava* plants have been shown to produce within their pitcher traps the volatile alkaloid coniine, which has a "mousy" odour. This compound not only entices the insects into the trap but also, because of its physiological activity, paralyses them so that they are more readily digested by this carnivorous plant (Mody *et al.,* 1976).

B. Insect Pheromones and Flower Scents

Insect behaviour is known to be controlled by chemical signals, which take the form of volatile organic constituents released by one insect to affect another. These substances are active in very small amounts and have been termed "pheromones", to indicate their relationship to the hormones of higher animals. Pheromones are involved in almost every aspect of insect life: feeding, sex, aggregation, oviposition, defense and laying trails. Chemically, many of the pheromones are simple aliphatic alcohols, acids or esters; others are closely related to the plant scents in being terpenoid in nature. Detailed accounts of insect pheromones are given by Law and Regnier (1971) and Jacobson (1972).

Pheromones will be discussed *inter alia* in later chapters of this book. Mention of them here is pertinent, since the action of a flower in producing a fragrant scent to attract a pollinator can be a similar signal to that of a pheromone released by one insect to attract another. Indeed the signals may sometimes get crossed, with interesting results, as will be mentioned below.

Because insects depend on volatile compounds for social communication, they can clearly become sensitive to similar molecules which may be present in flower scents. Plants may occasionally deceive insects by producing attractive odours to trap them (see above) or to draw them away from more rewarding pursuits (e.g. feeding). Insects "learn" to recognize the smells of individual flowers and it is this factor, perhaps more than any other, which is responsible for the phenomenon of flower constancy, where insects limit their attention to a few or only one plant species. It has ever been suggested, perhaps fancifully, that some plants produce hallucinogenic or narcotic substances in their scents, so that insects become "hooked" on them and a close symbiotic relationship may develop.

Three examples will now be given where pheromones and flower scents have become interwoven in pollination ecology. The first refers to the oriental fruit fly, *Dacus dorsalis*, which has the phenylpropanoid eugenol methyl ether (see Fig. 2.7) as sex pheromone. Pheromonal activity is exhibited both in feeding and in male aggregation. This same compound is produced in the blossoms of several plant species including *Cassia fistulosa*. As a result, male fruit-flies may congregate on *Cassia* trees and will perceive the signal as a sign to eat the leaves. Indeed, if there is sufficient methyleugenol in the atmosphere, the fly will continue to engorge the food of the plant, until it dies from over-indulgence.

This fruit-fly is perhaps, unusually sensitive to this flower scent. As little as 0·01 μg methyleugenol will produce a response from a single fly in a cage. The structure is very specific; synthesis of 34 analogues failed to produce another compound as active and most analogues were inactive. In passing, it is of interest that one active analogue methylisoeugenol, which differs only in the position of the side chain double bond, has also been shown to be a pheromone; it is an oviposition stimulant in carrot leaves to the female carrot rust fly *Psila rosae* (Berüter and Stadler, 1971).

The second example of pheromone-flower scent interaction is taken from recent studies on bee orchids by Kullenberg and Bergström (1975). The specific way that certain wild solitary bees of the genus *Andrena* are attracted to orchid flowers of the genus *Ophrys* for purposes of pollination has been appreciated for some time. The shape and colour of the orchid flower closely resembles that of the female bee of the species and the male descends on the plant, performing what is termed "pseudocopulation", and pollinating the flower in the process. What has not been realized until recently (Kullenberg, 1952) is that the visual lure of the orchid flower shape is closely associated with an olfactory attraction and that the orchid scent, in fact, mimics the sexual odours of the female bee, thus ensuring the presence of the male bee to trigger orchid pollination.

Following from these field observations, the scent of *Ophrys* has been analyzed. The major constituents are bicyclic sesquiterpenes of the cadinene series. Both (+)- and (−)-δ-cadinene have been identified and it is interesting that it can be shown in laboratory experiments that the male bee is excited by the (−)-isomer, but not by the (+)-form. Thus only compounds with the right stereochemistry produce maximal behavioural response in these insects.

The odour glands of the female *Andrena* bees have also been extracted and examined. Their "Dufour's gland" secretions contain open chain mono- and sesqui-terpene esters. *Trans*-farnesyl and geranyl hexanoates are the major substances in five *Andrena* species; the corresponding octanoates occur in a sixth species. Presumably, the bicyclic sesquiterpenes in the *Ophrys* scent are sufficiently similar in smell properties to the female sex pheromones that they "fool" the male bee into thinking he is approaching a real female.

A special feature of the odour compounds in the female bee secretions is that they have to perform two functions. Not only do they provide a sex pheromone, but also they are employed as nest lining material during the egg-laying process. The active constituents of the Dufour's gland in two other bee genera, *Colletes* and *Halictus*, have also been studied and characterized as macrocyclic lactones. One such compound is 18-octadecanolide. Again, these substances are dual-purpose. It is appropriate here to mention that very similar lactones have sex attractant properties in mammals, for example, civetone and muscone, the active odour compounds of the civet cat, *Viverra civetta,* and of the musk deer, *Moschus moschiferus* respectively (see also Chapter 7). Chemical structures of most of the compounds mentioned in the above paragraphs are shown in Fig. 2.11.

A final, third example, also taken from the bee orchid literature, records a case where male bees make use of flower scents as their sex pheromones. This happens with male euglossine bees which live in the tropical forests of central

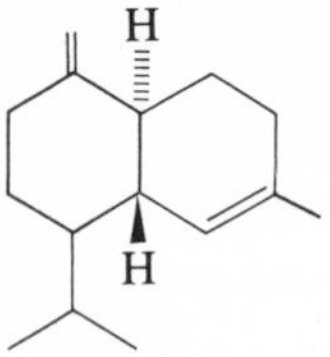

(+)-δ-cadinene 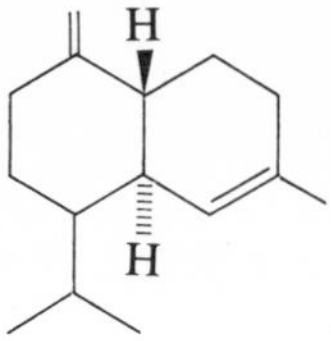   (−)-δ-cadinene

Ophrys scent constituents

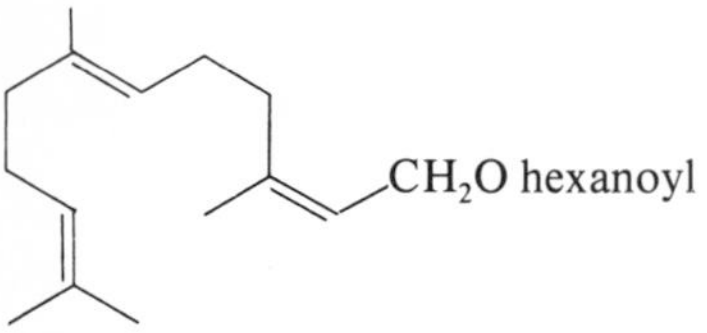

CH$_2$O hexanoyl   CH$_2$O-hexanoyl

trans-farnesyl hexanoate 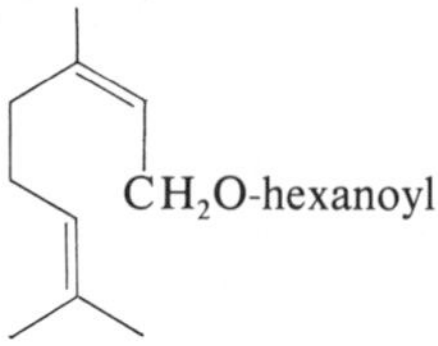   geranyl hexanoate

Female bee scents, genus *Andrena*

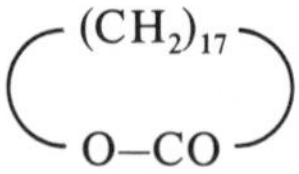

18-octadecanolide
Female bee scent, genus *Colletes*

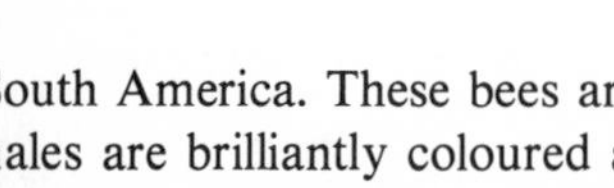

civetone 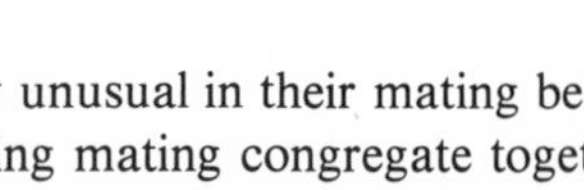   muscone

Fig. 2.11 Terpenoids and macrocyclic lactones involved in bee–orchid interactions

and South America. These bees are highly unusual in their mating behaviour; the males are brilliantly coloured and during mating congregate together into small swarms or "leks" in order to attract the females to them. The orchids which are pollinated by them have evolved a wide range of different floral scents, as part of these extensive speciation in the Neotropics. At least 60 chemically distinct fragrances have been recognized in these plants. While pollinating the orchids, several species of *Eulaema* bees collect the odour fragrances in their hind legs and use them to attract other males of the same species. They then form into swarms or leks, and when this is done, the females are attracted by visual means and mating takes place. Orchid compounds used in this way include eugenol, vanillin, cineole, benzyl acetate and methyl cinnamate. Different bee species are differentially attracted by only some of these odours. Thus, isolation mechanisms preventing different bee species from mating may be due to varying preferences for orchid scent compounds (Dodson, 1975).

IV. ROLE OF NECTAR AND POLLEN

A. Sugars of Nectar

One of the main reasons why animals visit flowers is to obtain the nectar and its nutritional properties are important to most pollinators, especially those who do not obtain nourishment in any other form (e.g. butterflies). Nectar clearly has no other function in the angiosperm flower other than to attract pollinating animals.

The majority of nectars that have been examined consist simply of a solution of sugars. Most are very sweet to taste, varying in sugar content from 15 to 75% by weight. The compounds present are the three common sugars of plant metabolism: glucose, fructose and sucrose (Fig. 2.12). Oligosaccharides also occur, usually in traces, in a number of plant nectars. Of these, the trisaccharide raffinose (6^G-α-galactosylsucrose) is the most frequent, occurring in nectars of Ranunculaceae, Berberidaceae and related families. Other sugars reported on occasion are the disaccharides maltose (glucosyl-α1→4-glucose), trehalose (α-glucosyl-α-glucose) and melibiose (galactosyl-α1→6-glucose) and the trisaccharide melezitose (2^F-α-glucosylsucrose).

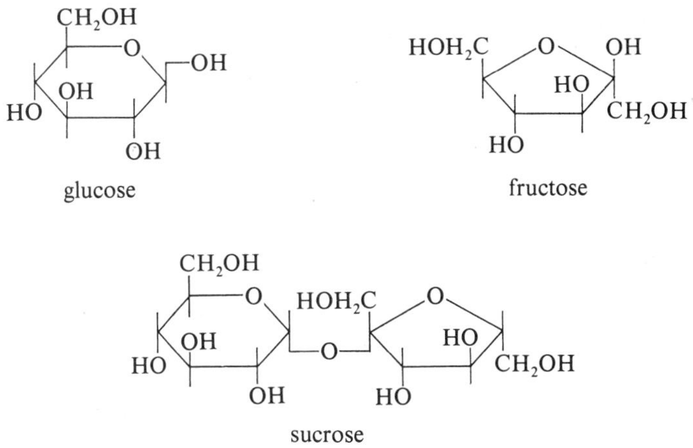

Fig. 2.12 Sugars of nectars

The distribution of the three common sugars in nectars has been surveyed in over 900 species (Percival, 1961) and it has been found that there are distinct quantitative differences between species. Indeed, angiosperm nectars can be divided into three broad groups: those in which sucrose is dominant (e.g. *Berberis, Helleborus*); those in which all three sugars occur in about equal amounts (*Abutilon*); and those in which glucose and fructose are dominant (crucifers, umbellifers, some composites). From these results, it could be concluded that there is an evolutionary trend within angiosperm from nectars with mainly sucrose to those with mainly glucose and fructose. The advantage of this to the pollinator would be the more readily assimilable sugar mixture, i.e. sucrose has to be broken down to glucose and fructose since it cannot be absorbed directly into the blood. More data, however, are needed to see whether such a trend really exists.

Table 2.5 Nectar classes within the genus *Rhododendron*

Nectar class[a]	No. species present in	% total	Example of species containing this nectar
Glc : Fru : Suc in 1 : 1 : 1 ratio	12	22	*R. phaeochrysum*
Suc with traces of Glc and Fru	8	15	*R. augustinii*
Glc : Fru : Suc (1 : 1 : 1) with oligosaccharide	3	5	*R. jasminiflorum*
Suc only	15	27	*R. camphylocarpum*
Glu and Fru only	17	31	*R. campanulatum*

[a] Abbreviations: Glc, glucose; Fru, fructose; Suc, sucrose.
  Oligosaccharide present is possibly raffinose; data from unpublished results of J. C. Cullen and J. B. Harborne.

We have analyzed nectars of *Rhododendron* species and found all three sugar types within the genus. Indeed, we were able to divide species into five nectar classes, based on the proportion of the three common sugars and the presence/absence of an oligosaccharide (Table 2.5). These nectar classifications followed sectional groupings within the genus, so that the method has possibilities from the taxonomic viewpoint.

A remarkable feature of these quantitative variations in nectar sugars is that the groupings remain consistent within the species and are not subject to diurnal or seasonal variations. Since sucrose is readily converted to glucose and fructose via enzymic reaction with invertase, one might expect considerable changes with age. Although invertase has been detected in nectars, it is presumably not present in sufficient quantity or sufficiently frequently or not present at the right time to change the patterns seriously. A recent survey of nectars for proteins (Baker and Baker, 1975) showed them to be generally absent, detectable amounts only being present in 14% of the sample.

B. Amino Acids of Nectars

It is curious that until very recently, the presence of amino acids in plant nectars lay largely undetected. Apart from a few earlier isolated reports (e.g. Ziegler, 1956), clearcut proof that amino acids are regular constituents of nectars did not appear until 1973 (Baker and Baker, 1973a, b). These two authors found them in minor but significant amount in 260 of 266 plant nectars surveyed.

The Bakers first looked for amino acids following the logical argument that certain pollinators, especially higher butterflies, were almost completely dependent on nectar for their nutrition; since they survived as adults for several months, they must clearly need nitrogen as well as sugar. These authors were also guided in their search by a number of naturalist observations, all indicating that these same butterflies took advantage of any nitrogen that might be available to them. Thus, tropical forest butterflies have been known to feed both on decaying crocodiles on the banks of the Amazon and on rotting, putrescent fruit of tropical legume trees. They have even been observed to absorb human sweat for its nitrogen content. There is an authenticated story of a hiker in Arctic Canada who took off his boots, while resting at midday, only

Table 2.6 Amino acid concentrations of nectars according to plant family

Relative advancement	Plant family	Total amino acid on histidine scale[a]
MORE	Asclepiadaceae	8·4
	Liliaceae	7·4
	Campanulaceae	7·0
	Leguminosae	6·9
	Amaryllidaceae	6·9
	Compositae	6·3
LESS	Rosaceae	3·9
	Myrtaceae	3·1
	Saxifragaceae	2·7
	Caprifoliaceae	2·2

[a] Ninhydrin colour on paper of single drops of nectar compared with same colours of histidine solutions. A score of 2 corresponds to a 98 μm solution of 4 to 391 μm, of 6 to 1·56 mM and of 8 to 6·25 mM (= c. 1 mg/ml). Data from Baker and Baker (1973b).

to be invaded by a swarm of butterflies collecting around his sweaty feet and socks.

The amounts of amino acid present in most nectars, although small, are sufficient to provide insects with a useful nitrogen supply. Thus 0·4 ml of a butterfly flower nectar contains about 840 nmol of amino acid, a daily intake of which would probably be sufficient to meet the nitrogen requirements. Baker and Baker (1973b), in their quantitative analyses of nectar nitrogen, noted significant variations in different angiosperms. Indeed, increase in amino acid content was correlated with increasing evolutionary advancement, woody primitive families tending to have lower amino acid scores than advanced herbaceous groups (Table 2.6). This is also correlated with the fact that the lower scoring families tend to be bee-pollinated, insects which can obtain nitrogen from other sources (e.g. pollen). By contrast, the higher scoring families have significantly more taxa which are pollinated by butterflies and, to a lesser extent, by humming birds. It thus appears almost as if plants have evolved to produce larger amounts of nitrogen in the nectar in response to the nutritional needs of their chosen pollinating vectors.

All the common protein amino acids are present in nectars (Baker and Baker, 1975). There is considerable qualitative variation and the number in easily detectable amounts may vary from one to twelve. The ten amino acids essential for insect nutrition (arginine, histidine, lysine, tryptophan, phenyl-alanine, methionine, threonine, leucine, isoleucine and valine) are better represented than others; glutamic and aspartic acids are also frequent. The variation in detectable amino acids between species is consistent and may be useful as a chemotaxonomic character (Baker and Baker, 1976). Nectars of hybrids between species with different amino acid profiles contain all the amino acids of the two parents; inheritance of nectar nitrogen is thus additive.

One other class of nutritional compound has been detailed in nectar: lipid. Lipids were reported in a few bee-pollinated members of the Scrophulariaceae by Vogel in 1969. A survey (Baker and Baker, 1975) has shown that lipids occur in a minority of nectars, being detected in some 34% of a 220 species sample. Lipids thus represent a minor energy source for some anthophilous animals.

Occasionally, nectars contain toxins, presumably derived initially from other plant parts. Honey produced by bees foraging on unusual plant sources are sometimes tainted by such compounds. The toxic diterpene acetylandromedol has actually been characterized in the nectars of *Rhododendron*. Alkaloids also occasionally appear and in the case of the nectar of *Sophora microphylla*, have been present in sufficient concentration to cause toxicity to the honey bees (Clinch *et al.*, 1972). Substances, which are harmless to man, may be toxic to bees. The glucoside arbutin from *Arbutus unedo* honey is apparently harmful to bees (Pryce-Jones, 1944). Again, the simple sugar galactose has been detected in the stigmatal exudates of tulip flowers and is also toxic to bees (Barker and Lehner, 1976). Our knowledge of nectar toxins is still very limited and as Baker and Baker (1975) put it "much more work is needed on substances potentially *unfavourable* to flower visitors".

C. Nutritive Value of Pollen

Any account of the nutritional benefit gained by animal pollinators from plants would be incomplete without some mention of pollen. The pollen is usually more accessible than the nectar and is collected and used by many flower visitors. Pollen is particularly fed on by beetles who have to chew it in order to break open the tough pollen walls. Bees benefit enormously from pollen, which they are able to digest. Pollen occasionally becomes mixed with the nectar, and in such conditions, the nutritional benefits may be available to animals (e.g. *Heliconius* butterflies) which feed solely on the nectar.

The chemistry of pollens has been exhaustively investigated (Barbier, 1970; Stanley and Linskens, 1974). Nutritionally, pollen is a rich source of food with 16–30% protein, 1–7% starch, 0–15% free sugar and 3–10% fat. Trace constituents present include various vitamins and inorganic salts. There are also varying amounts of secondary substances. Pollen is often coloured, especially by carotenoid but also by flavonoids and this is probably a signal to indicate its availability to insect feeders. The carotenoids of pollen are usually α- and β-carotene, lutein, zeaxanthin and their various epoxides. Deep red and purple pollens often have anthocyanidin for pigmentation (e.g. *Anemone*). Other flavonoids, especially the flavonol isorhamnetin, are frequently present in pollens and contribute to pale yellow colours.

Pollen has primary importance as the carrier of the male gametophytes, so that all use of pollen by animals for feeding is secondary and represents "pollen theft" as far as the plant is concerned. Competition between the two contrasting purposes of pollen is rarely a problem, since the majority of angiosperms are over abundant in pollen production. If insects did not capitalize on the excess pollen available to them, it would go to waste in other ways.

BIBLIOGRAPHY

Books and Review Articles

Baker, H. G. and Baker, I. (1973b). Amino acid production in nectar. In: Heywood, V. H. (ed.), "Taxonomy and Ecology", pp. 243–264. Academic Press, London.
Baker, H. G. and Baker, I. (1975). Nectar constitution and pollinator–plant co-evolution. In: Gilbert, L. E. and Raven, P. H. (eds.), "Coevolution of Animals and Plants", pp. 100–140. Texas Univ. Press, Austin.
Baker, H. G. and Hurd, P. D. (1968). Intrafloral ecology. *Ann. Rev. Entom.* **13**, 385–414.

Barbier, M. (1970). Chemistry and biochemistry of pollens. In: Reinhold, L. and Lipschitz, Y. (eds.), "Progress in Phytochemistry", Vol. 2, pp. 1–34. Wiley, London.

Crowe, L. (1964). Evolution of outbreeding in plants. I. The angiosperms. *Heredity* **19**, 435–457.

Dodson, C. H. (1975). Coevolution of orchids and bees. In: Gilbert, L. E. and Raven, P. H. (eds.), "Coevolution of Animals and Plants", pp. 91–99. Texas Univ. Press, Austin.

Faegri, K. and van der Pijl, L. (1971). "Principles of Pollination Ecology", 2nd edn. Pergamon Press, Oxford.

von Fritsch, K. (1950). "Bees, Their Vision, Chemical Senses and Language." Cornell, Ithaca, New York.

Goodwin, T. W. (ed.) (1976). "Chemistry and Biochemistry of the Plant Pigments", 2nd edn. Academic Press, London.

Grant, V. (1971). "Plant Speciation", 435 pp. Columbia Univ. Press, New York.

Grant, V. and Grant, K. A. (1965). "Flower Pollination in the Phlox Family." Columbia Univ. Press, New York.

Harborne, J. B. (1967). "Comparative Biochemistry of the Flavonoids", 383 pp. Academic Press, London.

Harborne, J. B. (1976). Functions of flavonoids in plants. In: Goodwin, T. W. (ed.), "Chemistry and Biochemistry of Plant Pigments", 2nd edn., pp. 736–779. Academic Press, London.

Jacobson, M. (1972). "Insect Sex Pheromones". 382 pp. Academic Press, New York.

Kullenberg, B. and Bergström, G. (1975). Chemical communication between living organisms. *Endeavour* **34**, 59–66.

Law, J. H. and Regnier, F. E. (1971). Pheromones. *Ann. Rev. Biochem.* **40**, 533–548.

Percival, M. S. (1961). Types of nectar in angiosperms. *New Phytol.* **60**, 235–281.

Piatelli, M. (1976). Betalains. In: Goodwin, T. W. (ed.), "Chemistry and Biochemistry of Plant Pigments", 2nd edn., pp. 560–596. Academic Press, London.

Proctor, M. and Yeo, P. (1973). "The Pollination of Flowers." Collins, London.

Smith, T. A. (1975). Recent advances in the biochemistry of plant amines. *Phytochemistry* **14**, 865–890.

Stanley, G. and Linskens, H. F. (1974). "Pollen: Biology Biochemistry and Management", 307 pp. Springer-Verlag, Berlin.

Literature References

Asen, S., Stewart, R. N. and Norris, K. H. (1972). *Phytochemistry* **11**, 1139–1144.

Baker, H. G. and Baker, I. (1973a). *Nature (Lond.)* **241**, 543–545.

Baker, H. G. and Baker, I. (1976). *New Phytol.* **76**, 87–98.

Barker, R. J. and Lehner, Y. (1976). *Apidologie* **7**, 109–111.

Beale, G. H. (1941). *J. Genet.* **42**, 197–213.

Berüter, J. and Stadler, E. (1971). *Z. Naturforsch.* **26b**, 339–340.

Brehm, B. G. and Krell, D. (1975). *Science* **190**, 1221–1223.

Clinch, P. G., Palmer-Jones, T. and Forster, I. W. (1972). *N.Z. J. Agric. Res.* **15**. 194–201.

Dement, W. A. and Raven, P. H. (1974). *Nature (Lond.)* **252**, 705–706.

Eisner, T., Eisner, M., Hyypio, P. A., Aneshansley, D. and Silbersgleid, R. E. (1973). *Science* **179**, 486.

Harborne, J. B., Heywood, V. H. and King, L. (1976). *Biochem. Syst. Ecol.* **4**, 1–4.

Hickman, J. C. (1974). *Science* **184**, 1290.
Horovitz, A. and Cohen, Y. (1972). *Amer. J. Bot.* **59**, 706–713.
Kullenberg, B. (1952). *Bull. Soc. Hist. Nat. Afr. du Nord.* **43**, 53.
Pryce-Jones, J. (1944). *Proc. Linn. Soc. London* 129–174.
Mody, N. V., Henson, R., Hedin, P. A., Kokpol, U. and Miles, D. H. (1976). *Experientia* **32**, 829.
Pijl, L. van der (1961). *Evolution* **15**, 44–59.
Scogin, R. and Zakar, K. (1976). *Biochem. Syst. Ecol.* **4**, 165–168.
Thompson, W. R., Meinwald, J., Aneshansley, D. and Eisner, T. (1972). *Science* **177**, 528–530.
Vogel, S. (1969). *Abstracts XI Int. Bot. Congr. Seattle*, p. 229.
Ziegler, H. (1956). *Planta* **47**, 447–500.

3 | Plant Toxins and Their Effects on Animals

I. INTRODUCTION

As Feeny (1975) has put it, the most conspicuous non-event in the history of the angiosperms is the failure of insects and other herbivores to attack plants on a wide scale. Green plants still dominate the landscape, in spite of the proven ability of insects—witness the devastation of locusts—to overeat and destroy them. It follows that all plants must be broadly repellent to animals as food and toxic in the widest sense. It is the selective ability of insects and grazing animals to overcome these defense mechanisms that allows them the limited feeding that we witness today.

The plant's defense is based on both physical and chemical factors. Physical defense mechanisms against herbivores are readily appreciated: tough epidermises, cuticular deposits, spines, thorns, prickles and stinging hairs. Defense may be purely strategic, as in the case of grasses which adapt to grazing by clinging close to the soil and by vegetative reproduction under the soil surface. Nevertheless, chemical defenses are also very important, provided by toxins and repellent substances of one type or another within the plant itself. These toxins have had and continue to have a key role in protecting plants from overgrazing.

Our views on plant toxins, the subject of the present chapter, have long been blinkered by the limited viewpoint that the only plants that are toxic are those that are dangerous to ourselves or to farm and domestic animals. On this view, relatively few plants are really poisonous and the toxin present is usually alkaloidal. This, however, completely neglects the fact that plants which are relatively harmless to us may be highly toxic to other groups of animals—birds, fish and especially insects. Plant insecticides such as nicotine, the pyrethrins and rotenoids are well known but less is known of the many other plant toxins inimical to insect life. McIndoo in 1945 drew up a list of 1,180 plant species containing insect poisons, the majority of which remain uninvestigated to this day. We are thus concerned here with toxicity in the very widest sense—to all animals which eat plants, from man to the humblest insect. Toxicity is present in most plants, not just those listed in the Flora with a P for poison against them.

The toxicity of a chemical is always relative, dependent on the dose taken in a given time period, the age and state of health of the animal, the mechanism of absorption and mode of excretion. The steroidal alkaloid solanine, for example, is present in all domestic potatoes but the amount present is so infinitesimal that it is rarely a dietary hazard. It is only when enormously large amounts of solanine accumulate in tubers that have been exposed above the soil surface and become "greened" that death from solanine poisoning is a reality. In such cases, victims have no time to adapt to dealing with the toxin and, unless they are sick, they die from respiratory failure. Whether death occurs on intake of a toxin depends therefore on whether the animal has time to become accustomed to small amounts of the poison in the diet, i.e. whether it has been able to develop detoxification mechanisms.

Toxins often have the role of feeding repellents, since plants usually advertise their presence by a warning signal of a visual or olfactory nature. Thus animals may be made aware of the presence of the toxins even before they start feeding. Mustard oils, for example, which occur in crucifers in bound form and are toxic to most insects, have a pungent acrid smell and are probably emitted continuously in trace amounts from the living plant. Other immediate warnings of danger may be provided through visual means by toxins deposited on the surface of leaves and other organs. Potentially toxic secondary compounds may occur in the surface waxes. Alternatively, glandular hairs on the leaf may secrete a toxic quinone, as in *Primula obconica*, or there may be a deposit of quinone on the leaf undersurface, as in a number of labiates. Again chemical defense is often "advertised" in woody plants when they exude resins from bark and fruit.

In the case of HCN, intact cyanophoric plants release no prussic acid, since the substrates and enzymes for HCN production are located in different organelles. It is only when the leaf is damaged by herbivores that the substrate and enzyme come together to produce the poison, which has a clear warning in its "odour of bitter almonds". In the case of alkaloids and saponins, the warning signal is only received after the animal has started feeding, in the form of a bitter taste. Most alkaloids and saponins are known to be bitter. Indeed, the standard for bitterness is quinine, the alkaloid of cinchona bark, which is still bitter to humans at a concentration of 1×10^{-6} M. Many other plant compounds are bitter, especially the triterpenoid cucurbaticins of the cucumber family, which clearly provide the basis of repellency to herbivores in these plants. The latexes which flow within plants such as chicory, dandelion and other composites also have an obvious role in herbivore deterrence, since they often contain bitter toxins among their constituents.

Finally an association of toxicity with a warning coloration can be seen in the brightly coloured, evil-looking purple black berries of the deadly nightshade, *Atropa belladonna*. The colour signal here is dual-purpose. It is a warning to predators (e.g. grazing mammals) which may be killed by the tropane alkaloids richly present in the berry. It is also a feeding signal to those animals which can safely tolerate the toxin, e.g. birds, which can then distribute the seed for the benefit of the plant.

The objectives in this chapter, then, are to present a brief account of plant toxins, with emphasis on more recently discovered classes, and to consider the ecological role of these toxins in plant–animal interactions.

II. DIFFERENT CLASSES OF PLANT TOXINS

A. Nitrogen-Based Toxins

Of the various nitrogen-based plant toxins (Table 3.1), the simplest in structure are the non-protein amino acids. These are widely present in plants and may be directly toxic in as much as they are anti-metabolites of one or other of the twenty protein amino acids (Fig. 3.1). In the simplest case, e.g. of azetidine 2-carboxylic acid, they may be mistakenly incorporated into protein synthesis, the organism produces unnatural enzymic protein which cannot function properly and death of the organism ensues. The toxic effect of other non-protein amino acids may sometimes be more complex. 3,4-Dihydroxyphenylalanine or L-DOPA, which is harmful to insects, interferes with the activity of tyrosinase, an enzyme essential to the hardening and darkening of the insect cuticle.

There are about 400 known structures of these plant amino acids (Fowden, 1970; Bell, 1976). While they are found in a number of unrelated families, they are particularly characteristic of legumes and occur mainly in the seeds. One

Table 3.1 Some nitrogen-based toxins in plants

Class of compound	Example(s)	Toxicity
Non-protein amino acids	L-DOPA in *Mucuna* seed	Insects, espec. bruchid beetles
	β-Cyanoalanine in *Vicia* seed	Fatal dose in rats 200 mg/kg body wt
Cyanogenic glycosides	Linamarin and lotaustralin in *Lotus corniculatus*	Universal; fatal dose of HCN in man *ca* 50 mg
Glucosinolates	Sinigrin in *Brassica*	Cattle and insects
Alkaloids	Senecionine in ragwort *Senecio jacobaea* leaves	Espec. cattle
	Atropine in *Atropa bella-donna* berries	Mammals, but not birds; LD_{50} in rats 750 mg/kg
Peptides	Amanitine in *Amanita phalloides*	Mammals
	Viscotoxin in *Viscum album* berries	Animals, but not birds
Proteins	Abrin in *Abrus precatorius*	Lethal dose in man 0·5 mg
	Phytohaemagglutinin in *Phaseolus vulgaris*	Bruchid beetles

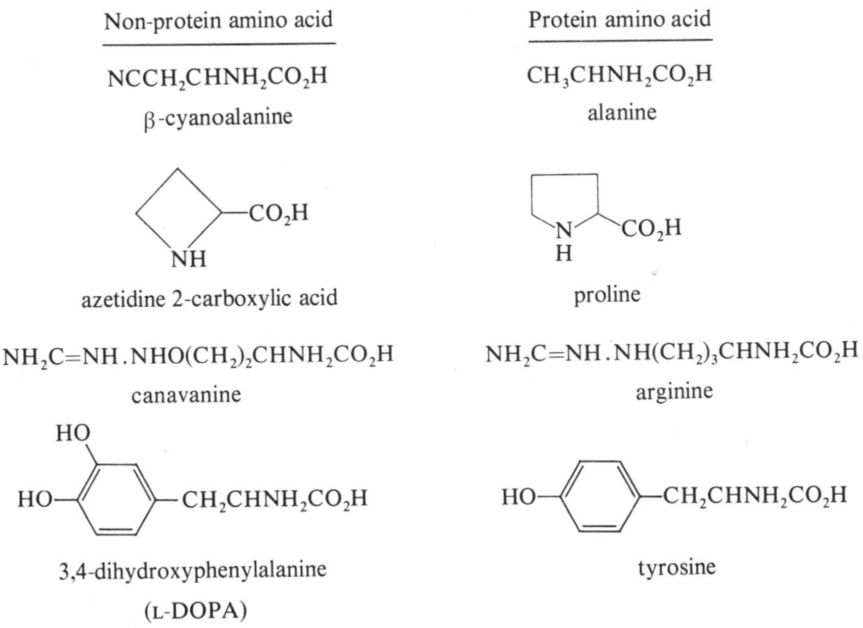
Non-protein amino acid
Protein amino acid
NCCH2CHNH2CO2H
β-cyanoalanine
CH3CHNH2CO2H
alanine
CO2H
NH
azetidine 2-carboxylic acid
N
H
CO2H
proline
NH2C=NH.NHO(CH2)2CHNH2CO2H
canavanine
NH2C=NH.NH(CH2)3CHNH2CO2H
arginine
HO
HO
CH2CHNH2CO2H
3,4-dihydroxyphenylalanine
(L-DOPA)
HO
CH2CHNH2CO2H
tyrosine

Fig. 3.1 Toxic non-protein amino acids and their protein amino acid analogues

which has been widely studied is azetidine 2-carboxylic acid, first isolated in quantity from *Convallaria majalis* (Liliaceae). It has a relatively wide distribution and occurs in several legumes. It is toxic because it interferes with proline synthesis or utilization. Plants which manufacture it in quantity like *Convallaria* are protected from its harmful properties because their protein-synthesizing machinery and more especially the proline *t*RNA-synthetase enzymes can recognize it and do not incorporate it into protein. Unadapted plants mistake it for proline and incorporate it into protein with fatal consequences.

The ecological function of toxic amino acids in legume seeds is fairly clear in that these seeds are particularly large and provide an especially rich source of nutrient to any herbivore. If there was no means of protection, the seeds would undoubtedly be over-eaten. Toxicity in these plants is provided by a variety of chemical structures (Bell, 1972). In *Vicia* species, β-cyanoalanine (or its γ-glutamyl derivative) is present; it is toxic to mammals, causing convulsions and death when injected into rats at a concentration of 200 mg/kg body wt. A more widespread legume toxin is canavanine, which occurs in seeds of the Jackbean *Canavalia ensiformis* to the extent of 4–6% fr wt and of *Dioclea megacarpa* to the extent of 7–10% fr wt. Canavanine is as toxic to mice as β-cyanoalanine is to rats, so presumably it provides protection in the seeds to a range of mammalian herbivores.

The major protective role of legume non-protein amino acids is, however, probably against insect feeding. One example is provided by the occurrence of L-DOPA in *Mucuna* seeds to the extent of 6–9%. While this substance is relatively non-toxic to mammals, being used medicinally in man for treating Parkinson's disease, it is dangerous to insects. On feeding, it causes mortality in the southern army-worm larvae, *Prodenia eridania*. Its ecological role has been discussed by Janzen (1969), in relation to the feeding of bruchid beetles, which attack *Mucuna* and other legume seeds in the natural habitat of the Brazilian forests. Two legume tree species may be growing adjacent to each other; the seeds of one, protected by L-DOPA, are essentially free from bruchid infestation, while the seeds of a second lacking a protective chemical are riddled with bruchid borings. Measurements of seed size and number in these contrasting situations indicate that the trees modify their seed production in relation to their content of deterrent chemical and its effectiveness in preventing beetle predation. Proof that many legume seeds contain insecticidal components has been further obtained in feeding experiments of seed meal to army-worms (Rehr *et al.*, 1973a).

Another structurally simple class of nitrogenous toxin are the cyanogenic glycosides. They are toxic not as such but only when broken down enzymically with release of HCN or prussic acid. The primary site of action of HCN is on the cytochrome system, terminal respiration is inhibited, oxygen starvation occurs at the cellular level and rapid death ensues. The distribution and ecological role of the bound forms of HCN will be discussed in a later section of this chapter. Like HCN, nitrite is toxic to a wide range of organisms and some plants, notably species of *Astragalus,* accumulate glucosides of organic nitro compounds, which are toxic due to the release of nitrite according to the scheme:

$$Glc{-}O{-}(CH_2)_3NO_2 \rightarrow HO(CH_2)_3NO_2 \rightarrow NO_2^-$$

Curiously, the toxicity of the above glucoside, miserotoxin, mainly affects cattle, although the human nervous system is not completely immune to nitrite poisoning. Incidentally, the legume genus *Astragalus,* which contains many species with miserotoxin or related nitro compounds (Stermitz *et al.,* 1972), is remarkably heterogenous in its toxic components. Other species accumulate selenium amino acids (e.g. *A. racemosus*) (see Chapter 1) and yet others (e.g. the loco weed *A. mollisimus*) so far unidentified animal poisons.

Glucosinolates (mustard oil glycosides) are closely related biosynthetically to cyanogenic glycosides and they can also be toxic to animals, when they occur in sufficient amount in plants, as in wild species of *Brassica.* Toxic symptoms include severe gastro-enteritis, salivation, diarrhoea and irritation of the mouth. Toxicity is actually due to the release of isothiocyanates (mustard oils), which are highly vesicant in their action. A further hazard of these substances is due to the fact that during their release from bound forms, the isothiocyanates produced can undergo rearrangement in part to the corresponding thiocyanates:

$$R{-}N{=}C{=}S \rightleftharpoons R{-}S{-}C{\equiv}N \ (R = \text{alkyl or benzyl})$$

the latter substances are harmful because they are goitrogenic, and produce hyperthyroidism in mammals. That glucosinolates are toxic to insects has been demonstrated by Erickson and Feeny (1974) who found that caterpillars of the black swallowtail butterfly (*Papilio polyxenes*) were killed by being fed on celery leaves which had been infiltrated with sinigrin (at a concn. of $0 \cdot 1\%$/fresh wt leaf).

The most familiar class of plant toxins are the alkaloids (Fig. 3.2). These substances have been used since time immemorial for poisoning purposes, an extract of hemlock leaves being used by the ancient Greeks to put the philosopher Socrates to death. The physiological effects of alkaloids on the central nervous system in man have been widely studied and alkaloids are utilized in modern medicine for a variety of purposes. There are at least 5,500 alkaloids of known structure and many more await structural elucidation. These bases occur widely, albeit sporadically, in the angiosperms, being present in about 20% of higher plant families. The term alkaloid covers an enormous range of chemical structures, from the simple monocyclic piperidine, coniine of hemlock *Conium maculatum* to the hexa- and heptacyclic alkaloids like

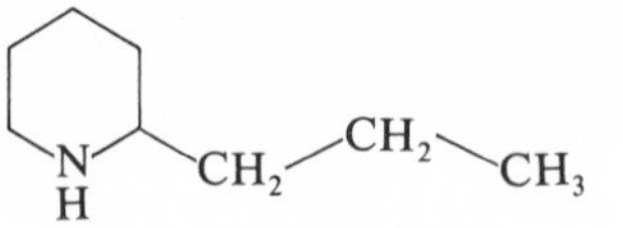

coniine, of *Conium maculatum*
(Umbelliferae)

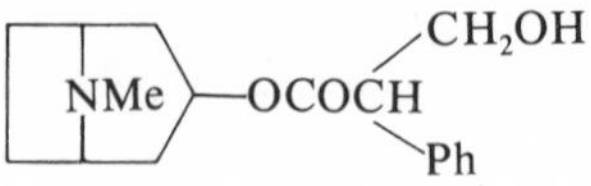

atropine, of *Atropa belladonna*
(Solanaceae)

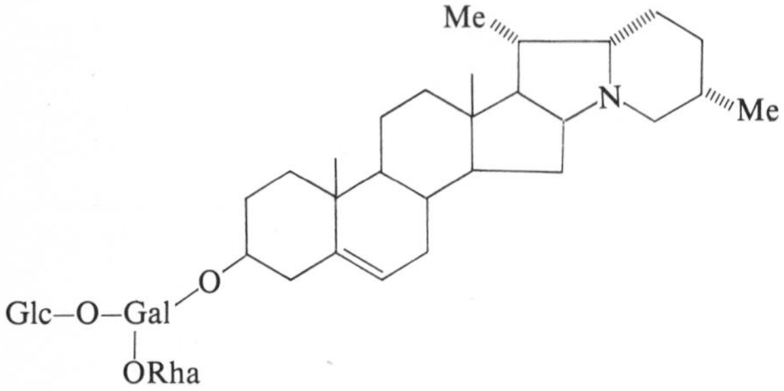

Glc—O—Gal
|
ORha

solanine, of *Solanum tuberosum*
(Solanaceae)

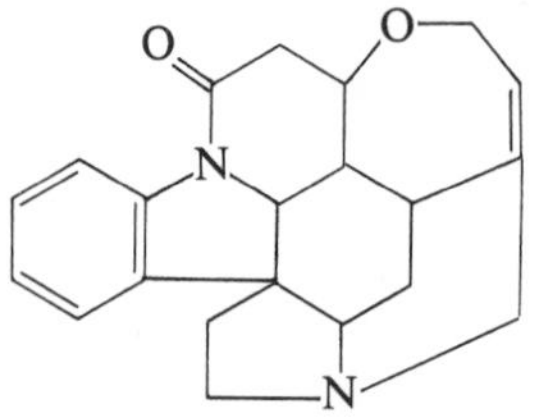

strychnine, of *Strychnos
nuxvomica* (Loganaceae)

Fig. 3.2 Some characteristic alkaloids of plants

solanine of *Solanum tuberosum* and strychnine of *Strychnos nux-vomica*. Not all alkaloids are highly toxic; few are as dangerous as, say, atropine, the principal toxin of deadly nightshade, *Atropa belladonna*. One highly toxic group are the pyrrolizidine alkaloids and their ecological function and toxicity will be mentioned in more detail later in this chapter (Section V.B.).

While the general toxicity of plant alkaloids in mammals, and especially in man and farm animals, is widely recognized, their teratogenic effects have only recently been recorded. Adult female cattle and sheep may imbibe alkaloids in their diet in insufficient amount to cause their death, but as a result of feeding on alkaloid-containing plants, congenital defects may occur in their offspring. Among alkaloids implicated in this way are the pyrrolizidine group, the nicotine group, those of *Lupinus* and also the simple piperidine derivative, coniine of hemlock (Keeler, 1975). The malformed offspring usually suffer various skeletal damage and defects of the digits or of the palate. Such livestock have very limited survival rates. In humans, teratogenic effects including skeletal damage as exhibited in the condition known as "spina bifida" have been attributed to over consumption by pregnant women of potato tubers, which contain the alkaloid solanine. The relationship between this human congenital defect and diet is, however, a complex one and the implication of potato constituents as the causative agents is still far from proven (see Kuc, 1975).

While plant proteins are not usually thought of as being toxic, there are a few which are highly dangerous to animals. One is abrin, the main protein of the seed of *Abrus precatorius* (Leguminosae), the lethal dose of which in man is as little as half a milligram. Since the seeds which are attractively coloured red and black, are employed by African natives for making necklaces, fatalities due to abrin poisoning do occasionally occur. Like most proteins, abrin can be denatured by heating and the toxic effects disappear when the temperature is raised above 65°C. A second well-known protein toxin is ricin, the protein of the castor bean, *Ricinus communis*. It is a protoplasmic poison, the lethal dose, as measured in mice, being 0·001 µg ricin nitrogen/g body wt.

A number of legume seeds, e.g. soybean *Glycine max,* contain proteins which are trypsin inhibitors. While these are not toxic as such, they presumably have a protective role against animal feeding, since they reduce the nutritional value of the protein in seeds containing them. Another class of proteins present in legume seeds are the phytohaemagglutinins, so called because of their ability to coagulate the erythrocytes of human blood. These glycoproteins, which are used routinely in the identification of certain human blood groups, are widely present in plant seeds, both in the Leguminosae and in the angiosperms generally (present in 79 of 147 families tested) (Toms and Western, 1971). The ecological significance of these proteins has largely been neglected, but a recent study by Janzen *et al.* (1976) suggests that they, too, may provide protection in seeds to insect attack. These authors were able to show that the reason why bruchid beetles *Caliosobruchus maculatus* can eat cowpeas (*Vigna unguiculatus*) and not black beans (*Phaseolus vulgaris*) is because while the former are phytohaemagglutinin-free, the latter are rich in these proteins. Indeed, "artificial" seeds made from cowpea flour containing from 1 to 5% phytohaemagglutinin of black beans were found to be lethal when eaten by the beetles. In this case, trypsin inhibitors were present in seeds of both legumes and thus were not implicated in insect repellency.

How far protein toxins generally protect angiosperm seeds from over-predation by animals has not really been studied, but the above examples illustrate the potentialities of plant proteins in this ecological role. Peptides may also be utilized in a similar way and toxic peptides are known both from higher plants (viscotoxin from mistletoe, *Viscum album*) and from fungi (the cyclic heptapeptide amanitine of *Amanita phalloides*).

B. Non-Nitrogenous Toxins

It is not always appreciated that a plant substance does not have to be an alkaloid or even to contain a nitrogen atom in the structure to be toxic to animals. There are many poisonous compounds which are terpenoids or even fairly simply hydrocarbons. For example, many of the plant extracts used as

Table 3.2 Some non-nitrogenous toxins in plants

Class of compound	Example(s)	Toxicity
Cardiac glycosides	Ouabain in *Acokanthera ouabaio*	Heart poison, LD_{50} in rats 17·2 mg/kg
Saponins	Medicagenic acid in *Medicago sativa* leaves	Fish, insects
Flavonoids	Rotenone in *Derris* root	Mainly insects and fish
Quinones	Hypericin in *Hypericum perfoliatum* leaf	Mammals
Polyacetylenes	Cicutotoxin in *Cicuta virosa* roots	Mammals
	Oenanthetoxin in *Oenanthe crocata* roots	Mammals
Aflatoxins	Aflatoxin B_1 from *Aspergillus flavus* infection on peanut	Birds and mammals

arrow poisons by natives in Africa contain cardiac glycosides, such as ouabain, as active ingredients. These steroidal substances are heart poisons. Again, the so-called "five-finger death" caused by the consumption by humans or cattle of the oddly shaped roots of water dropwort, *Oenanthe crocata*, is caused by the presence of polyacetylene hydrocarbons, such as oenanthetoxin, not of alkaloids.

One of the simplest of all non-nitrogenous toxins is monofluoroacetic acid, CH_2FCO_2H, which occurs in certain South African plants, such as *Dichapetalum cymosum*. It is poisonous because it stops respiration, through inhibition of the Krebs tricarboxylic acid cycle; the fatal dose in man is 2–5 mg/kg body wt.

A selection of the known non-nitrogenous toxins are listed in Table 3.2 and some of their structures are given in Fig. 3.3. Among the terpenoids, two particularly toxic groups are mentioned—the cardiac glycosides (or cardenolides) and the saponins. There are other structures in addition, for example the toxic principles of *Rhododendron* leaves and flowers are diterpenes. Also, the sesquiterpene lactones, compounds widely distributed in the Compositae, include some substances which are either toxic in insects (Burnett *et al.*, 1974) or repellent in having allergenic skin effects in animals (Mitchell, 1975). The ecology of terpenoid toxins has yet to be widely examined, but something is known of the cardiac glycosides and this will be considered in more detail later (Section IV).

Some non-nitrogenous toxins in plants are also notable for causing photo-sensitization in farm animals. The quinone hypericin (see Fig. 3.3) of *Hypericum perforatum,* for example, is a photodynamic compound which is

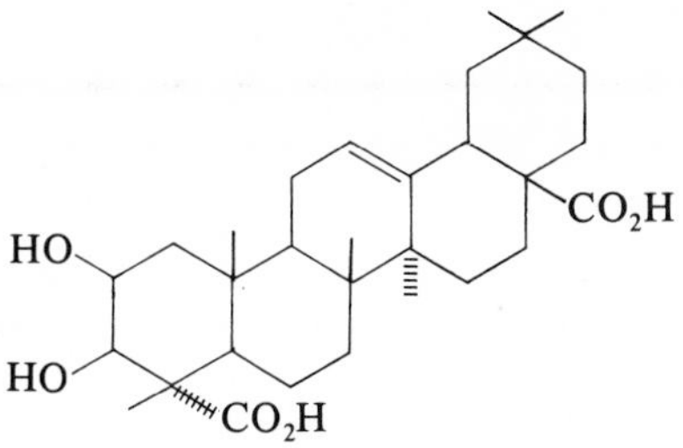

medicagenic acid, from
Medicago sativa (lucerne)

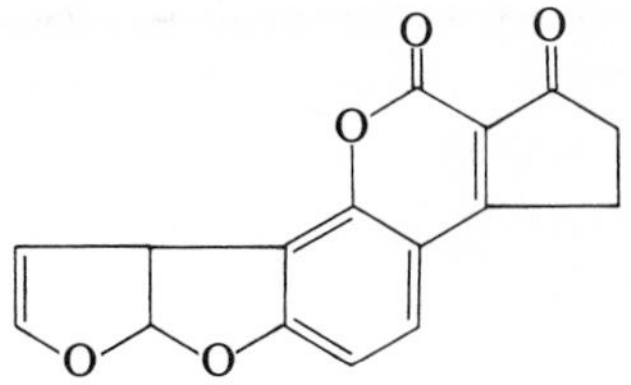

aflatoxin B_1, from *Aspergillus flavus*
growing on peanuts *Arachis hypogea*

$$HOCH_2CH=CH(C\equiv C)_2(CH=CH)_2(CH_2)_2CHOH(CH_2)_2CH_3$$

oenanthetoxin, from *Oenanthe crocata*

$$HOCH_2(CH_2)_2(C\equiv C)_2(CH=CH)_3CHOH(CH_2)_2CH_3$$

cicutoxin, from *Cicuta virosa*

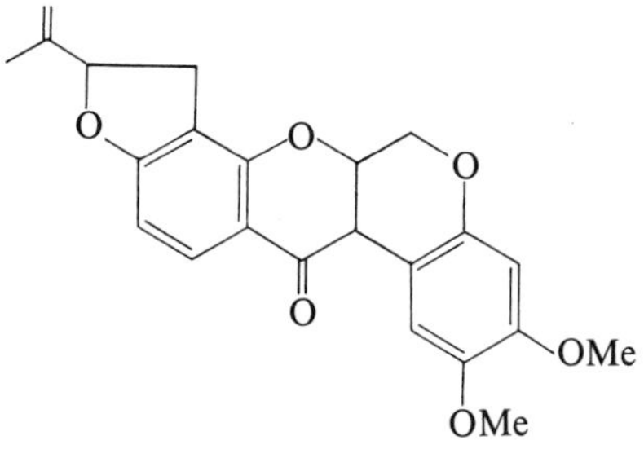

rotenone, from *Derris* root

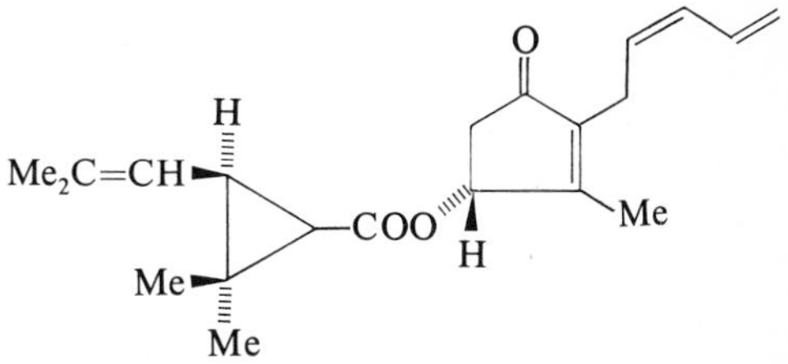

pyrethrin I, from
Chrysanthemum cinearifolium

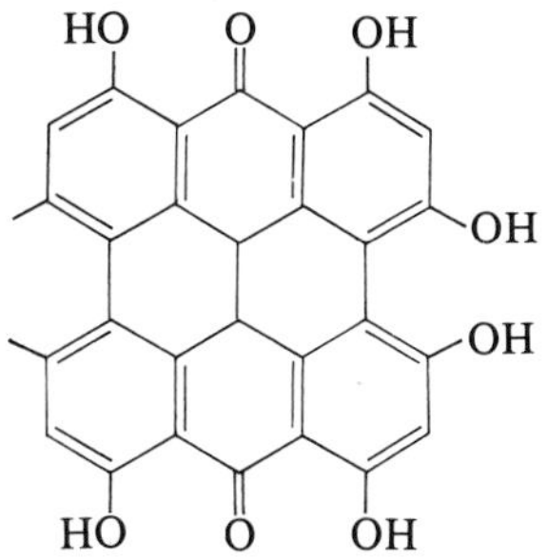

hypericin, from *Hypericum
perforatum* (St. Johns wort)

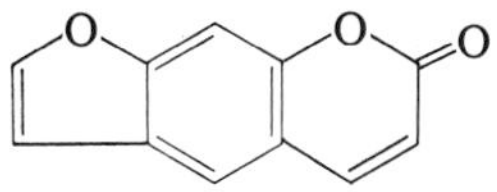

psoralene from umbellifer
leaves and stems

Fig. 3.3 Some non-nitrogenous plant toxins

absorbed by the animal and enters peripheral circulation. When exposed to sunlight, the animal as a result becomes susceptible to sunburn and other damage; serious necrosis of the skin can occur, with subsequent infection and starvation. Among other photodynamic compounds present in plants are furanocoumarins such as psoralen, which are responsible for photosensitization in sheep which have fed on spring parsley *Cymopterus watsonii* (see Keeler, 1975).

One recently discovered group of plant toxins—the aflatoxins—are exceptional in that they are not higher plant products at all but of microbial origin. The first aflatoxins were discovered in peanuts, which were incorporated into the diet of turkeys and other poultry and caused what at first seemed to be a mysterious "turkey-X" disease. The cause of death was traced to the contamination of the peanuts, after harvesting, by a fungus *Aspergillus flavus*. Indeed, the fungus when grown on peanuts produces a series of oxygen heterocyclic compounds, and it was these substances that killed the poultry. There are at least four major aflatoxins produced by *A. flavus* of which aflatoxin B_1 is representative (see Fig. 3.3). The recognition of the cause of poisoning as being due to mould products was made easy in this case by the intense UV fluorescence of the toxins. The pure compounds are carcinogenic in higher animals, with death being due to liver damage. The lethal dose in ducklings is 20 μg, with death occurring after 24 hr. The LD_{50} in mg/kg body wt ranges from 0·35 in ducks and 0·5 in dogs to 9·0 in mice. While both pigs and cattle suffer from the toxin, sheep are relatively impervious.

Following the discovery of aflatoxins in peanuts infected with *A. flavus*, it has been realized that a number of other fungi which are capable of infecting plant foodstuffs produce similar toxins and the general term mycotoxins is now in regular use (Moss, 1972). The discovery of these substances represents a significant threat as dangerous contaminants in foodstuffs of plant origin. Whether such toxins have any importance in natural ecological systems is not yet clear but the fact that higher plants live in a symbiotic relationship with many kinds of lower plant suggests that it is at least conceivable for a higher plant to protect itself from animal predators by harbouring a fungus or bacteria within its tissues which is able to manufacture a lethal toxin of this type.

All the toxins so far mentioned have their effects on the higher forms of animal life; there are also a range of non-nitrogenous substances which appear to be synthesized by plants specifically to ward off insect attack. Two of the best known groups of insecticide of plant origin are the rotenoids, which occur in legume roots, and the pyrethrins, from *Chrysanthemum cinearifolium* flower heads. Other lesser known groups of compounds, not obviously poisonous to higher animals, have also been shown to have toxic consequences in insects. Several common flavonol glycosides including rutin, quercitrin and isoquercitrin, are toxic to a number of insects, including *Heliothis zea, H. virescens* and *Pectinophora gossypiella* (Shaver and Lukefahr, 1969). The role of these substances in insect feeding and deterrence to feeding will be discussed later in Chapter 5.

III. CYANOGENIC GLYCOSIDES, TREFOILS AND SNAILS

A. Occurrence of Cyanogenic Glycosides in Plants

One of the most intriguing examples of plant toxins affecting plant–animal interactions is that involving cyanogenic glycosides, their variable occurrence in clover and birdsfoot trefoil and the differential eating of these plants by slugs and snails. We owe the major development of this work to D. A. Jones, who has described his results in two major reviews (Jones, 1972, 1974). Only a brief outline can be given here, the reader being referred to these reviews for further details.

Cyanogenesis is the ability of plants to synthesize compounds (cyanogenic glycosides) which liberate prussic acid or hydrogen cyanide (HCN) upon hydrolysis. One of the classic sources of HCN is the seed of the bitter almond *Prunus amygdalus*, which contains the glycoside amygdalin. The characteristic odour of HCN, which not everyone can smell, is thus "of bitter almonds". The toxicity of HCN is such that many cases of livestock poisoning and occasional human deaths are recorded each year. HCN is toxic to a wide spectrum of organisms, since its site of action is inhibition of the cytochromes of the electron transport system.

The fact that HCN is easily detected by a spot test using picrate paper (it turns from yellow to red or brown in the presence of the gas) has meant that the distribution of cyanogenesis has been widely studied. Besides their presence in clover and birdsfoot trefoil, at least 800 species representing 70 to 80 families contain cyanogens. The actual structures of the substances releasing HCN have been studied in a smaller sample and some 30 compounds have been fully characterized. Apart from some recently discovered cyanogens which are part lipid in structure from the Sapindaceae (Siegler, 1975), the known cyanogens have the same general structure, shown in Fig. 3.4.

The enzymic release of HCN within the plant is strictly controlled and all plants which make a glycoside contain a specific glycosidase which will

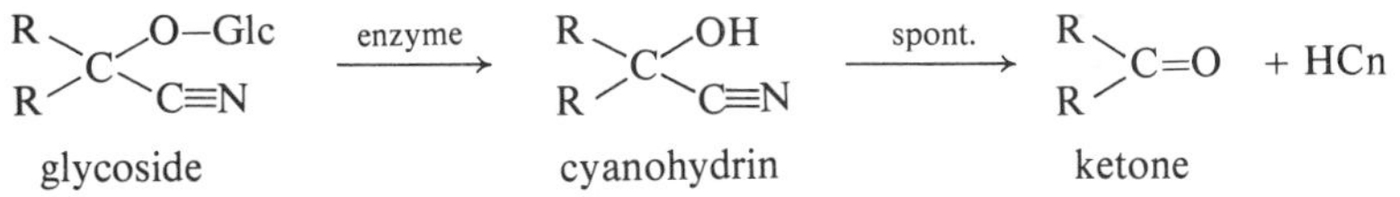

Fig. 3.4 Pathway of release of HCN from cyanogenic glycosides

hydrolyse it. These glycosidases differ in these substrate specificities from the common β-glucosidase and are usually named according to their substrate, e.g. linamarase for linamarin and so on. Hydrolysis of the glycoside releases the sugar (usually glucose) and an intermediate cyanohydrin, which then spontaneously decomposes producing a ketone or aldehyde and HCN (Fig. 3.4).

Probably linamarin (dimethyl substituted) and lotaustralin (methyl, ethyl substituted), the two glycosides of clover and birdsfoot trefoil, are the two commonest cyanogens in nature. These occur in other legume fodder plants, in flax (*Linum*) and in several Euphorbiaceae and Compositae. Aromatic substituted cyanogenic glycosides are also known, such as amygdalin, present in seed of bitter almonds to the extent of 1·8%, and dhurrin, occurring in the cereal *Sorghum vulgare*.

One final point about the cyanogenic glycosides needs stressing—their biosynthetic origin from protein amino acids. It is difficult to believe that plants

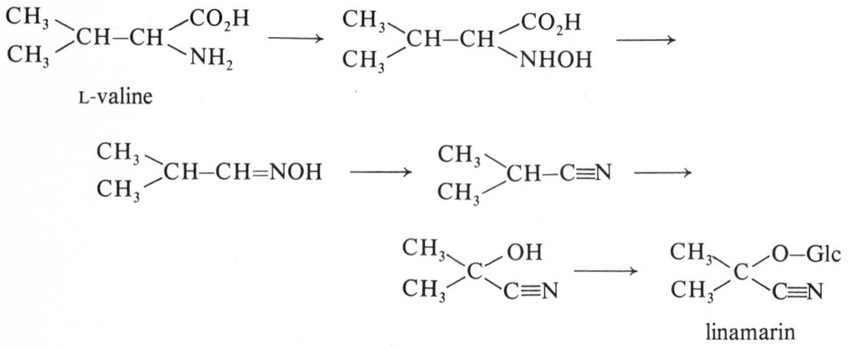

Fig. 3.5 Pathway of biosynthesis of linamarin from valine

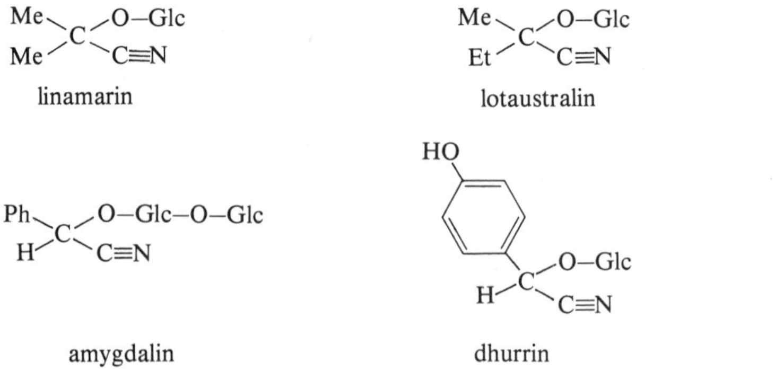

Fig. 3.6 Structures of representative cyanogenic glycosides

directly utilize significant amounts of essential amino acids in this way unless some functional benefit is attached to these products. The frequent earlier suggestions that cyanogens are waste products of primary metabolism seems particularly untenable in the case of substances so immediately formed from protein amino acids and containing their amino acid nitrogen locked up in this way.

The pathway to linamarin synthesis begins with the amino acid valine and takes place in five steps as outlined in Fig. 3.5. Lotaustralin is similarly derived from isoleucine and the aromatic cyanogenic glycosides (Fig. 3.6) come from phenylalanine or tyrosine.

B. Polymorphism of Cyanogenesis

The two plants used by Jones (1972) in the study of the ecological role of cyanogenesis are the clover *Trifolium repens* and birdsfoot trefoil *Lotus corniculatus*, two common pasture plants of temperate grasslands. The enormous advantage of using these two plants is that cyanogenesis is a genetically variable character in populations of both species. The function of cyanogenesis should thus be revealed by comparing plants with and without the character.

This variability or chemical polymorphism in clover was early recognized by geneticists and breeding experiments between cyanogenic and acyanogenic forms soon showed that two genes, G and E, controlled its production. G controls the synthesis of cyanogenic glycoside (e.g. linamarin) and E the enzyme (e.g. linamarase) needed to break it down to give HCN. Natural populations fall into four genotypes (GE, Ge, gE and ge) which can be identified phenotypically by suitable chemical tests.

Fresh leaves are placed in a test tube, crushed briefly with a glass rod in the presence of a drop of chloroform and the tube is stoppered, with a piece of filter paper soaked in picric acid solution hanging down from the stopper. Coloration (to red brown) within an hour indicates cyanogenesis and the dominant type GE. Coloration after 24 hr standing indicates the genotype Ge, since some HCN is liberated non-enzymically from the glycoside during this period. The process can be speeded up by adding some linamarase after the first 1-hr period.

If no colour is given after the 24-hr period, the leaf sample must be gE or ge. In order to finally distinguish between these two possibilities, it is necessary to add a small amount of linamarin to the tube. A colour change now indicates gE; samples still giving no colour can be registered ge, since they lack both glycoside and enzyme. Only the doubly dominant type GE is registered as cyanogenic, all the other three types being acyanogenic in the field.

The fact that clover populations are so readily scored for this character must have been at least partly responsible for Daday (1954) choosing to study the frequency of cyanogenesis in different populations. He soon found remarkable differences in frequency between different European populations. The only factor linking frequency in any given population seemed to be the January mean temperature. A remarkably close correlation was indeed apparent in his results between frequency of cyanogenesis in a given clover population and the winter isotherm at that geographical site. Thus in British populations when the January isotherm is higher than 5°C cyanogenesis runs from 70 to 95% frequency, while in central Russia where the winter temperature is very low, clover populations are acyanogenic. Mid-European populations are intermediate in both senses, with cyanogenic frequencies of 25–50%.

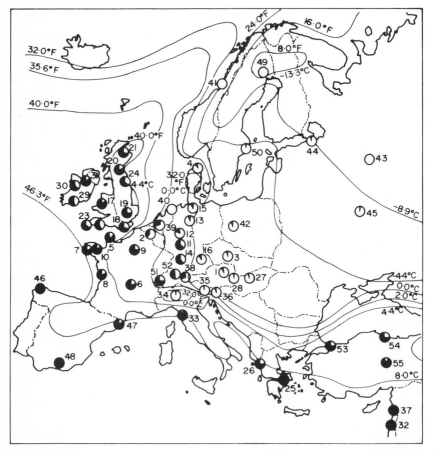

Fig. 3.7 Correlations between cyanogenic frequency and January isotherms of clover populations in Europe (from Jones, 1972)

No one was successful in explaining this peculiar correlation between two such apparently unrelated phenomena until Jones (1966) showed conclusively that slugs and snails, which are significant predators on both plants, show preferential eating for acyanogenic forms of *L. corniculatus*. Taking this new factor into account, one can now interpret Daday's data coherently.

The reason why cyanogenesis is high in British populations is probably because the high winter isotherm means that predators like slugs and snails are active all the year round. When clover and the trefoil start germinating in the spring, the young seedlings are very vulnerable to herbivores at the critical stage in their development and HCN is of considerable selective advantage to deter feeding. By contrast, cyanogenesis is low in frequency or absent from Russian populations of these plants because the icy cold winter forces most animal predators to hibernate. By the time the herbivores are active in the late spring, the clover seedlings will have developed sufficient leaf material not to require protection from feeding, as in England.

Although field studies are still needed to confirm this hypothesis, laboratory studies have shown that differential eating occurs on both *Lotus* and *Trifolium* plants. Of 13 species of slugs and snails examined, seven showed preferences for the acyanogenic forms, while the other six showed no selection. Some predator species are thus tolerant to cyanogenesis and have developed resistance to it by means of detoxification, a process which is now well understood (see Section C below). In ecological terms, then, cyanogenesis still does not provide these plants with complete protection from attack, since only 50% of species of predators are repelled by the toxin. However, this partial protection is clearly still sufficient to make the metabolic expenditure of amino acid precursor on cyanogenic glycoside synthesis worthwhile to these plants. The system is probably one that is actively undergoing selection. The fact that the cyanogenic character is not yet fixed in the population confirms both its partial ineffectiveness as a feeding repellent and also its high metabolic cost to the plant in terms of its requirement for nitrogen.

C. Other Protective Roles of Cyanogens

When snails and slugs feed on trefoil or clover, it is evident that some species are adapted to cyanide in the diet. Adaptation to HCN has been studied in farm animals and there is much evidence that detoxification occurs in sheep and cattle. Detoxification is by means of an enzyme rhodanese which converts the cyanide ion to thiocyanate:

$$CN^- + S \xrightarrow{\text{rhodanese}} CNS^-$$

The sulphur comes from β-mercaptopyruvic acid, $HSCH_2COCO_2H$, which in turn is converted to pyruvate. A similar process is involved in the clinical treatment of cyanide poisoning in man, when sodium thiosulphate is administered intravenously:

$$CN^- + Na_2S_2O_3 \rightarrow CNS^- + Na_2SO_3$$

Evidence that sheep are adapted to feeding on cyanogenic clover has been obtained by feeding them continuously with small amounts of the toxin in their diet. While unadapted sheep can be killed with a dose of 2·4 mg/kg body wt, animals that have become adapted can tolerate as much as 15–50 mg HCN/kg body wt. Sheep respond to the effects of mild HCN poisoning by ceasing to feed until the toxin clears from their systems.

It is thus clear that mammals are usually only killed by feeding on cyanogenic plants when presented with a single large dose at any one time. Such exposure occurs, for example, when tree stumps of the cyanogenic legume *Holocalyx glaziovii* produce young saplings just at the time when grass is scarce in Brazilian prairies. Cattle eat the saplings and die from the high intake of HCN. The protective function of cyanide to the plant is very clearly demonstrated in such instances (da Silva, 1940).

Humans are also subject to HCN poisoning, since cassava roots, used as a staple food in West Africa, contain significant amounts of cyanogenic glycoside, even after powdering and conversion to flour. It has been estimated that people living on cassava receive a daily dose of 35 mg HCN, half the lethal dose. Adaptation is clearly via rhodanese detoxification. However, high levels of thiocyanate may occur as a result and although this is not toxic, it has well-known goitrogenic properties and the long term effects of living on cassava may be early mortality (see Siegler, 1975).

The ecological role of cyanogenic glycosides in plants other than clover and *Lotus* has not generally been explored in such detail, but some information is available on the genus *Acacia*. Here cyanogenesis has a role *vis-à-vis* species which are protected by colonies of ants. Some of the central American species of this large, mainly Australian genus of legume trees have a close mutual association with ants of the genus *Pseudomyrmex*. The plants provide the ants with shelter and food (from nectaries), while the ants provide the trees with protection from herbivores. When disturbed, they viciously attack any approaching marauder. Such *Acacia* species have no need of a chemical defense and, indeed, chemical analyses show that none is present.

There are, however, non-ant *Acacia* growing in the same region of the World and analyses here showed, interestingly enough, that chemical defense is present in the form of cyanogenic glycoside. There is also some evidence in these plants of a second type of toxin, which acts synergistically with HCN in these plants. Feeding of the leaves to army-worms, which are relatively tolerant to HCN, still caused rapid mortality (Rehr *et al.*, 1973b).

The ecological importance to *Acacia* of having an anti-herbivore defense system is nicely illustrated by the fact that if the ant colonies of a young ant-*Acacia* species are deliberately removed, the tree rarely survives beyond another 6 to 9 months (Janzen, 1975). While it is not possible to do the same experiment with a cyanogen-containing *Acacia* species, it can at least be inferred from this that cyanogens are equally vital for survival in non-ant *Acacias*.

Finally, it may be observed that defense by HCN production is not confined to the plant kingdom. It is a protective device in animals, millipedes producing it to ward off attacks by ants. Some red warning-coloured moths also produce HCN at all stages in the life-cycle to make themselves unpalatable feeding to their predators.

IV. CARDIAC GLYCOSIDES, MILKWEEDS, MONARCH BUTTERFLIES AND BLUE-JAYS

What is now the classic example of plant–animal co-evolution in which secondary plant compounds have a key role is the interaction between milkweeds, monarch butterflies and blue-jays. It is an interesting case where insects have capitalized on the plant toxins and used them in their own defense against higher predators. It has the intriguing biological feature of warning coloration in that the insects involved are aposematic.

The various organisms—plants, insects, and birds—involved in this interaction are shown in Table 3.3. The chain of events linking these organisms has been worked out by the principal investigators, who include Brower (1969), Roeske *et al.* (1976), Rothschild (1972) and Reichstein and coworkers (1968). It is briefly as follows:

(1) the milkweed produces several cardiac glycosides within its tissues as a passive defense against insect feeding. The substances are both bitter tasting and toxic to higher animals.

Table 3.3 Organisms of the milkweed–monarch butterfly–blue jay interaction

Plants	Insects	Bird
Asclepias curassavica (milkweed) and other *Asclepias* spp. (Asclepiadaceae) *Nerium oleander* (Apocynaceae)	*Danaus plexippus* (monarch) and four other danaid butterflies Other small insects	*Cyanocitta cristata bromia* (blue-jay)

(2) the monarch butterfly caterpillar learns to adapt to these toxins. They are sequested during feeding and then stored safely within the insect body. This milkweed becomes the preferred food plant of the insect, since there are very few other competing feeders.

(3) the adult butterfly flies away from the host plant with the protective cardiac glycosides stored within it.

(4) a blue-jay tries feeding on the butterfly. It receives a mouthful of bitter-tasting cardiac glycoside, causing it to vomit.

(5) presented with a second monarch butterfly, the blue-jay turns away in distaste, since it has learned to associate the bright coloration of the butterfly with the bitter cardiac glycoside. The blue-jay avoids feeding on this butterfly and any others with the same warning coloration.

The situation, in practice, is more complex than this. For example, the fact that the blue-jay learns to associate the warning colour with the toxic compounds means that colour alone can allow the insect some protection. Indeed, Brower has calculated that only 50% of any given butterfly population need to carry toxins in order for the toxins to provide 100% protection from

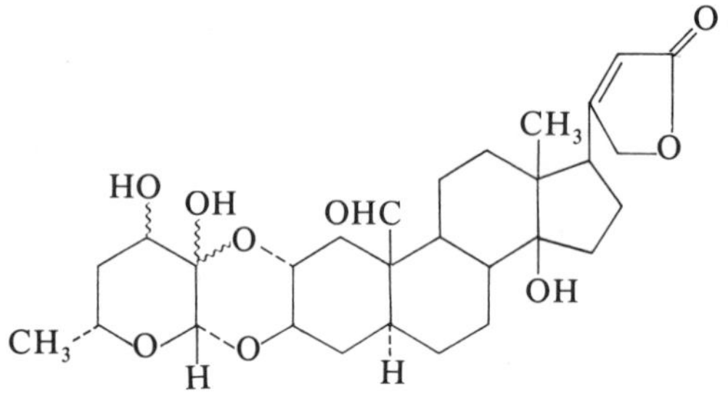

calotropin

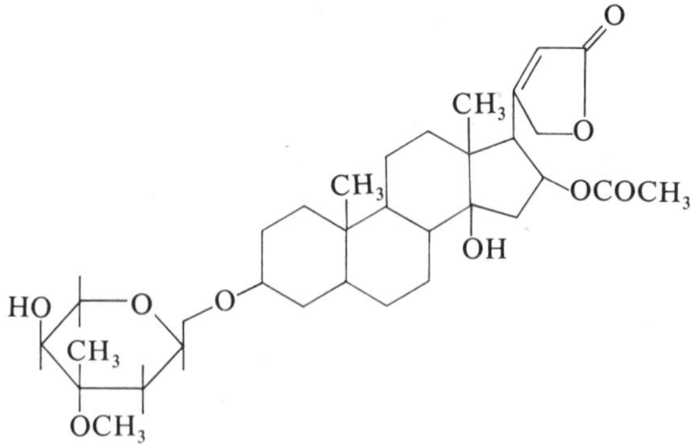

oleandrin

Fig. 3.8 Structures of two cardiac glycosides

blue-jays. This biological device is presumably a safety factor to allow for the fact that the host plants may vary in the quantity and quality of toxins they synthesize and which are available to the insect in any one year. The concentration of glycoside in the insect will vary with the season and with the particular species of the host plant fed upon. Furthermore, not all cardiac glycosides are unpalatable, so that insects may occasionally feed on *Asclepias* without accumulating emetic compounds.

The cardiac glycosides synthesized by the host plants include many different structures. Two examples are calotropin, one of the major glycosides of *Asclepias curassavica* and oleandrin, from *Nerium oleander* (Fig. 3.8). All the plant toxins seem to be absorbed and passed through into the insect's body. Thus, no less than ten glycosides, including calotropin, have been identified in the body tissue of monarch butterflies reared on milkweed. Similarly, eleven compounds have been found in the Lygaeid bug *Caenocoris nerii*, reared on oleander. Brower has calculated that the amount of cardiac glycoside stored on average in a single male butterfly is sufficient to cause five blue-jays to vomit 50% of the time! This odd statistic is a product of the particular method used for testing blue-jay feeding behaviour.

The protection cardiac glycosides afford to the monarch butterfly is also extended to other insects which live on milkweeds, namely four other aposematic butterflies, several Lygaeid bugs, Pyrgomorphid grasshoppers and beetles and one aphid. Finally, yet other butterflies mimic the colour pattern of the monarch and gain aposematic protection, although they do not feed on *Asclepias* nor do they sequester toxins.

Finally, there is the question why do the plants continue to synthesize toxins if the main benefactors are the insect feeders. The simple answer is that production of the toxins continue to provide the plant with protection not only from most insects but also from all grazing animals; cattle, for example, will avoid eating such plants. Also the caterpillars feeding on the plant may accumulate the repellent odour of that plant and serve to reinforce its effectiveness against predators. In addition, the presence of these insects on the plant can act as a lure to pollinators, who will be drawn to the flower and will achieve its pollination.

V, PYRROLIZIDINE ALKALOIDS, RAGWORTS, MOTHS AND BUTTERFLIES

A. Pyrrolizidine Alkaloids in Moths

A similar relationship to that linking milkweeds and butterflies in semitropical areas of north and central America has been discovered in temperate climates, indeed in the meadows around the University of Oxford in England. In this case, the plants are the groundsel, *Senecio vulgaris* and the ragwort, *S. jacobaea,* two very successful weeds of the Compositae family. These plants are powerfully protected from herbivores by containing in their leaves a series of alkaloids of the pyrrolizidine type. Many cases of cattle poisoning have been attributed to these *Senecio* alkaloids (Keeler, 1975). Nevertheless, the caterpillars of the tiger moth *Arctia caja* and the cinnabar moth *Tyria jacobaeae* feed with impunity on these two weeds and carry on their whole life-cycle on these same host plants.

Analysis of the caterpillars and adult moths show, indeed, that all six pyrrolizidine alkaloids of the ragwort are sequestered and stored by these insects. There are changes in the proportions of the alkaloids in plant and in insect and there is evidence that the insect transforms one alkaloid of the host plant into another *in vivo*. The most remarkable demonstration of the non-toxicity of the alkaloids in the insect is the fact that the alkaloids are even present in the insect eggs. The protection of both these moths from their bird and other predators again involves warning coloration, both the caterpillars and the adults being brightly coloured and patterned.

The interaction between *Senecio* and moth is complicated by variations in alkaloid content of the host plant with season, and geographical site. The tiger moth is relatively polyphagous and also feeds on foxglove *Digitalis purpurea* and can even store its cardiac glycosides. Both classes of toxin have been found in the same insect (Rothschild and Aplin, 1971). Presumably, the caterpillar modifies its feeding habits in order to ensure receiving sufficient toxin of one type or another to protect itself.

While the cardiac glycoside–monarch butterfly and *Senecio* alkaloid–moth interactions are the only two to have been fully investigated, it is apparent that such interactions are common in nature, particularly in aposematic insects. Rothschild (1973) has listed over 40 insect species (23 Lepidoptera, 1 Neuroptera, 7 Hemiptera, 5 Coleoptera, 1 Diptera and 6 Orthoptera) which have the ability to sequester and store plant toxins. Negative results were recorded for some 35 aposematic insects examined for toxins at the same time. While toxins were mostly alkaloids or cardiac glycosides, other substances involved were mustard oils (*Pieris brassicae* feeding on cabbage) and quinones (*Chrysolina brunsvicensis* feeding on *Hypericum*).

B. Pyrrolizidine Alkaloids in Butterflies

The ability of insects to feed on plants containing pyrrolizidine alkaloids and store them is remarkable in view of the high toxicity of these substances to other forms of life, particularly mammals. Recent research (Mattocks, 1972) suggests that the toxicity of pyrrolizidines lies not in their own structures, but in the one major *in vivo* metabolite to which they are converted. It appears as if

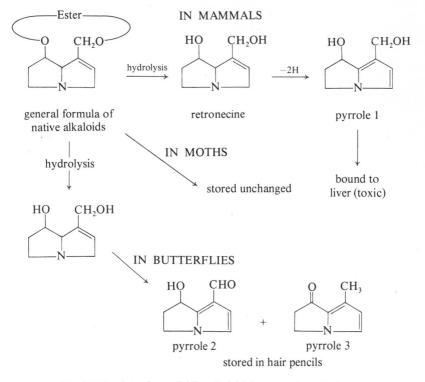

Fig. 3.9 The fate of pyrrolizidine alkaloids in mammals and in insects

mammals, in attempting to detoxify the pyrrolizidine molecule by dehydrogenation have accidentally produced a much more dangerous compound, with fatal consequences.

The pathway of metabolism in mammals (Fig. 3.9) involves hydrolysis of the ester groups of the alkaloid to give the main parent compound retronecine, and this is then dehydrogenated to pyrrole 1, which is the dangerous toxin. Because of its CH_2OH group in conjugation with the alkaloid nitrogen, it can be readily bound through this hydroxyl group to liver, where it interacts with vital cell constituents. It can, for example, act as a bifunctional alkylating agent and combine with macromolecules like DNA. While some of pyrrole 1 is conjugated and excreted in the urine, most binds to the liver or else circulates in the blood, reaching the lungs, where it also has fatal consequences.

That some insects can safely store *Senecio* alkaloids without modification is exemplified by the two moths which feed on these plants in Oxfordshire meadows (see above). That other insects can metabolize them, without fatal consequences, has become apparent from some recent observations on the

Asclepias-feeding Danaid butterflies, which were the main topic of an earlier section in this chapter.

It is clear that these butterflies have another secondary compound requirement, not provided for them by the milkweed (Edgar and Culvenor, 1974; Edgar *et al.*, 1974). This is of pyrrolizidine alkaloids, which are needed to manufacture aphrodisiacal substances which the male butterfly stores in its wing hair pencils and uses in its courtship display to attract the female. Two of the sex compounds are pyrroles 2 and 3 (see Fig. 3.9) which are clearly different in their oxidation level from pyrrole 1, the dangerous toxin in mammals. Pyrroles 2 and 3 are clearly of dietary origin, derived from *Senecio* alkaloids. Indeed, one of the unchanged ester alkaloids of *Senecio* has been found in the insect hair pencils.

Male danaid butterflies have been observed to visit both borages and *Senecio* plants in order to satisfy the feeding requirement. Plants of the Boraginaceae are one of the few other natural sources of *Senecio*-type alkaloids. How the adults, without mouth parts, actually obtain the alkaloid is something of a mystery. They tend to feed on dead or withered plants and are perhaps able to suck the alkaloid from the plant tissue. It is also possible the alkaloid occurs in the flower nectar of the plants in question.

One fascinating evolutionary feature of this unusual behaviour of Danaid butterflies is their failure to obtain the courtship display compounds from their feeding as caterpillars. It is, indeed, very rare for adult butterflies to have any other requirements than nectar during their remaining life. It is clearly connected with their need for two different classes of plant substance—cardiac glycoside (for protection against bird predation) *and* pyrrolizidine alkaloid (for courtship display). One simple explanation of their odd present-day behaviour

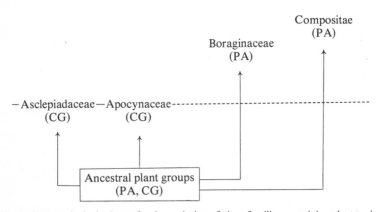

Fig. 3.10 Hypothetical scheme for the evolution of plant families containing plant toxins

is that Danaid butterflies originally fed as caterpillars on a plant containing *both* cardiac glycoside and alkaloid.

Going back in evolutionary time, one can envisage a scheme (Fig. 3.10) whereby some ancestral form of present-day Apocynaceae contained both types of toxin. Subsequent evolutionary pressures might have forced plants to choose between making either one or other of the two types of toxin, so that we reach the present-day situation, where the toxins are differentially distributed among Apocynaceae, Asclepiadaceae (cardiac glycosides) and Boraginaceae, Compositae (alkaloids). Such a theory would envisage that some primitive present-day Apocynaceae might conceivably still retain the capacity of synthesizing and accumulating both classes of toxin. A search for such a plant has, indeed, been successful and a species of *Parsonsia* contains both types of secondary compound (Edgar and Culvenor, 1975).

BIBLIOGRAPHY

Books and Review Articles

Bell, E. A. (1972). Toxic amino acids in the Leguminosae. In: Harborne, J. B. (ed.), "Phytochemical Ecology", pp. 163–178. Academic Press, London.

Brower, L. (1969). Ecological chemistry. *Scient. Am.* **220**, 22–29.

Feeny, P. (1975). Biochemical coevolution between plants and their insect herbivores. In: Gilbert, L. E. and Raven, P. H. (eds.), "Co-evolution of Animals and Plants", pp. 3–19. Texas Univ. Press.

Fowden, L. (1970). The non-protein amino acids of plants. *Progress in Phytochemistry* **2**, 203–266.

Janzen, D. H. (1969). Seed-eaters versus seed size, number, toxicity and dispersal. *Evolution* **23**, 1–27.

Janzen, D. H. (1975). Ecology of plants in the tropics. Studies in Biology No. 58. Edward Arnold, London.

Jones, D. A. (1972). Cyanogenic glycosides and their function. In: Harborne, J. B. (ed.), "Phytochemical Ecology", pp. 103–124. Academic Press, London.

Jones, D. A. (1974). Co-evolution and cyanogenesis. In: Heywood, V. H. (ed.), "Taxonomy and Ecology", pp. 213–242. Academic Press, London.

Keeler, R. F. (1975). Toxins and teratogens of higher plants. *Lloydia* **38**, 56–86.

Kuc, J. (1975). Teratogenic constituents of potatoes. *Recent Adv. Phytochem.* **9**, 139–150.

Mattocks, A. R. (1971). Toxicity and metabolism of *Senecio* alkaloids. In: Harborne, J. B. (ed.), "Phytochemical Ecology", pp. 179–200. Academic Press, London.

Mitchell, J. C. (1975). Contact allergy from plants. *Recent Adv. Phytochem.* **9**, 119–138.

Moss, M. O. (1972). Aflatoxins and related mycotoxins. In: Harborne, J. B. (ed.), "Phytochemical Ecology", pp. 125–144. Academic Press, London.

Riechstein, T., von Euw, J., Parsons, J. A. and Rothschild, M. (1968). Heart poisons in the monarch butterfly. *Science N.Y.* **161**, 861–866.

Roeske, C. N., Seiber, J. N., Brower, L. P. and Moffitt, C. M. (1976). Milkweed cardenolides and their comparative processing by monarch butterflies. *Recent Adv. Phytochem.* **10**, 93–167.

Rothschild, M. (1972). Some observations on the relationship between plants, toxic insects and birds. In: Harborne, J. B. (ed.), "Phytochemical Ecology", pp. 1–12. Academic Press, London.

Rothschild, M. (1973). Secondary plant substances and warning coloration in insects. In: van Emden, H. (ed.), "Insect–Plant Interactions", pp. 59–83. Oxford Univ. Press.

Siegler, D. S. (1975). Isolation and characterization of naturally occurring cyanogenic compounds. *Phytochemistry* **14**, 9–30.

Toms, G. C. and Western, A. (1971). Phytohaemagglutinins. In: Harborne, J. B., Boulter, D. and Turner, B. L. (eds.), "Chemotaxonomy of the Leguminosae", pp. 367–462. Academic Press, London.

Literature References

Bell, E. A. (1976). Personal communication.

Burnett, W. C., Jones, S. B., Mabry, T. J. and Padolina, W. G. (1974). *Biochem. Syst. Ecol.* **2**, 25–30.

Daday, H. (1954). *Heredity* **8**, 61–78; 377–384.

Edgar, J. A. and Culvenor, C. C. J. (1974). *Nature (Lond.)* **248**, 614–616.

Edgar, J. A. and Culvenor, C. C. J. (1975). *Experientia* **31**, 393–394.

Edgar, J. A., Culvenor, C. C. J. and Pliske, T. E. (1974). *Nature (Lond.)* **250**, 646–648.

Erickson, J. M. and Feeny, P. (1974). *Ecology* **55**, 103–111.

Janzen, D. H., Juster, H. B. and Liener, I. E. (1976). *Science* **192**, 795–796.

Jones, D. A. (1966). *Can. J. Genet. Cytol.* **8**, 556–567.

McIndoo, N. E. (1945). *US Dept. Agr. Bur. Entom. Plant Quarantine* **ET661**, 1–286.

Rehr, S. S., Bell, E. A., Janzen, D. H. and Feeny, P. P. (1973a). *Biochem. Syst. Ecol.* **1**, 63–67.

Rehr, S. S., Feeny, P. D. and Janzen, D. H. (1973b). *J. Animal Ecol.* **42**, 405–416.

Rothschild, M. and Aplin, R. T. (1971). In: de Vries, A. and Kochra, E. (eds.), "Toxins of Plant and Animal Origin". Gordon and Breach, London.

Shaver, T. N. and Lukefahr, M. J. (1969). *J. Econ. Entom.* **62**, 643–646.

Stermitz, F. R., Lowry, W. T., Norris, F. A., Buckeridge, F. A. and Williams, M. C. (1972). *Phytochemistry* **11**, 1117–1124.

da Silva, R. (1940). *Arq. Inst. Biologico (Sao Paulo)* **11**, 461–488.

4 | Hormonal Interactions Between Plants and Animals

I. INTRODUCTION

The idea of hormonal interactions between plants and animals seems remote and in the realms of science fiction when one considers how different their hormonal systems are. In animals, hormones are usually manufactured in special endocrine glands and are then transported to the site of action through the circulatory system. Animal hormones are mainly steroidal or peptidal in chemical structure and fall into easily grouped classes according to their effects.

By contrast, in plants, the ability to synthesize hormones is present in many cells. The site of synthesis varies as the plant develops and the hormones may only translocate relatively short distances. Chemically, plant hormones are very diverse, being of several structurally different types, i.e. purine-based (cytokinins), amino acid based (auxins) or terpenoid-based (dormins, gibberellins). One of the major plant growth hormones is even a gas, the compound ethylene, which exerts its effects through the air spaces between the plant cells.

That hormonal interactions do occur between plants and animals will be described in this chapter. They are possible at many levels and depend on the ability of physiologically active chemicals to interact between the different types of living organisms. In some cases, the animal is the dominant partner of the interaction; for example, when leaf cutting ants add auxin hormone to the fungal colonies on which they feed in order to maintain their growth and vitality. More frequently, the plant is dominant, exerting its effects by synthesizing animal hormones and pheromones and thus influencing the life and survival of its animal predators.

The fact that the endocrine system of animals is essentially absent from plants led scientists to reject early reports during the 1930s that mammalian female sex hormones occur in plant tissues. However, recent analytical experiments leave no doubt that both human male and female hormones are present in plants. Their function is, of course, still open to speculation and it is possible that they have a natural role in plants in relation to growth, flowering or sexual expression. Such an argument is supported in part by the discovery of a steroidal hormone, antheridiol, as a chemotactic sex substance in the water fungus, *Achlya bisexualis* (Hendrix, 1970). An alternative suggestion is made here that they are actually synthesized to deter mammalian feeding. Since hormonal activity is delicately balanced and depends on the right amount of a series of compounds arriving in sequence at the right site at the right time, an exogenous dietary source taken at the wrong time could have serious consequences in the reproduction of the female. The feeding deterrent view is supported by the presence in plants of several different compounds which resemble female hormones in structural terms and have oestrogenic activity. This topic of animal and plant oestrogens will be discussed in Section II of this chapter.

Support for the view that hormonal interactions occur between plants and animals has, however, come mainly from entomological studies and the discovery that not one but two classes of insect hormone occur in plants. They occur in relatively large quantities and with a variety of chemical structures. Their function is still speculative but it is clearly possible that they are deliberately produced by plants to interfere with insect metamorphosis and, hence, reproduction. The occurrences in plants of insect moulting hormones and of juvenile hormones will be considered in Sections III and V. One particularly interesting interaction involving insect moulting hormones, fruit-flies and cacti will be described in Section IV.

One further type of hormonal interaction is possible between plants and insects in relation to pheromones. This has already been briefly considered in the chapter on pollination ecology under flow scent (p. 48). The question considered here is the dietary origin of insect pheromones. It is possible that pheromones are synthesized *de novo* by the insect, are manufactured from plant substances of dietary origin or that plant compounds are sequestered and used directly without modification. One situation where all three possibilities are represented is the bark beetle–pine tree interaction and this will be presented in the final section of this chapter.

II. PLANT OESTROGENS

Reports of the presence of female sex hormones in seeds of the date palm and the pomegranate, which first appeared in the literature during the 1930s (e.g. Butenandt and Jacobi, 1933), were treated with scepticism. The methodology of chemical identification was relatively primitive at that time and this factor partly justified the critical attacks on these studies. However, in recent years, much more accurate analytical techniques have been applied to the same and other plant sources (Table 4.1) and the occurrence of both female and male sex hormones in plants is now beyond dispute. They occur in only trace amounts and there is at present the possibility of considerable quantitative variations between plant samples. The occurrence of as much as 17 mg/kg oestrone in pomegranate seeds recorded by Heftmann et al. (1966) has been disputed by Dean et al. (1971), who found much smaller amounts present. The latter authors however, noted its presence in seed, flower, leaf and root.

Whether these reports (Table 4.1) indicate that animal sex hormones are widespread in plants in trace amounts remains to be determined. There are considerable practical difficulties in screening plants for them, because of the low levels present and the time-consuming methods needed to prove their occurrence. Their production in plants could be completely accidental, as by-products of pathways leading to functionally more important plant sterols. Alternatively, they may be involved in plant growth and development or even

Table 4.1 Occurrence of human sex hormones in plants

Compound	Plant source	Concentration (mg/kg)
Oestrone	Date palm, *Phoenix dactylifera*	
	seeds	0·40
	pollen	3·3
Oestrone	Pomegranate, *Punica granatum*	
	seeds	17·0
Oestriol	Willow, *Salix*	
	flowers	0·11
Oestrone	Apple, *Malus pumila*	
	seeds	0·1
Testosterone	Scotch pine, *Pinus sylvestris*	
Androstenedione	pollen	0·08 and 0·59
Androstanetriol	Rayless golden rod, *Happlopappus heterophyllus*	—

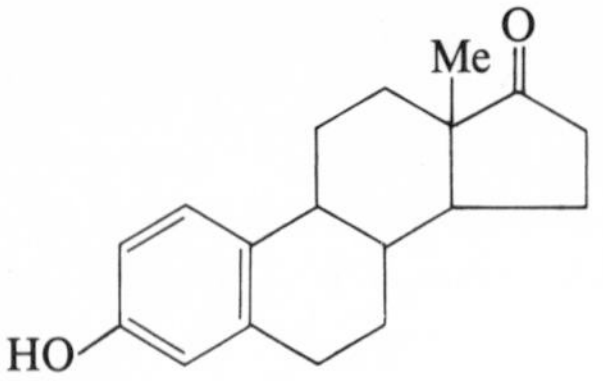

oestrone

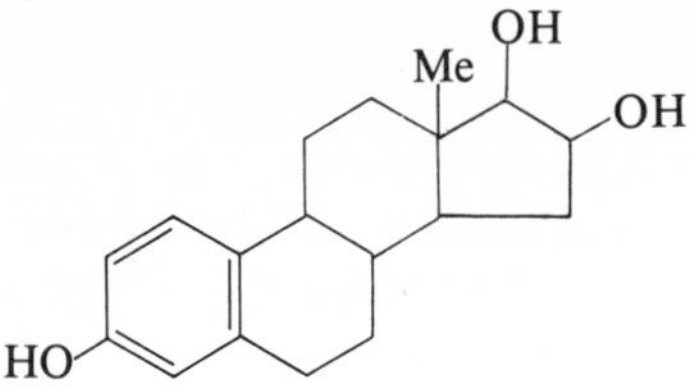

oestriol

OESTROGENS

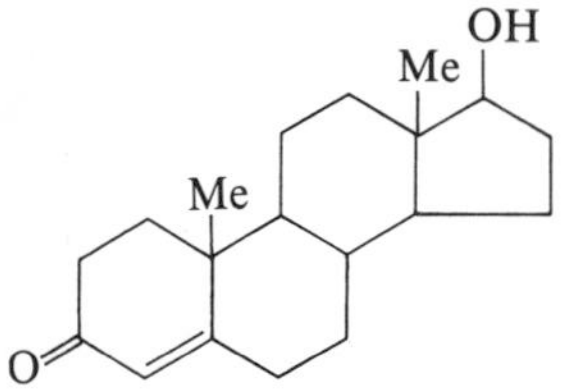

testosterone

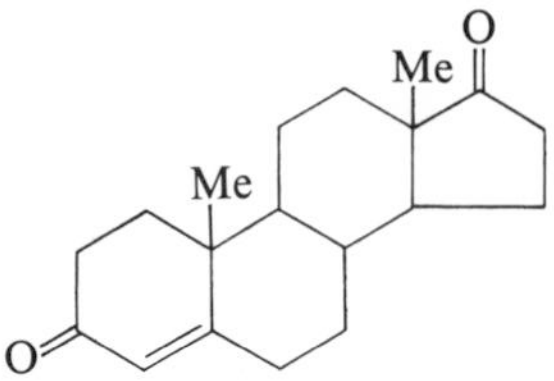

androstenedione

ANDROGENS

Fig. 4.1 Structures of human sex hormones found in plants

in the control of sexual expression in plants. Indeed, the effect of exogenous application of these hormones has been tested in a number of plant species. Among other effects reported are that: (1) oestrogens stimulate seed germination and growth; (2) oestrogens promote floral development; (3) both oestrogens and androgens increase the expression of femaleness in the cucumber; and (4) testosterone application to *Equisetum* increases the number of female prothalli (see Heftmann, 1975). These data are far from indicating that the sex hormones concerned have an endogenous role in plants. In none of these cases was either a male or a female hormone detected in the plant in question.

Reports of unidentified oestrogenic materials in many plant tissues, based on their effectiveness in upsetting the menstrual cycle in women, cows or ewes, suggest that oestrogens may be much more widespread than is indicated in Table 4.1. During the Second World War, for example, women in Holland correlated the eating of tulip bulbs, forced on them by food shortages, with menstrual upsets and ovulation failures. Among other food sources which have had effects on oestrus in women and cows are garlic, oats, barley, rye grass, coffee, sunflower, parsley and potato tubers. It is possible that some or all of these plant materials lack the hormones themselves but contain instead compounds which mimic their effect. This possibility is strengthened by the

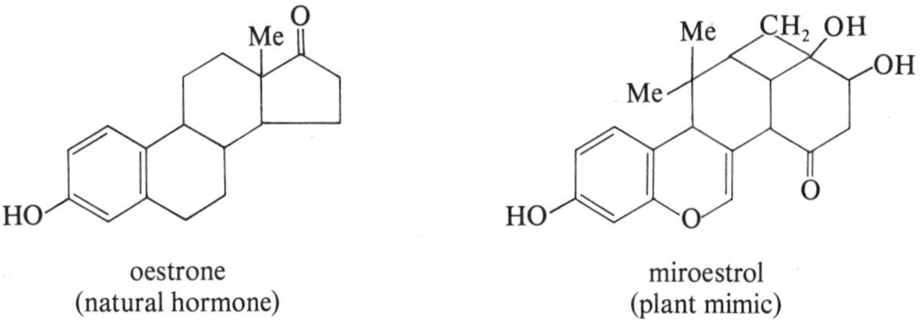

Fig. 4.2 Structural comparison between oestrone and miroestrol

fact that one such steroidal mimic, miroestrol, has been isolated, following a deliberate study of a plant source of known oestrogenic potency. Furthermore, a series of aromatic oestrogens were discovered in plants of the Leguminosae, because of their effects on oestrus in sheep. Indeed, the general term "phyto-estrogen" has been coined to describe any plant compound which has this activity.

The compound miroestrol was isolated, when scientists followed up a report that pregnant Burmese and Thai women used an extract of a legume tree root in order to bring on an abortion. The plant was identified as *Pueraria mirifica* and the active principle in the root characterized by Bounds and Pope (1960). Its structure, shown in Fig. 4.2, is remarkably close to that of the natural female hormone, oestrone. When given subcutaneously in multiple doses, miro-estrol is as potent as 17-β-oestradiol. Its particular effectiveness as an abortifa-cient is because of its activity when taken orally. It is over three times as potent as diethylstilboestrol, a synthetic compound used medicinally in place of oestrone because of its higher activity.

The discovery that isoflavonoids have oestrogenic activity in mammals was discovered during the 1940s when sheep in Australia were allowed to graze for longer periods than usual on pastures containing subterranean clover, *Trifolium subterraneum*. As a result of this practice, lambing percentages were seriously reduced (to less than 10%) and active material causing this infertility was traced to the clover plant. The principle was eventually isolated and identified as a mixture of two isoflavones, genistein and formononetin (Bradbury and White, 1954). Structural comparison (Fig. 4.3) with the hormone oestrone and the most active synthetic analogue, diethyl stilboestrol, shows why these isoflavones are oestrogens—they mimic the steroidal nucleus of the natural female hormone. They are, in fact, rather weak oestrogens on a molar basis (Biggers, 1959) but are presumably effective because of the relatively large quantity (about 1% dry wt) in the clover fodder.

A more active substance, coumestrol, was later isolated by Bickoff (1968) from alfalfa, *Medicago sativa,* and ladino clover, *Trifolium repens*. Although

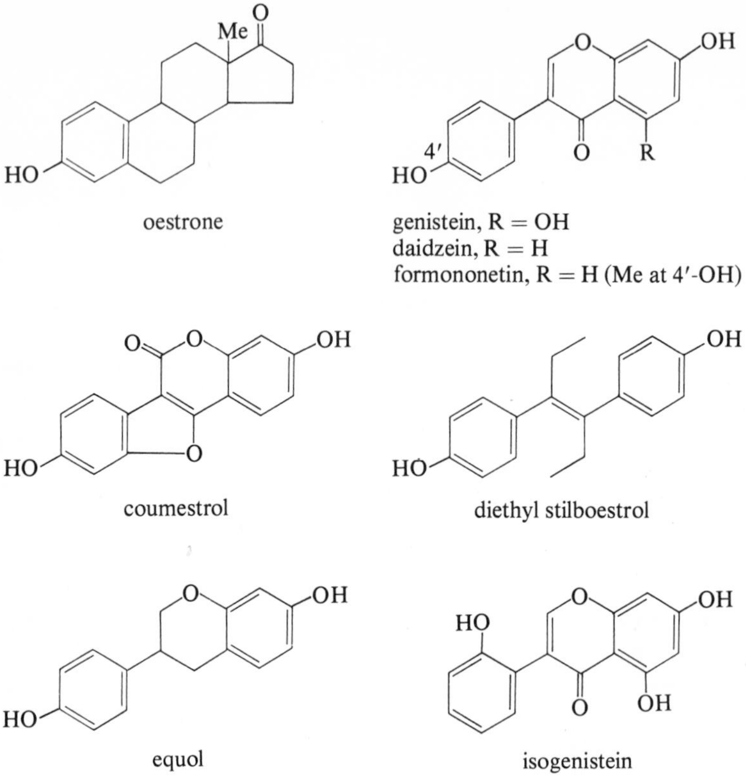

oestrone

genistein, R = OH
daidzein, R = H
formononetin, R = H (Me at 4'-OH)

coumestrol

diethyl stilboestrol

equol

isogenistein

Fig. 4.3 Isoflavonoids as oestrogenic mimics

coumestrol is 30 times more active than genistein or formononetin, its concentration in legume fodder plants is generally much lower, so that it is probably less effective *in vivo* than the isoflavones. In fact, recent research (Shutt, 1976) has shown that formononetin is the most important oestrogen in clover to sheep. This is because it is a pro-oestrogen, being converted (by demethylation and reduction) to a more active substance, the related isoflavan equol, within the animal body. This isoflavan was actually isolated form pregnant mares' urine as long ago as 1932, by Marrian and Haslewood. Comparative metabolic studies with genistein indicate that it is degraded in the rumen to inactive products, one of which is *p*-ethylphenol, so that the effective oestrogenic activity of clover when eaten by sheep is largely due to formononetin content.

All isoflavones are oestrogenic when given by parenteral injection to animals and much work has been done on structure–activity relationships in the isoflavonoid series using mice (Biggers, 1959). For example, it can be shown that the two *para*-substituted hydroxyl groups are needed for maximal activity; transfer of the 4'-hydroxyl in genistein to the 2'-position (to give isogenistein) reduces oestrogenic activity by 75% (Baker *et al.,* 1953).

From the agricultural viewpoint, the presence of isoflavonoids in clovers and other legume fodder plants is a hazard to farm animals, because of their effects on reproduction. Symptoms produced include difficult labour, infertility and lactation in unbred ewes. A survey of *Trifolium* has shown that 18 species have as high an isoflavone content as *T. subterraneum,* most other species having relatively small amounts. Plant breeding experiments have been carried out in the pasture clovers and strains with a safe, low isoflavone content are now available. Unfortunately, it is difficult to replace existing strains of subterranean clover in Australian pastures because they have become well adapted to their environment and have built up large reserves of seed in the soil. In spite of all attempts to reduce the feeding of breeding ewes on such pastures, it is estimated that each year one million Australian ewes fail to lamb because of "clover" disease. Immunization procedures are currently being developed to overcome this problem (Shutt, 1976).

Isoflavones are more or less restricted in their distribution to the Leguminosae, so that if these compounds have a deterrent function in nature, such a function can only operate in this family. There is no reason, however, why a variety of quite different chemical structures should not have the same purpose in other plant families. Weak oestrogenic activity has been, detected, for example, in some flavones and flavonols, two classes of compound which are widely present in the angiosperms.

The question remains—whether isoflavone synthesis is purely accidental to oestrogenic activity in mammals or whether these substances have been deliberately produced by the plant to interfere with the reproductive capacity of grazing animals. It may be significant that the isoflavone skeleton also provides the basis of disease resistance in legumes, since the phytoalexins formed in this family are nearly all reduced forms of genistein or formononetin (see Chapter 9).

That isoflavones do have an ecological role is supported by a recent report (Leopold *et al.,* 1976) that birds (quails) are also affected by the oestrogenic effects of pasture isoflavones. It appears that the birds feed on pastures rich in legume species and they use the presence of isoflavones as a form of population control. Thus in years of good rainfall, legumes that are eaten grow luxuriously and are relatively low in isoflavone on a fresh wt basis. There are no oestrogenic effects and egg laying is normal. However, in years of poor rainfall, the plants are less profuse in leaf and become richer in isoflavone on a fresh wt basis. An oestrogenic effect is exerted on the female quails, and egg-laying is curtailed. Thus, there is a self-regulating system whereby the increase in population is kept at a low level when the food available to the birds is limited. Natural population limitation is a feature of many animal communities and it is possible that phytoestrogens have a role in other species besides quails.

III. INSECT MOULTING HORMONES IN PLANTS

Before discussing the occurrence of insect hormones in plants, their role in the insect's life-cycle needs to be briefly stated. In the metamorphosis of insects, hormones are required to control the different stages in the life-cycle from larva to adult. They are required to initiate the changes in form that occur during growth, which in outline are as follows:

$$\underset{\text{1st stage}}{\text{Larva}} \xrightarrow{\text{MH/JH}} \underset{\text{2nd stage}}{\text{Larva}} \xrightarrow{\text{MH}} \text{Pupa} \xrightarrow{\text{MH}} \text{Imago}$$

the agents concerned being the juvenile hormone (JH) and the moulting hormone (MH). While the JH is required only at the initial metamorphosis from first to second stage larva, MH, which literally controls the moulting of the outer case or skin at each stage, is needed at every step up to the emergence of the adult. In more advanced insects, the juvenile form differs so much from that of the adult that several larval stages are needed before pupation.

For normal metamorphosis, then, these two hormones have a crucial role. They must be present in just the right amounts and at the right time in the cycle for development to proceed normally from larva to adulthood. While JH is synthesized in a pair of tiny cephalic glands, the corpora allata, MH is formed in the prothoracic glands located at the insect's anterior end.

That a moulting hormone was required in insect metamorphosis was first demonstrated over 40 years ago (see Wigglesworth, 1954). It was not, however, until 1954 that the pure hormone, named α-ecdysone, was isolated in sufficient amount for structural study. Butenandt and Karlson (1954) then isolated 25 mg of pure substance, starting from half a ton (500 kg) of silkworm pupae. It was not until 11 years later that the structure was determined by X-ray diffraction (Karlson et al., 1965) as a hydroxysterol with a clear resemblance in structure to cholesterol (Fig. 4.4). A second compound β-ecdysone, present in minor amount in silkworm, was identified as the 20-hydroxy derivative. Four further closely similar moulting hormones have subsequently been isolated from arthropods or crustacea, bringing the total number of zooecdysones to six.

So far, this account of insect hormones has been concerned solely with animals. A most amazing discovery, bringing this area of insect biochemistry and endocrinology into the realms of plant science, was made only a year or so after the structural elucidation of the two ecdysones. Takemoto et al. (1967)

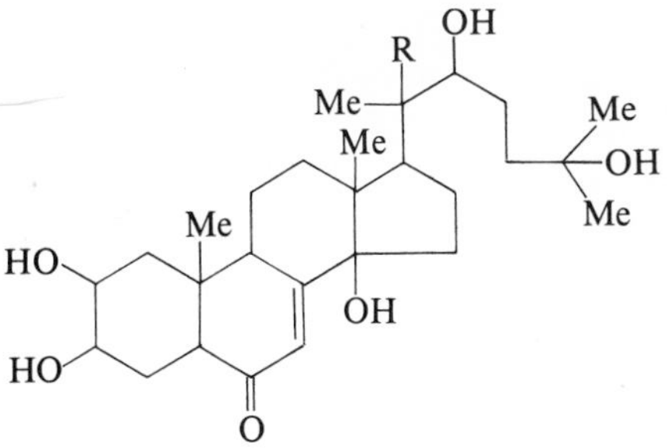

α-ecdysone, R = H
β-ecdysone, R = OH

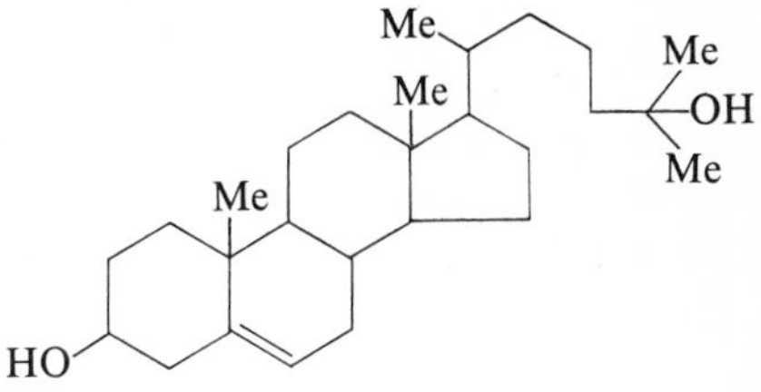

cholesterol

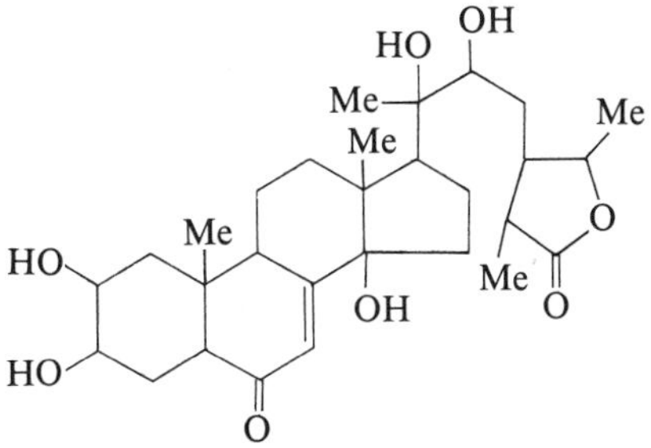

cyasterone

Fig. 4.4 Structures of insect moulting hormones

and Nakanishi (1968) jointly reported the presence of massive amounts of β-ecdysone in the leaves of the common yew, *Taxus baccata*. The amount of ecdysone (25 mg) produced by extracting half a ton of silkworms (i.e. 500 kilograms of insect tissue) was obtainable from as little as 25 g dried leaf or root of yew. An even richer source was found in the rhizomes of the common fern, *Polypodium vulgare*, 25 mg being obtained from only 2·5 g of rhizome.

The finding of insect hormone in such astonishing quantity in plants created a considerable sensation at the time. It was of immediate scientific value in providing an easy source of pure hormones for insect endocrine experiments. It was also of considerable practical interest, since such active materials or their analogues had potential in interfering with normal insect development and providing a means of pest control. What appeared to be a novel concept in insecticide chemistry, however, was, as Williams (1972) has put it, "a strategy which appears to be an ancient art invented by certain plants and practiced by them for tens of millions of years".

Plant surveys for ecdysones were rapidly initiated and they were found to occur regularly in ferns (in 22 of 43 spp. surveyed, especially in Polypodiaceae) and in gymnosperms (in 73 spp. of eight families, including Taxaceae and Podocarpaceae). Ecdysones do also occur in angiosperms, but much less frequently. While β-ecdysone is relatively ubiquitous in plants, the other zooecdysones are rare. Instead, a wide range of other structures are characteristic of plants. Over 30 phytoecdysones were characterized in the 4 years following the initial discovery in yew (Rees, 1971) and ten more have subsequently been added to the list (Nakanishi *et al.,* 1974).

The most fascinating property of many phytoecdysones is their enormous hormonal activity, as compared to α- and β-ecdysone. Some are up to 20 times more active. At such concentrations, they can have very damaging effects on insect development, partly because they resist the inactivation which α- or β-ecdysone undergo when applied to insects. For example, while α-ecdysone is 50% inactivated within 7 hr of being fed to an insect, cyasterone, a phytohormone from *Cycas*, is only inactivated to the same extent after 32 hr.

The biological effects of the plant hormones depend on whether they are applied cutaneously, by injection or by oral administration. Malformation, sterility and death is frequently the outcome of such administrations. The least effective route is via the mouth, probably because insects have developed methods of detoxification. Thus dietary hormones may undergo further hydroxylation, dehydrogenation at the 3-position, formation of conjugates or side-chain cleavage (Hikino *et al.,* 1975).

Finally, the question may be posed: do phytoecdysones have any ecological function or is their presence in plants purely coincidental to their occurrence in insects? Are these hormones a major defense mechanism produced by plants to ward off insect attack? While conclusive proof for such a role is very difficult to produce, there are an increasing number of experiments which support such a role for these substances (see Williams, 1972).

Some of the points that might be argued in favour of an ecological function for plant ecdysones are as follows:

(1) Phytoecdysones occur mainly in two groups of relatively primitive plants—the ferns and gymnosperms—which still appear to be relatively (but not completely) free of insect predation. Thus they may have emerged as a defense mechanism at one particular phase in evolution before the advent of the angiosperms. Their role as feeding deterrents appear to have been taken over in these latter plants by alkaloids or ellagitannins.

(2) When administered to insects, phytoecdysones produce major abnormalities in growth, leading ultimately to sterility and early death.

(3) While it is possible to show that some insects detoxify orally administered ecdysone, there may be others which are not able to deactivate it in time. The structural variation present in the phytoecdysones would provide

some protection against rapid deactivation. Insects are probably less able to cope with ecdysone entering through the cuticle and it is conceivable that some of the phytoecdysone may enter this way during insect feeding.

(4) Phytoecdysone synthesis is to be regarded as only one stage in a constant co-evolutionary situation between plants and insects. At the present time in evolutionary history, many insects might be expected to have partly or completely overcome this particular defense mechanism.

(5) Phytoecdysones do not necessarily have to be lethal to insects. Minor effects on metamorphosis or reproduction would probably be sufficient to reduce the fitness of the pest and keep its predation under reasonable control.

IV. THE FRUIT-FLY–CACTUS INTERACTION

A most unusual example of insect–host plant specificity has been recorded by Kircher and Heed (1970) in the Sonoran desert of Western United States. Here it has been found that four *Drosophila* species exhibit remarkable specificity in choosing to feed variously on rotting limbs of four cactus species growing in the area. The relationship between cactus and fruit-fly is highly consistent, as shown by the emergence records of adult flies from larvae taken from the different cacti (Table 4.2). Each fly species feeds on a specific cactus, with very few exceptions.

Two types of interaction occur involving secondary chemistry, both feeding attractants and feeding repellents (see Chapter 5 for definitions of these terms)

Table 4.2 Emergence records of *Drosophila* species on rotting cacti in the Sonoran desert

Cactus	Associated *Drosophila* species	Host plant specificity[a]
Senita *Lophocereus schottii*	*D. pachea*	862 : 1
Saguaro *Carnegiea gigantea*	*D. nigrospiracula*[b]	6803 : 1
Organ pipe *Lemairocereus thurberi*	*D. mojavensis*	28 : 1
Sina *Rathbunia alamosensis*	*D. arizonensis*	23 : 1

[a] Ratio of progeny of associated *Drosophila* sp. to number of progeny of non-associated species, i.e. on Senita, for every 862 *D. pachea* grubs emerging, one foreign species (*D. mojavensis*, etc.) was found. Data modified from Kircher and Heed (1970).

[b] *D. nigrospiracula* is unusual in that it will also live on two other host plants; *D. pachea* and *D. mojavensis* also each have one other possible host plant.

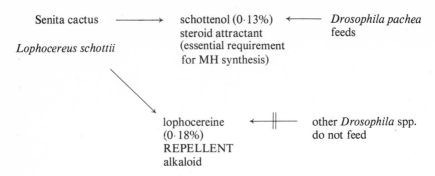

Fig. 4.5 Interaction between *Drosophila* and Senita cactus

being present (Fig. 4.5). The feeding attractant is common to all the cacti and is a sterol which permits the insects to synthesize their moulting hormone. Since insects cannot make the sterol nucleus *de novo*, they are dependent on plants for their starting materials. The common starting material is sitosterol (see Fig. 4.6) which is the major sterol in plant tissues and insects have to make a number of structural changes in order to convert this to α-ecdysone. These changes fall into three groups of reactions: (1) rearrangement of the double bond from the $\Delta5$ to the $\Delta7$ position; (2) removal of the 24-ethyl group (this is a structural feature which distinguishes almost all plant from animal sterols); and (3) various oxidations around the carbon skeleton to introduce three alcohol groups and one keto group.

While most insects have to carry out all these reactions, it is apparent that *Drosophila* species, by feeding on these cacti, can avoid carrying out the first step, the rearrangement of the $\Delta5$ double bond. This is because the major sterol in Senita cactus is not sitosterol, but the compound schottenol (for formulae, see Fig. 4.6) which is similar in structure, except that the double bond in the second carbon ring is already in the right position for ecdysone synthesis. By feeding on schottenol, the flies require less steps and less enzymes for synthesizing their moulting hormone. It is such an advantage to them that they have, indeed, become dependent on the host plant for this material. Laboratory-reared larvae fed on sitosterol are incapable of making ecdysone and thus do not develop into adult flies.

The second class of plant substances in this feeding syndrome are alkaloids. These apparently act as feeding deterrents to *Drosophila* species other than the one that is specifically associated with a particular cactus. Thus lophocereine occurs to the extent of 0·18% in Senita cactus; it is accompanied by a second alkaloid pilocereine (0·6%), a trimer of similar structure to lophocereine (Fig. 4.7). These two alkaloids act as repellents to other *Drosophila* feeders. Toxic effects can be shown in lab. feeding experiments, only *D. pachea* being

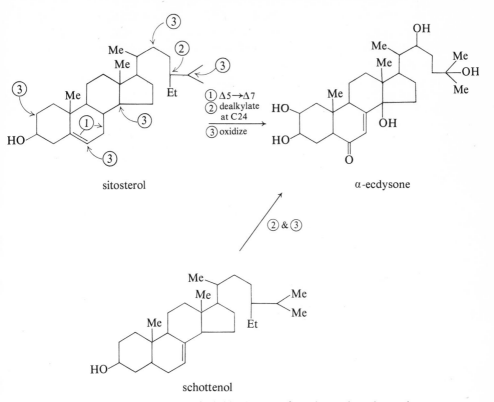

sitosterol

α-ecdysone

schottenol

Fig. 4.6 Pathway of synthesis of moulting hormone from sitosterol or schottenol

impervious to their effects. A second cactus, Saguaro, contains a different alkaloid carnegeine, which is now repellent to *D. pachea* but not to *D. nigrospiracula*, the species which feeds on Saguaro in preference to any other host plant.

lophocereine

repellent in Senita cactus to all except *D. pachea*

carnegeine

repellent in Saguaro cactus to all except *D. nigrospiracula*

Fig. 4.7 Alkaloids of cacti

In this interesting example of coevolution between plant and insect, the fruit-fly has reached the extreme of dependency on one or two species of host plant. Even a small change to a closely related plant is dangerous, causing death due to the presence of an unfamiliar alkaloid. The flies are also in a vulnerable position if their host plant disappears, since they will have to rapidly recover the ability to accomplish the $\Delta5 \longrightarrow \Delta7$ double bond shift. The plants have evolved a complex secondary chemistry in terms of both sterols and alkaloids, which at least partly limits the predation of insects on them. Since the flies feed on the decaying parts of the cacti, insect feeding is relatively harmless and even may be beneficial in removing the dying limbs more rapidly than otherwise.

V. INSECT JUVENILE HORMONES IN PLANTS

The requirement for a juvenile hormone at an early stage of insect growth has already been mentioned in Section III (p. 90). It is required to control growth and the build-up of necessary material for metamorphosis. It may exert its effects for up to 6 weeks, as in the *Cecropia* moth larvae. The hormone is synthesized in the corpora allata glands which regulate its release into the blood.

From the first demonstration that a juvenile hormone was present in insects, it took 20 years before it was chemically characterized. In 1967, Roller and co-

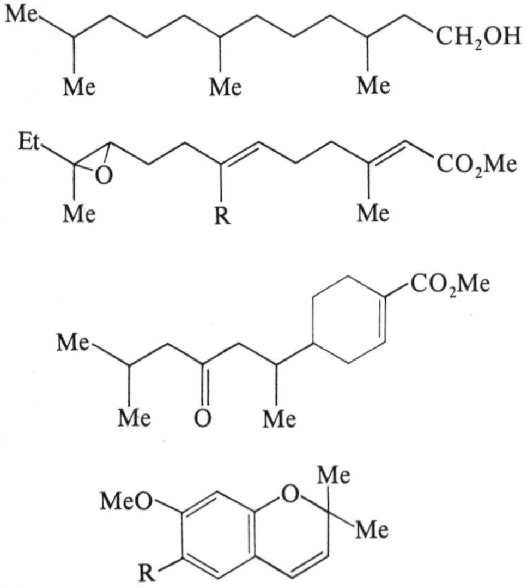

farnesol

JH I (R = Et)
JH II (R = Me)

juvabione

precocene 1 (R = H)
precocene 2 (R = OMe)
(anti-JH activity)

Fig. 4.8 Structures of juvenile hormones and analogues

workers elucidated the structure of JH I (see Fig. 4.8), using less than 300 µg of material isolated from *Cecropia* moth. It has a sesquiterpenoid structure related to farnesol which itself has some activity. A second compound JH II of closely similar structure was also found in *Cecropia*. Subsequently, two further closely similar variants of JH I have been found in other insects. The two compounds JH I and II represent the juvenile hormone activity of the majority of insects. Many related structures have been synthesized and the relationship between structure and activity established (Pfiffner, 1971).

The story of the discovery that materials with JH activity occur in plants is one of those interesting accidents which illuminate the pages of the history of science. The detection of the so-called "paper factor" arose when a Czechoslovak biologist, K. Sláma, was invited by C. M. Williams to Harvard University to culture his favourite experimental insect, the European bug *Pyrrhocoris apteris*. Mysteriously, all attempts to persuade the bugs to go through normal metamorphosis in the new surroundings failed. They obstinately remained in the fifth larval stage. A search of factors responsible for this failure in growth revealed that in moving to Harvard, Sláma had replaced the Whatman filter paper used in the petri dishes for growing the bugs on by U.S. paper towelling (Scott Brand 150). Substitution of the original filter paper led to normal growth and development. Clearly, some compound in the Scott Brand paper was continually providing juvenile hormone material to the bugs, thus arresting their normal metamorphosis.

A study of a range of paper products revealed that all U.S. newspapers and journals were highly active. By contrast, European and Japanese papers were completely inert. This difference in "paper factor" was then traced to the fact that American paper is manufactured largely from balsam fir, *Abies balsamea,* a tree which is not used in the European paper pulping industry. Thus some material present in the tree is carried through all the processes of paper manufacture and is still present on the printed page of the American journal *Science*. The corresponding English journal *Nature*, on the other hand, is completely free from this insect growth inhibitor, since different trees are used for making its paper.

Extraction of American paper eventually gave an active compound, juvabione, which was found to be a structural analogue of the natural insect hormone (Fig. 4.8). Juvabione, however, is only active for one family of insects, the Pyrrhocoridae, to which the European bug belongs. Treatment of the related Lygaeidae in the same group of insects, the Hemiptera, with juvabione gave no response. Plant juvenile hormones, therefore, seem to be rather selective in their effects.

The discovery of a second insect hormone in plant materials, following the phytoecdysone story (see Section III), led to interest and speculation about the possible ecological effects of such occurrences. Unlike the situation in the case of moulting hormones, however, no other structures besides juvabione and its dehydro derivative appear to have been reported. There is, however, evidence that materials with JH activity are distributed in a range of plants. Bowers (1968) examined 52 species at random and found hormone activity in the *Tenebrio* assay in six—a frequency of 12%. Other surveys have also been successful in revealing such activity in further plant sources.

Since compounds with juvenile hormone activity occur in plants and are effective in arresting embryonic development in insects, sometimes with lethal side-effects, there seems little doubt that a similar ecological role can be put forward for them, as for the plant-derived moulting hormones. These substances may be deliberately produced by plants as a sophisticated self-defence against insect predation. The effectiveness of such control can be seen in the fact that synthetic JH analogues have recently been marketed as insecticides against several agriculturally important pests.

Even more remarkable support for the viewpoint that secondary compounds provide hormonal defense in plants against insects is the recent discovery of anti-JH substances in plants. Two chromenes, called precocene 1 and 2 (see Fig. 4.8) have been isolated from the insect resistant composite plant, *Ageratum houstoniatum*. When added to insect diets, these two substances interfere with JH activity in such a way that precocious metamorphosis occurs. Thus, the nymphs of the milkweed bug miss out one or more larval states to become imperfect adults. The net result is usually sterility in the females (Maugh, 1976).

VI. PHEROMONAL INTERACTIONS AND THE PINE BARK BEETLE

Infestation of pine trees by various bark beetles is a serious cause of damage and loss in these commercially important timbers. Studies of the causes of these infestations have been carried out over a period of years, as part of a search for a means of control. One major tree affected in North America is the ponderosa pine, *Pinus ponderosa,* which has a range of pests including the Western pine beetle *Dendroctonus brevicomis* and the California five-spined ips, *Ips confusus.* The interaction clearly involves the monoterpenes of the pine but is a very complicated one. It is difficult, even today, to be sure of all the steps in this interaction. The present account mainly is restricted to the work on *D. brevicomis,* carried out by American entomologists (Silverstein *et al.,* 1968; Wood and Silverstein, 1970; Wood, 1973). The reader is referred to a review by Wood (1970) for the situation in respect of *I. confusus.*

An outline of the different stages in the infestation by *D. brevicomis* is indicated in Fig. 4.9. Some of the chemical substances involved are shown in Fig. 4.10.

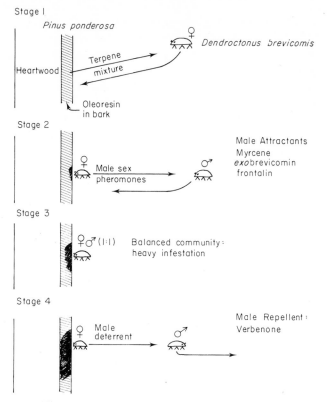

Fig. 4.9 The pine bark beetle–ponderosa pine interaction

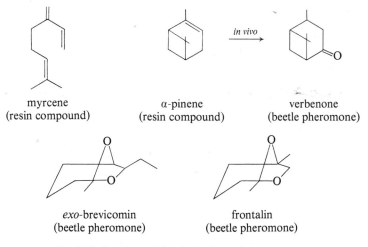

myrcene
(resin compound)

α-pinene
(resin compound)

verbenone
(beetle pheromone)

exo-brevicomin
(beetle pheromone)

frontalin
(beetle pheromone)

Fig. 4.10 Chemistry of the pine bark–beetle interaction

The oleoresin of pine bark is rich in volatile terpenes and traces of this vapour exude from the tree. This vapour, or certain of its components, attract the female beetle, which then settles to feed on the bark (stage 1).

Once the females are established, they begin to attract males to the site for reproductive purposes (stage 2). They employ a mixture of three components: myrcene, which is sequestered from the oleoresin and used directly; and two bicyclic ketals, *exo*-brevicomin and frontalin, which appear to be synthesized *de novo* by the beetle. The males, attracted by the pheromone mixture, duly arrive at the site, copulate with the females and a new generation of beetles emerge.

The female beetles, originators of the infestation, appear to control the sex ratio within the population by varying the proportions of the sex pheromone mixture exuded at any given period of time (stage 3). This is apparent from experiments in which all three components have been added artificially to the "frass" of a bark infestation. Such a mixture attracts males and females in a 1 : 1 ratio, whereas if frontalin is omitted, the ratio changes to 2 : 1 in favour of the males.

Finally, the area of infestation reaches its optimum size, when there is only enough food for the existing beetles. At this stage, the female beetle stops pheromone production and forms instead a male repellent, verbenone, which effectively prevents males reaching the infestation (stage 4). This ketone verbenone is formed from one of the major bark terpenes, α-pinene by a two-stage oxidation via the alcohol, verbenol. It is possible that verbenol also plays a role in the interaction at this stage.

From the ecological viewpoint, it is particularly interesting that the beetle makes use of dietary compounds in at least two ways, either without structural alteration (myrcene) or with minor modification (verbenol, verbenone). Another interesting aspect is that of synergism (Table 4.3), whereby the male attractant must contain all three components for maximum effectiveness. Addition of myrcene to the frontalin–brevicomin mixture doubles the effectiveness of the attractant. Furthermore, myrcene is essential and it cannot

Table 4.3 Synergistic effects of terpenoid mixtures on beetles

Pheromone mixture	Number males trapped in 24 hr period
Brevicomin + frontalin	193
Brevicomin + frontalin + myrcene	389
Brevicomin + frontalin + limonene	196
Frontalin + 3-carene[a]	34

[a] This mixture is highly attractive to the females.

be replaced by the closely related structure, limonene (Table 4.3). It may be noted that a mixture of frontalin and 3-carene, instead of attracting males, now is highly attractive to females. This mixture, of course, would be an ideal lure to attract females away from pine trees before they start infestations and it has been put forward as a means of control.

A further twist in this complex interaction may be due to micro-organisms, which are probably responsible for the *in vivo* conversion of α-pinene to verbenone within the beetle. Thus, a bacterium has been isolated from the gut of *Ips confusus* which can oxidize α-pinene to verbenol, while a symbiotic fungus of *Dendroctonus* has been shown to be able to further oxidize verbenol to verbenone (Brand *et al.*, 1976). It is conceivable, therefore, that the development of micro-organisms in the host plant may be important in influencing the behaviour of the beetle on a successfully colonized tree.

One final point—it is possible that the trees themselves may modify their oleoresin chemistry to provide resistance to beetle predation. It has been found that Douglas fir populations, which are preyed upon by their own beetle *Dendroctonus pseudotsugae*, vary clinally in the Western United States in their terpene content. In particular, the ratio of α- to β-pinene changes significantly with geography (Zavarin and Snajberk, 1975). This may be important in that the Douglas fir beetle is attracted by α-pinene but repelled by β-pinene (Heikkenen and Hrutfiord, 1965), so that trees with a high β-/α-pinene ratio may be less susceptible than other clones to beetle attack.

BIBLIOGRAPHY

Books and Review Articles

Bradbury, R. B. and White, D. E. (1954). Oestrogens and related substances in plants. *Vitamins and Hormones* **12**, 207–233.

Heftmann, E. (1975). Functions of steroids in plants. *Phytochemistry* **14**, 891–902.

Hendrix, J. W. (1970). Sterols in growth and reproduction of fungi. *Ann. Rev. Phytopath.* **8**, 111–130.

Kircher, H. W. and Heed, W. B. (1970). Phytochemistry and host plant specificity in *Drosophila. Recent Advance Phytochem.* **3**, 191–208.

Pfiffner, A. (1971). Juvenile hormones. In: Goodwin, T. W. (ed.), "Aspects of Terpenoid Chemistry and Biochemistry", pp. 95–136. Academic Press, London.

Rees, H. H. (1971). Ecdysones. In: Goodwin, T. W. (ed.), "Aspects of Terpenoid Chemistry and Biochemistry", pp. 181–222. Academic Press, London.

Shutt, D. A. (1976). The effects of plant oestrogens on animal reproduction. *Endeavour* **35**, 110–113.

Silverstein, R. M., Brownlee, R. G., Bellas, T. E., Wood, D. L. and Browne, L. E. (1968). Brevicomin: principal sex attractant in the frass of the female Western pine beetle. *Science* **159**, 889–890.

Williams, C. M. (1972). Hormonal interactions between plants and insects. In:

Sondheimer, E. & Simeone, J. B. (eds.), "Chemical Ecology", pp. 103–132. Academic Press, New York.

Wood, D. L. (1970). Pheromones of bark beetles. In: Wood, D. L. & Silverstein, R. M. (eds.), "Control of Insect Behaviour by Natural Products", pp. 301–316. Academic Press, New York.

Wood, D. L. (1973). Selection and colonization of ponderosa pine by bark beetle. In: Van Emden, H. (ed.), "Insect–Plant Relationships", pp. 101–118. Blackwells, Oxford.

Wood, D. L. and Silverstein, R. M. (1970). Bark beetle pheromones. *Nature* **225**, 557–558.

Literature References

Baker, W., Harborne, J. B. and Ollis, W. D. (1953). *J. Chem. Soc.* 1859–1863.

Bickoff, E. M. (1968). Rev. Ser. I. (1968). Commonwealth Bur. Pastures and Field Crops, pp. 1–39. Hurley, Berks.

Biggers, J. D. (1959). In: Fairbairn, J. W. (ed.), "Pharmacology of Plant Phenolics", pp. 51–69. Academic Press, London.

Bounds, D. G. and Pope, G. S. (1960). *J. Chem. Soc.* 3696–3705.

Bowers, W. S. (1968). *Bio-Science* **18**, 791–799.

Brand, J. M., Bracke, J. W., Britton, L. N. and Markovetz, A. J. (1976). *J. Chem. Ecol.* **2**, 195–199.

Butenandt, A. and Jacobi, H. (1933). *Z. Physiol. Chem.* **218**, 104–112.

Butenandt, A. and Karlson, P. (1954). *Z. Naturforsch.* **96**, 389–391.

Dean, P. D. G., Exley, D. and Goodwin, T. W. (1971). *Phytochemistry* **10**, 2215–2216.

Heftmann, E., Ko, S. T. and Bennett, R. D. (1966). *Phytochemistry* **5**, 1337–1339.

Heikkenen, H. J. and Hrutfiord, B. F. (1965). *Science* **150**, 1457–1459.

Hikono, H., Ohizumi, Y. and Takemoto, T. (1975). *J. Insect Physiol.* **21**, 1953–1963.

Karlson, P., Hoffmeister, H., Hummel, H., Hocks, P. and Spitelber, G. (1965). *Chem. Ber.* **98**, 2394–2402.

Leopold, A. S., Erwin, M., Oh, J. and Browning, B. (1976). *Science* **191**, 98–99.

Marrian, G. F. and Haslewood, G. A. D. (1932). *Biochem. J.* **26**, 1227.

Maugh, T. S. (1976). *Science* **192**, 874–877.

Nakanishi, K. (1968). *Bio-Science* **18**, 791–799.

Nakanishi, K., Goto, T., Ito, S., Natori, S. and Nozoe, S. (1974). "Natural Products Chemistry", Vol. I, p. 525. Academic Press, New York.

Roller, H., Dahm, K. H., Sweeley, C. C. and Trost, B. M. (1967). *Angew. Chem. Intern. Ed. English* **6**, 179–180.

Takemoto, T., Ogawa, S., Nishimoto, N., Arihari, S. and Bue, K. (1967). *Yakugaku Zasshi* **87**, 1414–1418.

Wigglesworth, V. B. (1954). "The Physiology of Insect Metamorphosis." Cambridge Univ. Press, London.

Zavarin, E. and Snajberk, K. (1975). *Biochem. System. Ecol.* **2**, 121–129.

5 | Insect Feeding Preferences

I. INTRODUCTION

Until recently, the role of secondary compounds in plants has remained largely obscure. Many plant physiologists have regarded them as waste products of primary metabolism and of no possible survival value to plants. This situation has been completely changed largely due to the attention paid to these substances by biologists interested in the complex and subtle interactions that take place between plants and insects. Fraenkel (1959), in a now classical article, was one of the first to voice the suggestion that secondary compounds are directly involved in the feeding behaviour of insects. However, it was not until the major review of Ehrlich and Raven (1965) on the probable factors controlling the coevolution of butterflies and plants that secondary substances became the cornerstone of a new theory of biochemical coevolution between animals and plants.

The conclusions from Ehrlich and Raven's article can best be presented here in their own words: "A systematic evaluation of the kinds of plants fed upon by the larvae of certain subgroups of butterflies leads unambiguously to the conclusion that *secondary plant substances play the leading role* in determining patterns of utilization. This seems true not only for butterflies but for all phytophagous groups ... In this context, the irregular distribution in plants of secondary compounds ... is immediately explicable. Angiosperms have, through occasional mutations and recombinations, produced a series of chemical compounds not directly related to basic metabolism. Some of these compounds by chance serve to reduce or destroy the palatability of the plant in which they are produced. Such a plant protected from phytophagous animals enters a new adaptive zone. Phytophagous insects, however, can evolve in response to physiological obstacles ... selection (from insect populations) could carry a recombinant or mutant (in turn) into a new adaptive zone. Here it would be free to diversify largely in the absence of competition from other feeders. Thus, the diversity of plants not only may tend to augment the diversity of phytophagous animals, the converse may also be true."

Subsequent to the publication of Ehrlich and Raven's review, the role of such compounds as alkaloids, terpenoids and flavonoids has been extensively explored in this coevolutionary situation of plants with their insect herbivores. Important recent reviews of this topic are those of Dethier (1972), Feeny (1975), Fraenkel (1969), Meeuse (1973) and Schoonhoven (1968, 1972). It should be pointed out that there are still those who object to the view that secondary compounds have a function (Mothes, 1973) and there are a number of others who have largely ignored the evidence available to them (see e.g. Goodwin and Mercer, 1972).

The theory rests on a variety of observations but seven main points may be discerned.

(1) The theory explains why there are three major areas of *enormous diversity* in biology—in the angiosperms, the insect kingdom and in secondary compound chemistry. In the case of angiosperms, well over a quarter of a million species are estimated to be present in the world. Estimates of the species diversity in insects vary between 0·5 and 2 million; the Lepidoptera alone has 15,000 species. Finally, with regard to secondary compounds, the total of known structures must be in the region of 30,000; at least 6,000 alkaloids and 10,000 terpenoids have been characterized. A much greater number of structures await recognition in the vast number of plants not yet sampled or chemically analysed.

(2) The theory explains a conspicuous non-event (Feeny, 1975), namely that the destructive potential of herbivorous insects has not prevented the green plants from dominating the earth, i.e. higher plants must possess effective defenses against over-predation.

(3) Most herbivorous insects discriminate between plants in feeding and many feed on a small number of related species belonging to the same genus, tribe or family.

(4) The host plants of a given insect may share similar secondary compounds but be different in general morphology and anatomy.

(5) Many secondary compounds are highly toxic to insects. This applies not only to alkaloids, but to many terpenoids and oxygen heterocyclic compounds (see Chapter 3).

(6) Plants can arrive at the same solution to an ecological problem (e.g. animal predation) by a variety of routes, i.e. they practice chemical mimicry. For example, a repellent bitter taste in plants may be produced by the synthesis of an alkaloid (e.g. quinine), a saponin, a cardiac glycoside, a triterpenoid (e.g. cucurbitacin), a sesquiterpene lactone (e.g. lactopicrin) or a flavanone glycoside (e.g. naringin).

(7) All angiosperms tend to have at least one type of secondary compound in major concentration, i.e. they accumulate these substances in sufficient amount to be effective in controlling insect attack. The plant may have alkaloid *or* flavonoid *or* terpenoid; it is rare to find a plant rich in a variety of *different* classes of secondary substances.

In any theory involving the considerable time span taken for the angiosperms to evolve to the present day (some 135 m.years), a great deal rests on circumstantial evidence. However, as with the Darwinian theory of evolution, it is possible to devise experiments among present day plants and insects to test these co-evolutionary ideas. There are, however, particular problems associated with testing this theory which have to be borne in mind in interpreting the data available to us. Thus, the toxicity of a secondary substance may be subtle, incomplete or difficult to measure accurately. Intake of the compound only needs to slightly reduce the fitness of the invading insect population to be ecologically significant; alternatively its effect may take the form of a hormonal interference (see Chapter 4).

In seeking a secondary substance involved in insect feeding, it is necessary to distinguish this function from other ecological roles, e.g. it may be an agent in plant–plant interactions (see Chapters 8 and 9). There are also problems in determining which of many related structures present in a particular plant may be active in coevolution. Many trace components in plants may be biosynthetic intermediates and not relevant from the functional viewpoint. Finally, there are considerable problems in bioassay. Many oligo- or monophagous insects are reluctant to feed on an abnormal diet and it may be difficult to test the effectiveness of isolated plant fractions. Some insects may prefer to die from starvation rather than accept a diet lacking their normal feeding stimulant—this is true of the larvae of the cabbage white butterfly which live on crucifers (see p. 114).

In this chapter, it is planned to consider briefly the biochemical basis of insect feeding preferences and then provide a number of selected examples where secondary compounds act as attractants or deterrents to particular insects. The question of the feeding preferences of higher animals, which have a similar biochemical basis, is reserved for the chapter following this one.

II. BIOCHEMICAL BASIS OF PLANT SELECTION BY INSECTS

A. Coevolutionary Aspects

The choice of plants for feeding by present-day insect populations has to be considered within an overall evolutionary context. The situation observed today has been produced by evolutionary forces operating in the past and the interaction between plants and their insect predators is a dynamic one and likely to be subject to continual variation and change. At any one instance, the plant or the insect may appear to have the advantage. Both partners in the interaction, however, adapt themselves in different ways to the changing conditions. Other environmental pressures (e.g. climate, disease, etc.) also have their effect on the interaction:

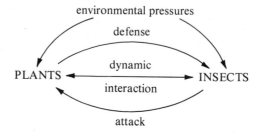

The plants that provide the source of food to insects—and this applies to practically all members of the Angiospermae—have evolved to avoid being overeaten. This can be achieved in a variety of ways. Morphological modifications, clearly produced in response to herbivore attack, include the armouring of the more attractive and accessible plant parts with spines, prickles, thorns or stinging hairs. Emigration via the seeds to new habitats represents another method by which plants can avoid over-predation. For example, a move by a plant from a mainland situation to an adjacent island may often be successful in "throwing off" an animal pursuer.

Undoubtedly though, the most significant type of defense a plant can erect is in the realms of chemical armoury. Effective and often drastic reduction in insect feeding may be achieved by altering the chemical components of the plant leaves. This can be done either by reducing the edibility or nutritive status of the leaves or more positively by introducing a toxin, an unpleasant taste or an offensive odour into the leaf tissue.

Insects evolve in this dynamic interaction by overcoming the plant's defenses. Because insects are highly specialized organisms, they have a greater variety of responses available to them. They can adapt biochemically and anatomically to the digestion and assimilation of new plant foods. They can develop new feeding habits and new taste preferences. They are more mobile than plants and can move away to new pastures, when faced with an unpalatable or inedible species. Finally, they are adept at developing detoxification mechanisms and can neutralize the potency of a toxin, so that it no longer acts as a barrier to feeding. Such detoxification usually involves a chemical modification of the toxin *in vivo*, its conversion to a non-toxic conjugate or else its sequestration in special storage tissues within the insect.

B. Plant Chemicals as Defense Agents

As has already been mentioned in Chapter 3, the chemistry of plant defense is essentially the production of a variety of secondary metabolites. These compounds can be of many different structures. Toxicity to insects, for example, can be achieved by the synthesis of any one of a range of secondary compounds, be it an alkaloid, a terpenoid or a flavonoid. Frequently, mixtures of several closely related structures of the same class are produced by plants and it is likely that synergism occurs, one substance enhancing the effectiveness of a second substance as a feeding deterrent.

In order to repel insect feeding, a plant may not necessarily have to produce a substance that is highly toxic to the insect. It may be sufficient to produce a compound that is unpleasant or distasteful. Also, an effective barrier to most insect feeding can be erected by reducing the nutritional value of the plant. Thus it is apparent that the synthesis of some secondary compounds, especially of tannins, has this effect on insect behaviour.

Two terms are widely used to refer to chemicals involved in insect feeding preferences: chemical attractants (or feeding stimulants) and chemical repellents (or feeding toxins). It can be confusing to the uninitiated that the same type of compound is often ascribed a role as an attractant to one insect *and* as a repellent to a second insect. This apparently contradictory situation can only be appreciated when the evolutionary aspects are taken into account. It is clear that *any* chemical substance implicated in insect–plant interactions has a defensive role, irrespective of whether it is a repellent or an attractant in any particular instance.

The hypothesis is that all secondary compounds affecting insects (and other animals) were first synthesized by plants (and continue to be synthesized) as a general defense against animal feeding. In this situation, one insect species evolves the means to detoxify the repellent (or toxin) and then begins to feed exclusively on that plant. The insect can do this because the repellent is no longer harmful to it. However, the original compound is still highly effective in repelling other insects from feeding so that it also has the enormous advantage that it does not have to compete with other species for its food.

To the successful insect, the toxin through its smell or taste becomes a valuable signal to guide it to its favoured host plant. Indeed, the substance becomes an attractant, because of its close association with this plant. In many cases, the insect becomes dependent on the presence of the attractant, so much so that it becomes an essential feeding stimulant to the insect. Indeeed, a substance that is an attractant has its own hazards to the insect, because of this dependency, and the insect may become so "hooked" on the substance that it is unable to feed on a diet lacking this component. Eventually, the size and success of the insect population may be closely controlled by the availability of the necessary host plant required for feeding.

To summarize, any chemical affecting insect feeding is basically a plant's defense against insect attack and even in situations where its role has been reversed into that of an attractant by one particular insect species, it still has its dangers to the successful predator.

C. Insect Feeding Requirements

Insects vary enormously in their responses to the plant world. Those that prey exclusively on other insects are clearly unaffected by plant chemistry but the vast majority of insects are phytophagous, i.e. are able to discriminate between plants through their chemical senses. Within this broad category, insects are divided into those that are polyphagous, oligophagous or monophagous.

Polyphagous insects are those that eat any plant which they are presented with. Locusts fall into this category, though even with these pestilential insects, it is possible to demonstrate some differential feeding habits (Chapman, 1976). Leaf cutting ants are another group which utilize a wide variety of plant species for feeding purposes (see p. 123). The Chrysanthemum leaf-minor *Phytomyza atricornis*, in spite of its name, is another omnivore, feeding on over a 100 different host plants besides Chrysanthemums.

Oligophagous insects, probably making up the majority of phytophagous insects, are those which feed on a relatively few related species belonging to one or only a few plant genera or families. They are selective in their feeding, being guided by other factors than purely nutritional requirements in their search for food. Of the many examples here, one may quote the danaid butterflies (see p. 75), which feed almost exclusively on plants of the Apocynaceae and Asclepiadaceae. Most aphids are oligophagous, generally feeding on plants in a single genus or single family (van Emden, 1972). Many other insect pests are also oligophagous, such as the oak leaf roller and the various pine bark beetles.

Finally, there are monophagous insects, which feed on a single plant species. The best known is the silkworm, *Bombyx mori,* which is restricted to mulberry leaves, *Morus nigra.* The condition of monophagy may be imposed on an oligophagous insect in certain habitats by a depauperate flora. The survival of some of the butterflies in the British fauna depends on particular host species being available to them. The swallowtail butterfly, *Papilio machaon,* will only feed in England on the umbellifer *Peucedanum palustre,* although in other European countries it will live on several related umbellifers. The close dependency of Lepidoptera on their preferred host plants is nicely illustrated in the book of Mansell and Newman (1968) on British butterflies, since each insect is shown against a background of one of its characteristic host plants.

There has been much debate in the past whether the preferential feeding behaviour of insects is solely determined by nutritional requirements or solely by its response to hostile chemicals within the leaf or other tissue. It is now generally agreed that both nutritional and other chemical agents guide insects to plants. The relative importance of nutrition versus secondary chemistry probably varies from insect to insect. However, secondary chemistry is usually the controlling factor, since all plants are relatively similar in nutritional value. Since the primary biochemical processes within the leaf are practically identical in all green plants, the relative amounts of sugar, lipid, poly-saccharide, amino acid and protein are inevitably very similar. Again, physiological processes (e.g. senescence) are more likely to affect nutritional status in the plant than anything else. There is, in addition, little concrete evidence from insect feeding studies to suggest that certain plants are avoided because they are nutritionally inadequate (van Emden, 1973).

The main taste response of insects is to sweetness and free sugar, present universally in leaf tissue, is a major nutritional requirement. Other major requirements are for nitrogen (protein or free amino acid), vitamins and phospholipids. Trace elements are also important. Finally, there are the sterol requirements, which have already been discussed under insect metamorphosis in Chapter 4.

III. SECONDARY COMPOUNDS AS FEEDING ATTRACTANTS

A. General

The role of secondary substances as feeding stimulants in insects has been widely studied and a wide range of plant structures have been implicated in such interactions. A selection from the many examples available in the primary

Table 5.1 Plant secondary compounds as feeding attractants

Insect class and species	Plant host	Chemical attractants	Reference
APHIDS			
Brevicoryne brassicae	*Brassica campestris* (cabbage)	Glucosinolate: sinigrin	van Emden, 1972
Acyrthrosiphon spartii	*Sarothamnus scoparius* (broom)	Alkaloid: sparteine	Smith, 1966
BEETLES			
Agasicles sp.	*Alternanthera phylloxeroides*	Flavone: 6-methoxy-luteolin 7-rhamnoside	Zielske *et al.*, 1972
Diabrotica undecimpunctata	*Citrullus vulgaris* (cucumber)	Triterpenoids: cucurbitacins	Chambliss and Jones, 1966
Scolytus mediterraneus	*Prunus* spp.	Flavonoids: taxifolin, pinocembrin, dihydrokaempferol	Levy *et al.*, 1974
S. multistriatus	*Ulmus europea* (elm)	Flavonoid: catechin 7-xyloside Triterpenoid: lupeyl cerotate	Doskotch *et al.*, 1973
BUTTERFLIES			
Papilio ajax	*Foeniculum vulgare* (fennel)	Essential oils: various	Dethier, 1941
Pieris brassicae	*Brassica campestris* (cabbage)	Glucosinolate: sinigrin	Schoonhoven, 1968
MOTHS			
Bombyx mori	*Morus nigra* (mulberry)	Flavonoids and essential oils (see Table 5.2)	Hamamura *et al.*, 1962
Ceratomia catalpae	*Catalpa* spp.	Iridoid glycosides: various	Nayer and Fraenkel, 1963
Serrodes partita	*Pappea capensis* (wild plum)	Quebrachitol	Hewitt *et al.*, 1969
WEEVILS			
Sitonia cylindricollis	*Melilotus alba*	Coumarin	Akeson *et al.*, 1969

literature is presented in Table 5.1. Further examples are discussed in the reviews of Dethier (1972) and Schoonhoven (1968, 1972).

Three general points may be noted. First, almost every class of secondary substance has been implicated in such interactions. Compounds representing at least eight different structural types are mentioned in the table. Second, compounds which are toxic or repellent generally are particularly prominent, e.g. the bitter cucurbitacins, the poisonous alkaloid sparteine, the acrid mustard oil allyl isothiocyanate and so on. Third, in the majority of cases, more than one compound has been implicated as feeding attractants. In one case, as many as fourteen components are active, e.g. the feeding of the Catalpa sphinx moth.

Some of the above points will now be discussed in more detail, in relation to specific plant–insect interactions. The feeding attractant of the silkworm, the cabbage butterfly and the cabbage aphid will be particularly mentioned, since these have been most intensively studied; many of their behaviour responses are undoubtedly shown by many other phytophagous insects as well.

B. The Silkworm–Mulberry Interaction

Because of the valuable silk fibres it spins, the silkworm *Bombyx mori* has become one of the most beneficial insects to mankind. For this reason, more time and effort has been spent on the study of its feeding behaviour than on that of any other comparable insect. Scientifically, it is interesting in that it feeds exclusively on the leaves of the black and white mulberry trees, *Morus nigra* and *M. alba*. As a result of the experiments of Hamamura *et al.* (1962), it is apparent that a range of chemicals in the leaf are concerned in this very specific feeding behaviour. The substances can be divided into three groups: olfactory attractants, biting factors and swallowing factors (Table 5.2). Each

Table 5.2 Chemical factors of mulberry leaves associated with silkworm feeding

Attractants	Biting factors	Swallowing factors
ESSENTIAL OILS:	FLAVONOIDS:	INORGANIC ELEMENTS:
Citral	Isoquercitrin	Silicate
Terpinyl acetate	Morin	Phosphate
Linalyl acetate	TERPENOID:	CELL WALL COMPONENT:
Linalol	Sitosterol	Cellulose
β,γ-Hexenol	SUGARS:	
	Sucrose	
	Inositol	

From Hamamura *et al.* (1962).

group has a specific role in the insect feeding response. While some of the compounds listed are generally present in all plants, others are secondary constituents some at least of which are specifically associated with the host plant.

The olfactory attractants of mulberry leaf are a mixture of monoterpenes, which exert their primary effect by attracting the insect larvae to feed through their sense of smell. It has been shown that *Bombyx* larvae are sensitive to these monoterpene mixtures as soon as they approach within 3 cm of the leaf, their olfactory sense being relatively acute at this distance. The importance of smell as an attractant can be demonstrated by surgical removal of the insect's oral sense receptors. Insects so treated immediately lose their power of discrimination and they start biting into almost any plants which are presented to them.

The second group of substances involved in silkworm feeding are the biting factors (Table 5.2). Three of the compounds included here—sucrose, inositol and sitosterol—are essential dietary requirements and they must all act as general feeding stimulants to most insects. The other two substances—morin and isoquercitrin—are much more restricted in their natural distribution and clearly have a different role, since they are not important dietary constituents. These two compounds, together with the essential oils in the leaf, must provide the specific basis for the attraction of the silkworm to its favoured food source. While one of these two flavonoids, isoquercitrin (or quercetin 3-glucoside) is relatively common in angiosperm leaves, the other, morin, is almost completely exclusive in its occurrence to this particular plant.

The structural requirements of these two flavonoids seem to be absolute in that substitution of closely related structures in the insect diet is ineffective in producing a feeding response. Indeed, if quercetin 3-glucoside is replaced by either the 3-rhamnoside or the 3-rutinoside (see Fig. 5.1 for formulae), a receptor site sensitive to repellent chemicals is triggered and the insect is put off feeding. It is noteworthy that simple substitution of one sugar (rhamnose) for another (glucose) in the flavonoid molecule can have such a dramatic effect on insect feeding. However, other examples are known in the flavonoid series where a change in the nature of the substituted sugar can dramatically alter taste properties (see Horowitz, 1964). Reversal of taste properties can also occur with other types of simple molecules. Thus, the amino acid L-alanine, $CH_3CH(NH_2)CO_2H$, is a feeding stimulant to the European corn borer while the structurally related isomeric β-alanine, $NH_2CH_2CH_2CO_2H$, is a deterrent (Beck, 1960).

The final stage in the silkworm feeding is the act of swallowing and here relatively common chemicals provide the necessary stimulus. These are the cellulose, richly present in the cell wall of this plant, and the mineral elements, silicate and phosphate. These substances provide the necessary "bulk" to the

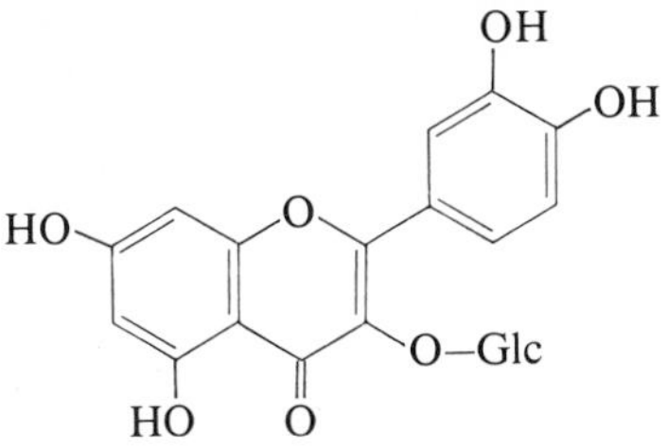

isoquercitrin
(*Bombyx mori*)

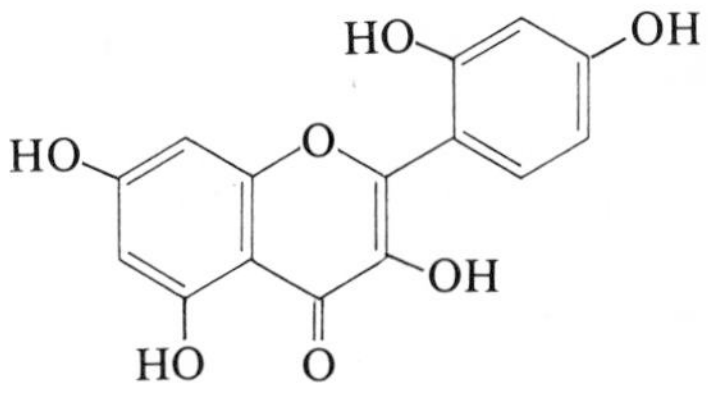

morin
(*Bombyx mori*)

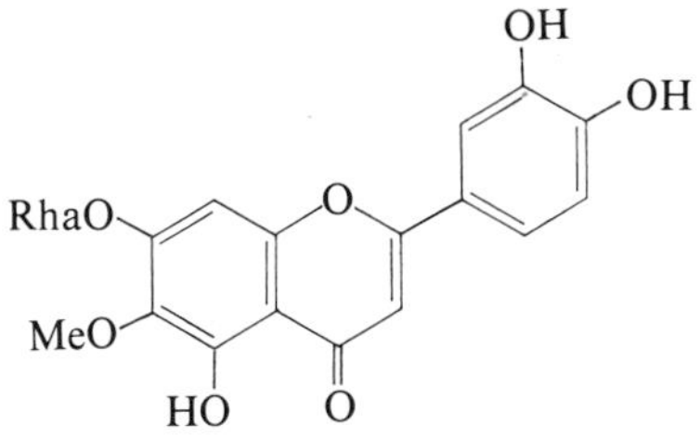

6-methoxyluteolin
7-rhamnoside (*Agasicles*)

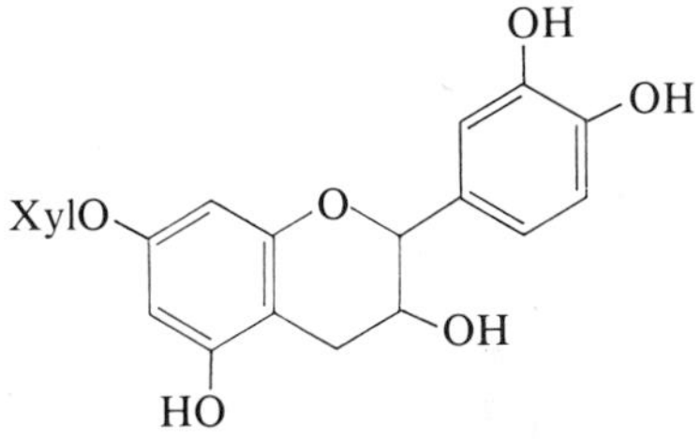

catechin 7-xyloside
(*Scolytus multistriatus*)

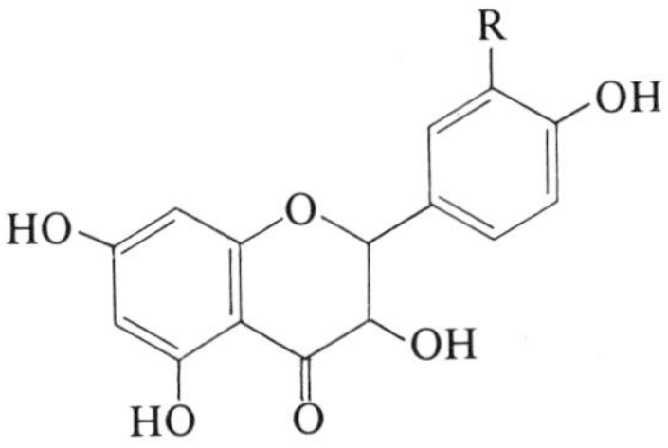

dihydrokaempferol (R = H)
taxifolin (R = OH)
(*Scolytus mediterraneus*)

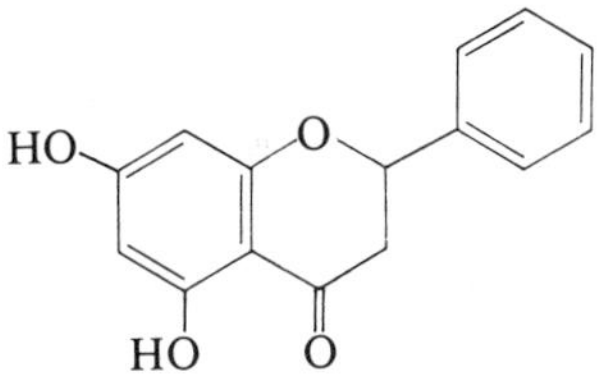

pinocembrin
(*Scolytus mediterraneus*)

Fig. 5.1 Flavonoids as feeding attractants to insects

insect alimentary canal in just the same way as "roughage" is a needed requirement in mammalian diets.

C. Glucosinolates as Feeding Attractants in the Cruciferae

The best documented case of repellent substances becoming attractants is in the feeding behaviour of crucifer insect pests. Two particular insects have been

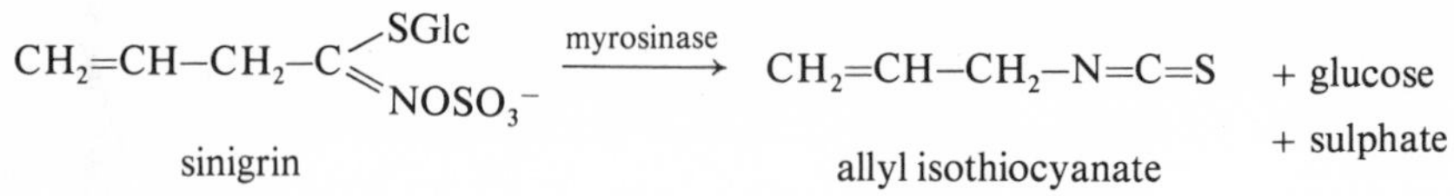

$$CH_2=CH-CH_2-C\begin{matrix}SGlc\\NOSO_3^-\end{matrix} \xrightarrow{\text{myrosinase}} CH_2=CH-CH_2-N=C=S \quad + \text{glucose}$$

sinigrin   allyl isothiocyanate   + sulphate

Fig. 5.2 Enzymic release of allyl isothiocyanate from sinigrin

studied in detail—the cabbage butterfly *Pieris brassicae* and the cabbage aphid *Brevicoryne brassicae*—but what applies to these insects is undoubtedly also true for other predators on members of the cabbage family, the Cruciferae. The repellent substances, whose role has been dramatically reversed by these insects, are the acrid-smelling mustard oils present in these plants. The volatile oils occur in the plants in bound form as the corresponding glycosides (called glucosinolates) and are released enzymically by the action of the enzyme myrosinase which co-occurs with the glucosides in crucifer leaves. Although a range of different glucosinolates occur within the Cruciferae, the major compound of the cabbage and the one upon which most work has been done is sinigrin. This releases allyl isothiocyanate, its mustard oil, following enzymic hydrolysis according to the reaction shown in Fig. 5.2.

Allyl isothiocyanate is the acrid, sharp-tasting principle of mustard and, although taken by man in small amounts as a table condiment, it is generally a feeding repellent to most animals. That it is not only a repellent but can actually be toxic to insects has been demonstrated by Erickson and Feeny (1974). Since insects will usually refuse sinigrin in the diet, these authors fed the substance to larvae of the black swallowtail butterfly *Papilio polyxenes* by infiltrating a 0·1% solution (based on leaf fresh wt) of sinigrin into one of its normal food plants, namely celery. This was sufficient to cause 100% mortality, the concentration of sinigrin in the celery being close to that present in crucifer plants. The authors argue from this that sinigrin in cabbage plants has a clear defensive function against insects not normally feeding on this family of plants.

The fact that this same sinigrin is a positive feeding stimulus to both cabbage butterflies and aphids has been demonstrated in a number of experiments (see Dethier, 1972). Thus larvae of the cabbage butterfly can generally be persuaded to feed on an artificial diet but it is essential that mustard oil (or the glucosinolate) be added to it. It is possible to take newly hatched larvae and get them to feed on a diet devoid of mustard oil, but even with these insects addition of glucosinolate to the diet immediately increases feeding intake by 20%. The dependency of the larvae on this feeding stimulant is most significantly demonstrated in the case of insects fed from the start on cabbage leaves. When these larvae are transferred to an artificial diet lacking sinigrin, they refuse to eat and, in fact, prefer to die rather than accept food lacking what has become an essential attractant. The importance of sinigrin to

Pieris brassicae is shown in other aspects of their life-cycle. The adult female, for example, uses the same substance as an oviposition stimulant. Indeed, its effectiveness is apparent in that the butterfly can be fooled into laying its eggs on a piece of filter paper, as long as the paper has been previously soaked in a solution of sinigrin.

The cabbage aphid is similarly attracted to the same host plant by the presence of sinigrin. While the aphid is highly specific to crucifers, it can be persuaded to feed on a non-host plant such as the broad bean *Vicia faba* by the simple expedient of infiltrating the bean leaves with a solution of sinigrin. Factors controlling the feeding of aphids on cabbage leaves have been studied by van Emden (1972) who concludes that there are two major chemical controls in aphid behaviour—the concentration of sinigrin and the free amino acid balance in the leaves.

The aphids use the presence of sinigrin as a sensitive guide to the host plant when they arrive at a new site for infestation. They may alight on non-host plants, but once they have inserted their sucking stylets and found sinigrin to be absent, they immediately fly off in search of a plant containing the essential stimulant. Once settled on a host plant, they are also guided to the most suitable site for feeding by the sinigrin content. Thus, young cabbage leaves have a very high sinigrin concentration, so much so that aphids avoid feeding on these tissues. It is the more mature leaves with medium sinigrin levels that they prefer to feed on. They also avoid senescent plants; here it is not a drop in sinigrin content which turns them off feeding but a change in the amino acid balance. In particular, older leaves contain *inter alia* more than average amounts of γ-aminobutyric acid and variation in this and other amino acids is apparently detected by aphids.

Aphids are thus highly sensitive to plant chemistry: to the feeding stimulant, its absolute concentration, and to nutritional factors, especially the amino acid balance. van Emden's reference (1972) to "aphids as true phytochemists" is a very apt description for these highly perceptive insect feeders.

D. Other Feeding Attractants

As discussed above, the major attractants of the silkworm are essential oils and flavonoids, while that of the cabbage butterfly and aphid is the glucosinolate sinigrin. These are not exceptional cases and it is apparent (Table 5.1) that practically every type of secondary constituent has been assigned a role as a feeding stimulant in a particular plant–insect interaction. The poisonous alkaloid sparteine, for example, acts as a stimulant to feeding of the broom aphid on *Sarothamnus scoparius*. Here, the aphid alters in feeding site according to where the highest concentration of sparteine occurs within the plant. Thus, it begins feeding on the young shoots in the Spring and eventually moves during the Summer months onto the flower buds and fruit pods as the sparteine content varies with the life-cycle of the plant (Smith, 1966). Again, it proved possible in this case (see also above, p. 115) to make these aphids transfer to a non-host plant *Vicia faba* by infiltrating the leaves with a sparteine solution.

Essential oils, which act as olfactory stimulants to silkworm feeding on mulberry leaves, probably provide a signal to many other oligophagous insects that they are approaching their favoured host plant. Experiments with larvae of the Swallowtail butterfly, which feed exclusively on members of the Umbelliferae, show them to be sensitive to at least eight different components in umbellifer essential oils. Besides containing mono- and sesqui-terpenes, the oil fraction of umbellifer species often have aromatic phenylpropanoids present, which are also volatile and physiologically active. Undoubtedly, these phenylpropanoids (see Fig. 5.3) have a role in feeding attraction, although they have yet to be tested on a wide scale. One of them, methylisoeugenol, occurs in carrot leaf and is known to be an oviposition stimulant to the carrot root fly (Beruter and Stadler, 1971). Another, myristicin, which occurs in fruit, leaf or root of a range of umbellifers (Harborne *et al.*, 1969) is reputed to have hallucinogenic properties in man and could well be an attractant to some of the

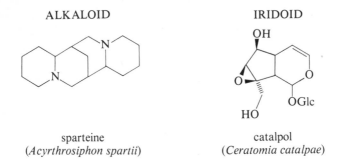

ALKALOID

IRIDOID

sparteine
(*Acyrthrosiphon spartii*)

catalpol
(*Ceratomia catalpae*)

PHENYLPROPANOIDS

methylisoeugenol
(*Psila rosae*)

myristicin
(*Papilio ajax*?)

Fig. 5.3 Structures of some characteristic insect attractants

butterflies which feed specifically on Umbelliferae. The repellent properties of myristicin to insects has been established by the experiments of Lichtenstein and Casida (1963).

Many other terpenoids can be active in feeding behaviour. One complex interaction is that of the catalpa sphinx moth feeding on *Catalpa* leaves (Bignoniaceae) since a mixture of fifteen iridoid glycosides, including catalpol (see Fig. 5.3) are concerned in feeding attraction. It is interesting that a related monoterpene lactone nepetalactone, occurring in a related family, in *Nepeta cataria* (Labiatae) is an olfactory attractant to the domestic cat *Felis domestica*. Thus, the same type of molecule can be olfactory stimulant in both plant–insect and plant–mammal interactions.

Finally, a word may be said about flavonoids as feeding attractants in plants other than the mulberry. A range of other structures have been found to be active (Fig. 5.1). Thus, the *Agasicles* beetle is attracted to feed on alligator weed *Alternanthera phylloxeroides* by the presence of a particular flavone, 6-methoxyluteolin 7-rhamnoside. On the other hand, the elm bark beetle is attracted to elm leaves by a flavanol, (+)-catechin 7-xyloside. This vacuole–soluble compound operates in conjunction with a triterpenoid, lupeyl cerotate, which presumably occurs on the leaf surface. Interestingly, flavanones have been implicated as feeding attractants to another beetle, which feeds on the bark of fruit trees belonging to the genus *Prunus* (see Table 5.1). In this case, three compounds as active: taxifolin, pinocembrin and dihydrokaempferol. A fourth flavanone in the bark, naringenin (5,7,4'-trihydroxyflavanone) is curiously inactive.

IV. SECONDARY COMPOUNDS AS FEEDING DETERRENTS

A. The Winter Moth and Oak Leaf Tannins

A few typical examples of secondary substances acting as deterrents to insect feeding are shown in Table 5.3. Some other cases have already been mentioned earlier in this chapter. The types of compound, as with the attractants, span the whole range of structural types from terpenoids and alkaloids to quinones and flavonoids. It is among this latter class of secondary compound that the most important barrier is provided in the angiosperms against herbivore feeding. These particular substances are the plant tannins, which occur very widely in relatively high concentration in the leaves of woody plants. There are, in fact, two groups of tannin present: the hydrolysable and the condensed tannins. The hydrolysable tannins are derivatives of simple phenolic acids such as gallic acid and its dimeric form, hexahydroxydiphenic acid, combined with the sugar, glucose. The condensed tannins have a higher molecular weight and are oligomers formed by condensation of two or more hydroxyflavanol units. Some typical structures are illustrated in Fig. 5.4.

Table 5.3 Plant secondary compounds as feeding deterrents

Insect class and species	Plant host	Chemical repellent	Reference
ANT			
Atta cephalotes	*Citrus* fruit	Monoterpene: limonene	Cherrett, 1972
BEETLES			
Leptinotarsa decemlineata	*Solanum demissum*	Alkaloid: demissine	Sturchkow, 1959
Monochamus alternatus	*Pinus densiflora*	Hydrocarbon: ethane	Sumimoto et al., 1975
Scolytus multistriatus	*Carya ovata*	Quinone: juglone	Gilbert et al., 1967
BOLLWORM			
Heliothis zea	*Gossypium barbadense* (cotton)	Terpenoid: gossypol Flavonoids: quercetin glycosides	Shaver and Lukefahr, 1969
MOTH			
Operophtera brumata	*Quercus robur* (oak)	Flavonoids: tannins	Feeny, 1970
Spodoptera ornithogallii	*Vernonia glauca*	Sesquiterpene lactone: glaucolide-A	Burnett et al., 1974

HYDROLYSABLE TANNINS

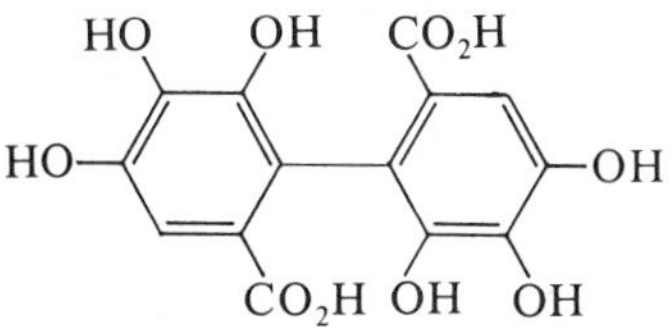

CONDENSED TANNINS

hexahydroxydiphenic acid
(linked to glucose)

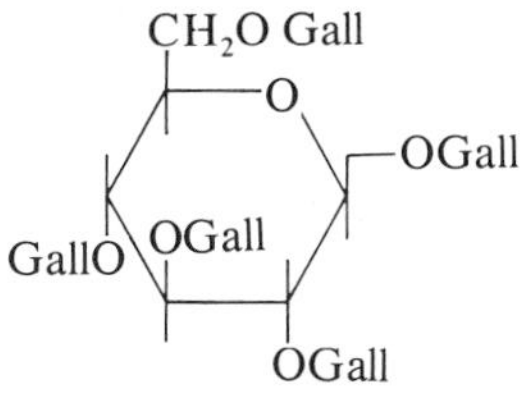

pentagalloylglucose
(Gall = galloyl residue)

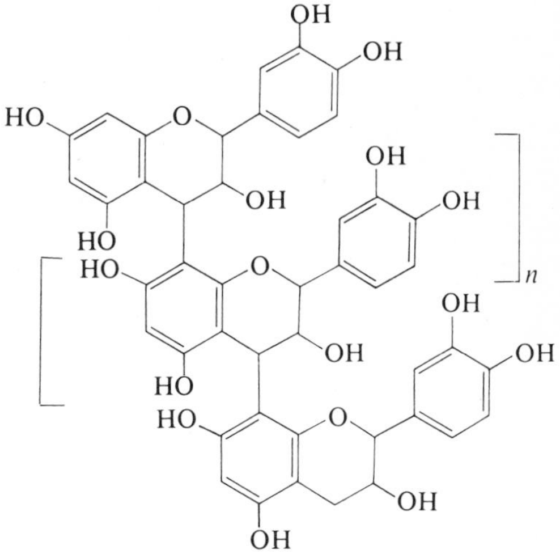

procyanidin
($n = 1-10$)

Fig. 5.4 Characteristic tannins of the oak

Tannins, by definition, have the ability to tan animal hide to form leather, i.e. they combine with protein, often irreversibly, by forming bonds with the peptide and other functional groups. Such bonding prevents proteins from being attacked by trypsin and other digestive enzymes, the significance of which will be apparent later. The other property of tannins, linked with their tanning ability, is their taste—an astringency which causes the puckering of the tongue. This astringency is repellent to higher animals, birds, reptiles and probably also insects (see p. 139).

The importance of tannins in controlling the feeding of winter moth larvae on oak trees has been established by the work of Feeny (1970). He was interested in the curious behaviour of these caterpillars, which feed happily on oak leaves in the Spring but abruptly cease feeding on oak in mid-June, turning to other tree species for sustenance. In seeking an explanation for this odd feeding behaviour, Feeny compared oak leaves growing in the Spring with those growing in June in terms of nutritional status but could find no obvious differences. The odd behaviour was also not explicable in terms of other environmental parameters, e.g. an increase in bird predation on these insects. It was only when he measured tannin content that real differences became apparent (Fig. 5.5), a sharp increase occurring just at the time when insect feeding ceased.

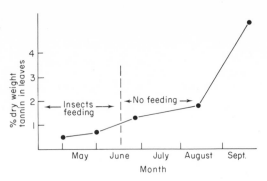

Fig. 5.5 Correlation between tannin content and insect feeding behaviour on oak

Chromatograms of leaf tannin extracts (Fig. 5.6) made on the two dates showed not only qualitative but also quantitative differences, leaf maturity being associated with an increasing number of tannin components. While the hydrolysable tannins were present equally in April and June leaves, the condensed tannins only appeared in significant amount in the older leaves.

The immediate cause of the change in feeding habit in the winter moth is thus certainly due to the increasing repellency of the leaf, because of the astringent taste of the tannin. The reason behind this change in food habit is undoubtedly more complex, involving a change in the nutritional value of the protein present in the leaf. As the larvae bite into oak leaf, the tannin and protein, normally compartmentalized in different parts of the cell, are brought

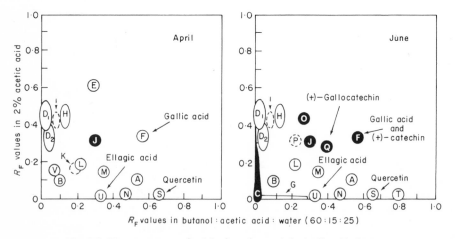

Fig. 5.6 Chromatograms of oak leaf tannins made in April and in June

together and the protein undergoes complex formation if not a tanning process. As tannin content increases during the season, more and more of the protein becomes complexed. This has the effect, already pointed out, of seriously reducing the digestibility of the protein, i.e. its capacity to undergo tryptic hydrolysis to free amino acid within the insect body.

One can conclude, therefore, that the tannin produced by the oak tree in its leaf tissues ultimately provides a significant barrier to insect feeding by affecting the nutritional value of the protein present in the same leaf. It may also be noted that the effectiveness of tannins to inhibit the digestibility of proteins is greatest at low pHs (e.g. 4·2) and least at high pHs. Significantly, the gut pH of the winter moth larvae is about 9·2 and this high value may be solely an adaptation in order to increase the amount of nitrogen available to the insect from protein–tannin complexes.

What is true for the winter moth may well apply to the other insect predators feeding on oak. While no less than 110 species of Lepidoptera have been recorded in oak trees in early June, only 65 of these species can be found on the same trees in mid-August. Furthermore, the density of insects on oaks undergoes a dramatic decline about the same time. While the tannin increase is the major determinant in this interaction, increasing toughness of the leaf is also a factor. Clearly, the tree, in response to insect predation, produces increasing amounts of tannin to avoid complete defoliation. The trees also respond to insect attack by producing "lammas" shoots and the photosynthetic area after the attack is largely restored by late June. During the summer months then, the oak can carry out sufficient photosynthesis to build up energy to store for the winter months ahead.

The oak leaf–winter moth interaction may be an unusual form of symbiosis, established in the above terms largely because oak trees live to such an enormous age and because insect predators have had time to adapt, at least partly, to the secondary compound deterrents. Feeny (1976) has recently suggested that a distinction can be drawn between long-living woody plants such as the oak tree and ephemeral annuals (e.g. crucifers) in terms of their chemical defense strategies. Long-living plants he terms "apparent", since they are easily found by insects and are unlikely to escape insect predation. They adopt a defense such as tannins, which are synthesized in bulk and which are generally repellent to most feeders. By contrast, herbs with a short life-cycle are "unapparent", since they can more easily escape being fed upon. Their chemical defense is thus more likely to involve the production of specialized chemicals (e.g. glucosinolates or alkaloids) which are produced in small quantity and which insects can more readily detoxify. The above hypothesis fits in with the studies done so far on the oak leaf–winter moth and the crucifer–butterfly interactions, but more quantitative measurements are needed in other interactions to see whether the theory is of general application.

B. The Colorado Beetle and *Solanum* alkaloids

The Colorado beetle *Leptinotarsa decemlineata*, with its brightly coloured yellow and black marking, is a familiar and serious pest of the potato crop. Although it has been excluded from Great Britain, it is prevalent both in North America and in continental Europe. It can produce serious crop loss due to leaf damage. A search for potatoes resistant to Colorado beetle attack has, therefore, been an important goal in potato breeding. Resistance was first discovered not among cultivated varieties but among related wild tuber-bearing *Solanum* species, native to South America. In particular, resistance was recognized in *S. demissum* and the source of resistance was traced to the major steroidal alkaloid of the leaf, to a substance called demissine. Although demissine has a structure closely related to that of solanine, the major alkaloid of the cultivated potato *S. tuberosum*, it is apparently sufficiently different to repel beetle attack (Fig. 5.7).

HARMLESS

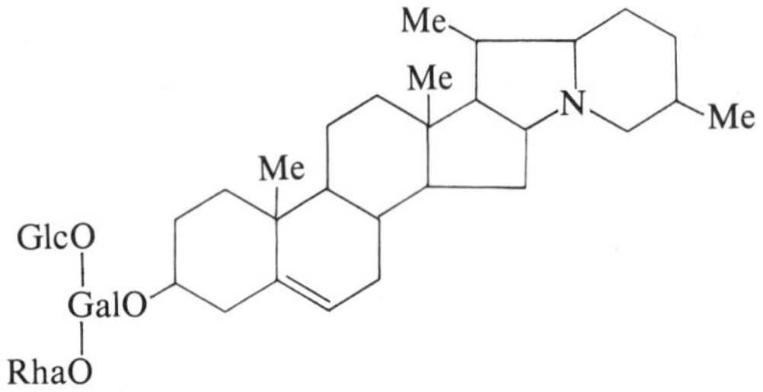

solanine
(alkaloid of *Solanum tuberosum*)

REPELLENT

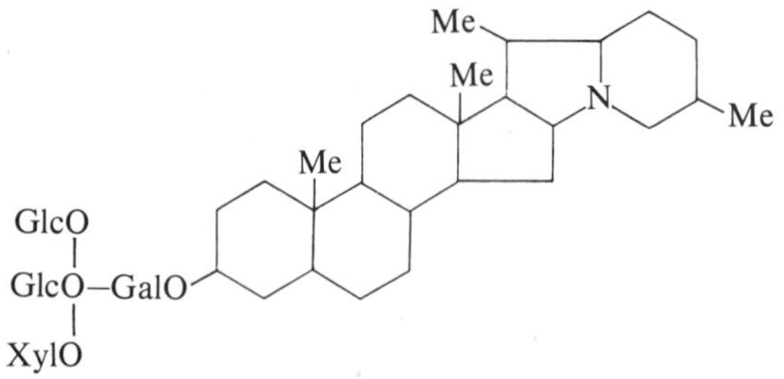

demissine
(alkaloid of *Solanum demissum*)

Fig. 5.7 Structures of *Solanum* alkaloids affecting Colorado beetle feeding

A number of other *Solanum* alkaloids have been tested for activity and the relationship between repellency and molecular structure has been at least partly established. The three key features in the structure of demissine which are important for deterrence are: (1) the presence of a tetrasaccharide sugar at the 3-position; (2) the presence of xylose as one of the four sugar moieties; and (3) the absence of a Δ5-double bond. As soon as the 3-sugar is reduced to a trisaccharide, xylose is lost and the Δ5-double bond introduced, as in solanine, all repellency disappears. Tomatine, a major alkaloid in the tomato and also in several potato relatives, has a tetrasaccharide containing xylose and lacks a Δ5-double bond. It is, indeed, as repellent as demissine. Infiltration of potato leaves with tomatine solution, at a concentration of 2 mM/kg causes 50% reduction in beetle feeding while a concentration of 3 mM/kg leaf results in 100% larval mortality. Thus like most other feeding deterrents, it can have toxic consequences to the insect invader.

It is interesting that deterrence to beetle attack is closely dependent on chemical structure and small changes in part of the deterrent molecule can completely abolish the deterrence value. This may be because the deterrent acts on the insect at the membrane level, possibly interfering with the absorption of the phytosterols of the potato leaf, which are required by the beetle for ecdysone synthesis (see p. 90). Since alkaloids of the *Solanum* are in fact steroidal molecules, it is also possible that they have a direct effect in blocking ecdysone biosynthesis.

Information on the deterrent properties of demissine is clearly of practical value, since breeding experiments with *S. demissum* and *S. tuberosum* might yield a potato resistant to beetle attack. In fact, such a breeding programme has been developed and potato plants resistant to the potato beetle have been obtained. How long this resistance persists in the field is another matter, since it is clearly possible for the beetle to adapt to demissine and detoxify it in a harmless form. Hence, the Colorado beetle may rise once more and predate upon an unprotected potato harvest.

C. Other Feeding Deterrents

Apart from the two examples discussed in Sections IV.A and IV.B, feeding deterrents have not otherwise been well studied and much of our present information depends on limited observations. The feeding behaviour of leaf-cutting ants of the species *Atta cephalotes* and *A. octospinosus* is complicated by the symbiosis of these insects with their fungal colonies and their indirect use of leaf material as food (Cherrett, 1972). The leaf-cutting ant is an insect which can thus afford to seek novelty in feeding and this probably accounts for its polyphagous habits. It does not seem to be affected by most secondary compounds, although latex-containing plant species are rarely attacked. Older

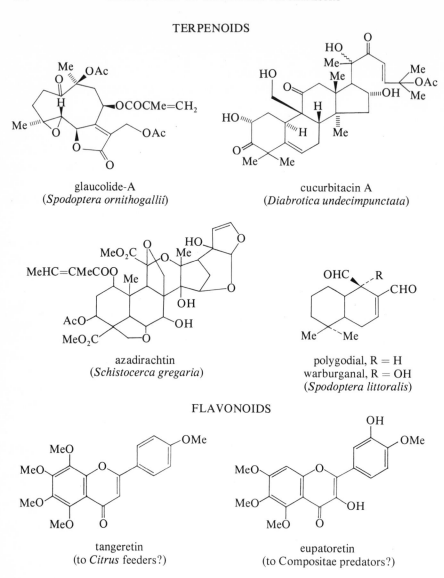

TERPENOIDS

glaucolide-A
(*Spodoptera ornithogallii*)

cucurbitacin A
(*Diabrotica undecimpunctata*)

azadirachtin
(*Schistocerca gregaria*)

polygodial, R = H
warburganal, R = OH
(*Spodoptera littoralis*)

FLAVONOIDS

tangeretin
(to *Citrus* feeders?)

eupatoretin
(to Compositae predators?)

Fig. 5.8 Some insect feeding deterrents

leaves of host plants are generally avoided, perhaps because of the build-up of tannin in them. *Atta cephalotes* is repelled by the monoterpene limonene in the peel oil of grapefruit flavedo, but this seems to be a special case and due to the fact that the oil is maintained in the flavedo under some pressure.

How far monoterpenes can act as feeding repellents generally is not clear, although, as has been mentioned earlier (Chapter 4, Section VI), changes in the α/β-pinene ratios in pine oleoresins can apparently limit the feeding of some pine bark beetles. However, not all beetles are affected by these olfactory compounds. In the case of *Monochamus alternatus* which feeds on pine needles, ethane gas is the active repellent and *not* the five monoterpenes which are present in the needle vapour. It is remarkable that such a simple compound as ethane, C_2H_6, can be effective in this way. As little as 0.60 µl of the gas are produced from one gram of pine needles, but this is sufficient to cause feeding to cease (Sumimoto *et al.*, 1975).

Higher terpenoids (see Fig. 5.8) are undoubtedly significant deterrents in many instances. Glaucolide-A, a sesquiterpene lactone of *Vernonia* plants, has been shown to deter not only the yellow striped army-worm (see Table 5.3) but also other insects which try to feed on these composite species. Glaucolide-A is effective in feeding diets at concentrations between 0.1 and 1%.

The most bitter and distasteful triterpenoids in plants are probably the cucurbitacins, a series of twenty tetracyclic triterpenes occurring in the cucumber and other members of the Cucurbitaceae. While serving as attractants to the cucumber beetles, they are repellent to most other insects. For example, cucumber beetles, offered a choice of non-bitter and bitter fruits to eat, will feed almost exclusively (in a ratio of $11:1$) on the bitter fruits. By contrast, the honey bee, *Apis mellifera*, faced with the same choice, not surprisingly opts for the fruit lacking cucurbitacin (in a ratio of $1:7$).

One other notable triterpenoid antifeedant is the compound azadirachtin, which was discovered following repeated observations that the neem tree *Azadirachta indica* (Meliaceae) which grows in Africa, is never eaten by the desert locust *Schistocerca gregaria*. The active principle was isolated and characterized by Nakanishi (1975) and shown to have a highly complex chemical structure (for formula, see Fig. 5.8). Simpler sesquiterpenoid antifeedants, e.g. warburganal, have been isolated by the same workers from the bark of the East African trees *Warburgia stuhlmannii* and *W. ugandensis* (Kubo *et al.*, 1976). Warburganal is a less general repellent than azadirachtin, since while active against larvae of army-worm, it does not have any deterrent effect on locust feeding. Interestingly, the antifeeding compounds in *Warburgia* taste "hot" to humans; whether insects can detect this taste and are thus deterred from feeding remains for future study.

One group of secondary compounds which may be important deterrents are the various flavone and flavonol glycosides which accumulate in leaves of most angiosperms. They accumulate particularly in herbaceous species and appear to replace, at least in part, the condensed tannins which occur so characteristically in leaves of woody angiosperms (Harborne, 1972). The toxicity of the common flavonol glycosides such as rutin and isoquercitrin to several insects feeding on cotton or tobacco plants has already been referred to (see Table 5.3). Flavonoid toxicity may well be enhanced by extra substitution of hydroxyl and/or methoxyl groups in the molecule. Compounds based in 6-hydroxyluteolin and quercetagetin are indeed commonly found in the leaves of many Tubiflorae families and especially in composites. The danger of these compounds to mammalian feeding is emphasized by reports of the neonatal lethality of the flavone tangeretin in rats and of the cytotoxicity of the flavonol eupatoretin present in *Eupatorium* leaves (Stout *et al.*, 1964; Kupchan *et al.*, 1969). One suspects that these molecules could be highly dangerous to insects, too.

Other examples of insect feeding deterrents can be found in two recent reviews: one on nutritional aspects by Beck and Reese (1976) and one on toxic aspects by Rhoades and Cates (1976).

V. EVOLUTION OF FEEDING DETERRENTS IN HIGHER PLANTS

A summary of the information on herbivore feeding and plant chemistry discussed in this and the last two chapters is presented diagrammatically in Fig. 5.9. This outline indicates that as angiosperms have evolved, they have developed different modes of protection from animal feeding. These modes encompass the synthesis of a range of deterrent molecules. Some deterrents are highly sophisticated in their action, i.e. by affecting the hormonal balance within the animal. Other deterrents are highly toxic (e.g. cyanogens, alkaloids) and deter largely on account of their poisonous nature. Yet other deterrents essentially reduce palatability (e.g. the cucurbitacins) or else reduce the nutritional status of the plant (e.g. tannins).

Within the evolutionary series: ferns → gymnosperms → woody angiosperms → herbaceous angiosperms, there is a trend towards chemical complexity in deterrent structures. Any one of the three main biosynthetic pathways may be brought into operation: the terpenoid (mevalonate), the phenolic (shikimic) or nitrogen (amino acid) pathway. Other biosynthetic routes not included in Fig. 5.9 are occasionally important, e.g. the toxic polyacetylenes in umbellifer roots are derived from the fatty acid pathway. One plant family may concentrate on one type of deterrent molecule, e.g. the Cruciferae with their mustard oils. Other families may diversify their toxins, e.g. the Leguminosae with their non-protein amino acids, alkaloids, cyanogens and isoflavones.

All these many and varied compounds are produced by plants in the first instance as protective devices against insect feeding. However, in almost every instance, insects and other animals have evolved defense or detoxification mechanisms. Indeed, almost every type of toxin is utilized by a particular insect in a positive way as a feeding stimulant or attractant. This is true of the

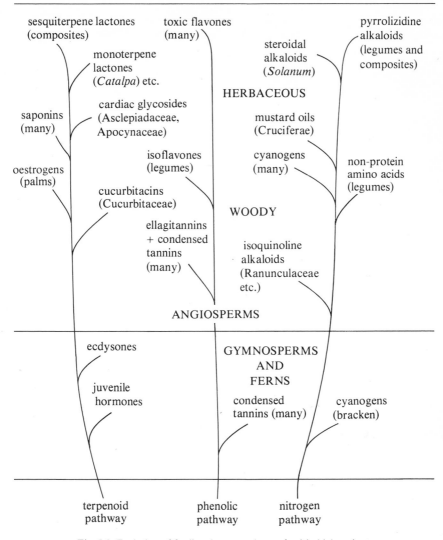

Fig. 5.9 Evolution of feeding deterrents (*sensu latu*) in higher plants

alkaloids (sparteine), the mustard oils (sinigrin), the cardiac glycosides, and the cyanogens. The only exception at present seems to be the condensed tannins, which have not been reported as yet as positive attractants to any insect. The role of tannins in protecting plants from mammalian feeding will be taken up in the next chapter, which deals with the feeding preferences of higher animals, including man. Many biochemical parallels between insects and other animals will become apparent.

BIBLIOGRAPHY

Books and Review Articles

Beck, S. D. and Reese, J. C. (1976). Insect–plant interactions: nutrition and metabolism. *Recent Adv. Phytochem.* **10**, 41–92.

Cherrett, J. M. (1972). Chemical aspects of plant attack by leaf-cutting ants: Harborne, J. B. (ed.), "Phytochemical Ecology", pp. 13–24. Academic Press, London.

Dethier, V. G. (1972). Chemical interactions between plants and insects. In: Sondheimer, E. and Simeone, J. B. (eds.), "Chemical Ecology", pp. 83–102. Academic Press, New York.

Ehrlich, P. R. and Raven, P. H. (1965). Butterflies and plants: a study in co-evolution. *Evolution* **18**, 586–608.

Feeny, P. (1975). Biochemical co-evolution between plants and their insect herbivores. In: Gilbert, L. E. and Raven, P. H. (eds.), "Co-evolution of Animals and Plants", pp. 3–19. Univ. Texas Press, Austin, Texas.

Feeny, P. (1976). Plant apparency and chemical defense. *Recent Adv. Phytochem.* **10**, 1–40.

Fraenkel, G. (1959). The raison d'etre of secondary plant substances. *Science* **129**, 1466–1470.

Fraenkel, G. (1969). Evaluation of our thoughts on secondary plant substances. *Ent. expl. et appl.* **12**, 474–486.

Meeuse, A. D. J. (1973). Co-evolution of plant hosts and their parasites as a taxonomic tool. In: Heywood, V. H. (ed.), "Taxonomy and Ecology", pp. 289–316. Academic Press, London.

Mothes, K. (1973). Pflanze und tier ein vergleich auf der ebene aes Sekundärstoff-wechsels. *Österr. Akad. Wissensch.* abt. I, **181**, 1–37.

Rhoades, D. F. and Cates, R. G. (1976). A general theory of plant herbivore chemistry. *Recent Adv. Phytochem.* **10**, 168–213.

Schoonhoven, L. M. (1968). Chemosensory bases of host plant selection. *Ann. Rev. Entom.* **13**, 115–136.

Schoonhoven, L. M. (1972). Secondary plant substances and insects. *Recent Adv. Phytochem.* **5**, 197–224.

van Emden, H. F. (1972). Aphids as phytochemists. In: Harborne, J. B. (ed.), "Phytochemical Ecology", pp. 25–44. Academic Press, London.

van Emden, H. F. (ed.) (1973). "Insect–Plant Relationships." Blackwell Scientific Pub., Oxford.

Literature References

Akeson, W. R., Haskins, F. A. and Gorz, H. J. (1969). *Science* **163**, 293–294.

Beck, S. D. (1960). *Ann. Entomol. Soc. Amer.* **53**, 206–212.

Beruter, J. and Stadler, E. (1971). *Z. Naturf.* **26b**, 339–340.

Burnett, W. C., Jones, S. B., Mabry, T. J. and Padolina, W. G. (1974). *Biochem. System. Ecol.* **2**, 25–29.

Chambliss, O. and Jones, C. M. (1966). *Science* **153**, 1392–1393.

Chapman, R. G. (1976). "A Biology of Locusts." Studies in Biology, No. 71. Edward Arnold, London.

Dethier, V. G. (1941). *Am. Naturalist* **75**, 61–73.

Doskotch, R. W., Mikhail, A. A. and Chatterji, S. K. (1973). *Phytochemistry* **12**, 1153–1156.

Erickson, J. M. and Feeny, P. (1974). *Ecology* **55**, 103–111.

Feeny, P. (1970). *Ecology* **51**, 565–581.

Gilbert, B. L., Baker, J. E. and Norris, D. M. (1967). *J. Insect Physiol.* **13**, 1453–1459.

Goodwin, T. W. and Mercer, I. E. (1972). "An Introduction to Plant Biochemistry." Pergamon Press, Oxford.

Hamamura, Y., Hayashiya, K., Naito, K., Matsuura, K. and Nishida, J. (1962). *Nature (Lond.)* **194**, 754–755.

Harborne, J. B. (1972). *Recent Adv. Phytochem.* **4**, 107–141.

Harborne, J. B., Heywood, V. H. and Williams, C. A. (1969). *Phytochemistry* **8**, 1729–1732.

Hewitt, P. H., Whitehead, V. B. and Read, J. S. (1969). *J. Insect Physiol.* **15**, 1929–1934.

Horowitz, R. M. (1964). In: Harborne, J. B. (ed.), "Biochemistry of Phenolic Compounds", pp. 545–572. Academic Press, London.

Kubo, I., Lee, Y. W., Pettei, M., Pilkiewicz, F. and Nakanishi, K. (1976). *J.C.S. Chem. Comm.*, 1013–1014.

Kupchan, S. M., Sigel, C. W., Knox, J. R. and Udayamurthy, M. D. (1969). *J. Org. Chem.* **34**, 1460–1463.

Levy, E. C., Ishaaya, I., Gurevitz, E., Cooper, R. and Lavie, D. (1974). *J. Ag. Fd. Chem.* **22**, 376–382.

Lichtenstein, E. P. and Casida, J. E. (1963). *J. Ag. Fd. Chem.* **11**, 410–415.

Mansell, E. and Newman, L. H. (1968). "The Complete British Butterflies in Colour." Ebury Press & Michael Joseph, London.

Nakanishi, K. (1975). *Recent Adv. Phytochem.* **9**, 283–298.

Nayer, J. K. and Fraenkel, G. (1963). *Ann. Entomol. Soc. Amer.* **56**, 119–122.

Shaver, T. N. and Lukefahr, M. J. (1970). *J. Econ. Entom.* **62**, 643–646.

Smith, P. (1966). *Nature (Lond.)* **212**, 213–214.

Stout, M. G., Reich, M. and Huffman, M. N. (1964). *Cancer Chemother. Rep.* **36**, 23–24.

Sturchkow, B. (1959). *Z. Vergl. Physiol.* **42**, 255–302.

Sumimoto, M., Shiraga, M. and Kondo, T. (1975). *J. Insect Physiol.* **21**, 713–722.

Zielske, A. G., Simons, J. N. and Silverstein, R. M. (1972). *Phytochemistry* **11**, 393–396.

6 | Feeding Preferences of Vertebrates, Including Man

I. INTRODUCTION

Apart from nutritional considerations, the selection of plant species as foods by vertebrates is based on taste and aroma, a complex response from tongue and nostril. Rejection of otherwise nutritious plants may therefore, be due to either the absence of an agreeable flavour (i.e. no positive response to the species) or the presence of disagreeable chemicals or toxins. The experimental problems of determining food selection by higher animals are, however, very considerable, compared to those with insects. It is, for example, highly expensive to test the effects of plant alkaloids on feeding behaviour in large farm animals, simply because of the number of fatalities that would inevitably arise in a statistically significant sampling. Again, to examine the feeding preferences of wild deer is complicated by the facts that they feed over wide areas and that there are practical problems in observing the behaviour of such shy creatures at close quarters. Much of the information available, therefore, is circumstantial or based on limited observations of the natural history type.

    The very fact that chemical substances can play a role in feeding, social and reproductive behaviour of mammals has taken some time to be generally accepted. Animals undoubtedly live in a world linked by chemical communication systems. While chemical signals are important in influencing food selection, as will be shown in this chapter, they are also involved in social and reproductive behaviour. Although unsuspected for many years, there are now known to be female sex pheromones in higher apes and man; simple organic acids have been identified as pheromones in human vaginal excretions and other odour compounds in the sweat have been implicated in male–female recognition encounters (see Chapter 7).

The chemicals of taste and smell are detected in man by receptor sites in the mouth and nose and much is known about the physiology of these responses (Moncrieff, 1967; Harper *et al.*, 1968). In the case of taste buds these are grouped in papillae on the surface of the tongue and most papillae appear to be sensitive to more than one taste. However, there are regions of distribution of the four main types of receptor: the sweet taste is more easily sensed on the tips of the tongue, the bitter taste at the back, the sour taste at the edges and the saltiness on the tip and at the edges. These taste buds are highly sensitive to dilute solutions of appropriate chemicals The threshold of salty taste is, for example, at a sodium chloride concentration of about 0·05% and that for bitterness is at a concentration of brucine of 0·0001%.

The olfactory receptors of man number over a million and are situated in a small 5 cm^2 region at the top and towards the rear of the nose. These receptors are tightly packed in this region and are protected from direct contact with the exterior environment by means of a series of folds. Attached to each olfactory receptor are a number of short and long cilia or hair-like filaments, which lie within a mucoid material bathing the receptor region. Receptor cells connect directly with the olfactory bulb in the brain and are capable of transmitting some 10^8 bits of information per second. One of the many remarkable features of the olfactory stimulus is that only a small number of molecules are required for perception to take place. For methyl mercaptan, for example, it has been estimated that a minimum of 40 molecules distributed over several receptors is sufficient for perception.

With both taste and smell, individuals vary in their response and there is a degree to which genetic factors control the ability to detect different chemicals. Blindness to the bitter taste of various phenylthiocarbamides and thioureas has been extensively explored by geneticists and it has shown to be inherited as a recessive character in a simple Mendelian fashion. The parent compound phenylthiocarbamide is non-bitter to some 5% of humans. Individuals who cannot detect a certain smell are similarly described as being blind to that smell or "anosmic". The frequency of anosmia within human populations varies with the smell. Thus, the skunk-like odour of *n*-butylmercaptan, which is obnoxious at a concentration of 0·0075% in 90% methanol, cannot be detected by about one person in a thousand (Harper *et al.*, 1968a). By contrast, trimethylamine,

Table 6.1 Some characteristic odours and chemicals that can represent them

Odour	Chemical[a]	Odour	Chemical[a]
Almond-like	Nitrobenzene	Metallic	n-Nonyl acetate
Aromatic	Benzaldehyde	Minty	Menthol
Burnt	Methyl benzoate	Musk-like	Exaltolide
Cool	Camphor	Onion-like	Dimethylsulphide
Disinfectant	Phenol	Petrol-like	Benzene
Faecal	Skatole	Rancid	Valeric acid
Fishy	Trimethylamine	Soapy	Stearic acid
Floral	Hydroxycitronellal	Sour	Acetic acid
Fragrant	β-Ionone	Spermous	1-Pyrroline
Fruity	Benzyl acetate	Spicy	Eugenol
Heavy	Coumarin	Sweaty	Iso-Valeric acid
Malty	Isobutyraldehyde	Sweet	Vanillin

[a] Based on the opinion of seven odour experts (Harper, 1975). Assessment of the odour of a particular chemical is subjective and the same compound can represent different odours to different people. In addition, with most odours, more than one individual chemical may be chosen to represent it.

the fishy primary odour, is not apparent to as many as 7% of human subjects (Amoore and Forrester, 1976).

Selection of food by man and other mammals is inevitably a complex matter involving flavour, taste, palatability, colour and odour. It is often difficult to determine the controlling factor in situations where the detection system is so highly sophisticated. Although human tastes are classified within four groups—salty, sweet, bitter, sour—the palate can respond to and recognize a variety of shades within these groups and similarly the human nose can differentiate between many scents and odours (see e.g. Table 6.1). However, as with insects, a major attractant in mammals is undoubtedly to sweetness. Indeed, if we are to believe Yudkin (1972), man's insatiable sweet tooth is a dangerous feature in his makeup, leading him to overconsume sugar and then develop a variety of disease symptoms as a consequence. By contrast to the attraction of sweetness, repellents are sharpness, bitterness and astringency. In man, whose taste responses are highly developed, a balance between sweetness and acidity or astringency is often necessary and both tastes are commonly present in foods and drinks; otherwise there is insipidity (Bate-Smith, 1972).

While we know a lot about taste responses of man and can infer much about the taste responses of insect herbivores, it is difficult to obtain much information about the enormous range of animals in between. Can we assume that there is a common basis for taste responses in animals generally? Evidence that tastes are indeed basically similar in hedgehogs, rats and man has been obtained in a rather odd test, devised because of wartime shortage of food, on the palatability of wild birds' eggs to these three groups of feeders (Bate-Smith, 1972). The results showed that all three groups responded to bitterness in the eggs to the same degree. Furthermore all three classes of subject were equally repelled by this bitterness. One should not, of course, conclude from this experiment that all animals respond to bitterness to the same degree. Swain (1974) has shown that reptiles, and especially tortoises, are relatively insensitive to the bitterness of quinine in solution, their sensitivity being only one-tenth that of man himself.

In the present chapter, it is intended to consider in turn the available information on feeding preferences of domestic animals, wild animals and of man. Much of the data discussed has been derived from the reviews of Arnold and Hill (1972), Bate-Smith (1972) and Rohan (1972), which should be consulted for most of the references in this field. More recent references will be included in the text, where appropriate.

II. DOMESTIC ANIMALS

A. Responses to Individual Chemicals

In choosing animal species in which to study food preferences, farm animals clearly have the advantages of availability and docility. Also, information obtained may be of direct practical value to the farmer. One of the problems of learning about the taste responses of such animals is, of course, their inability to express their preferences in human terms. It is an experimental disadvantage that cows cannot talk! However, the problem can be overcome to some extent by studying the response of cows and sheep to pure dilute solutions of chemicals, as a part of their normal daily water intake. Such studies do not reflect the natural situation where the animals have a wide choice of plant species in pastures, whose tastes and flavours are compounded of many different chemicals. Nevertheless, such work clearly indicates the importance of taste and smell to these animals in their choice of food.

Five basic substances in solution have been used to represent the main tastes in such experiments: sodium chloride (saltiness); sucrose or glucose (sweetness); acetic or citric acids (sourness); quinine (bitterness); and tannic acid (astringency). In general, the chemicals are detected at a fairly low threshold concentration and are accepted; increasing the concentration eventually leads to rejection. On a molar basis, bitterness is the first taste response to be rejected (Fig. 6.1). In general, the results clearly illustrate the fact that farm animals discriminate between chemicals and respond variously in degree to these major tastes (Arnold and Hill, 1972).

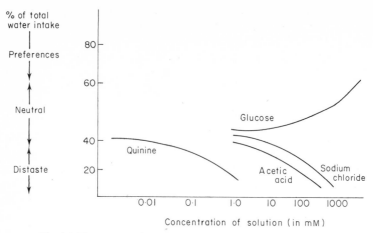

Fig. 6.1 The taste responses of sheep to solutions of pure chemicals

As may be expected, there are minor variations in response between individuals of the same species and also between different breeds of the same species. Larger differences in response occur when comparisons are made between cattle and goats, sheep and goats and cattle and sheep. In most cases, cattle are the most sensitive to chemical solutions, with goats being intermediate and sheep being the least sensitive. Only in the case of bitterness is this order reversed, goats being more sensitive than sheep with cattle showing the least sensitivity. To conclude, the results suggest at least that ruminants are not all that different from humans in their ability to recognize basic tastes and flavours in the plants they eat.

B. Responses to Chemicals Present in Plants

What is known of the sensory responses of ruminants to pure chemicals provides a guide to the way that these animals respond to stimuli from chemicals present in plant tissues. All sorts of complexities have to be taken into account in relating these feeding experiments to the situation in the field. Nutritional aspects are clearly important, but even here it is clear that animals cannot possibly respond to such commonly measured features of fodder plants as total nitrogen, crude fibre or ash content. Their nutritional response must be at the molecular level to specific chemical substances.

Although there is still much surmise, something can be said about the probable responses of most cattle, sheep and goats to several of the major classes of plant substance found in fodder plants. These data are discussed briefly in the following paragraphs.

Sugars. Sweetness is a clear preference in feeding, one shown by all ruminants that have been examined. There is also evidence that the form of the sugar can affect the response. Thus, calves show a greater response to sucrose solutions than to solutions of other sugars, while sheep appear to prefer glucose to sucrose at high concentrations. The importance of the response to sweetness in leaf can be gauged by the fact that cattle will eat normally unacceptable "dung-patch" herbage after it has been sprayed with sucrose solution. Objectionable stimuli can thus be swamped or suppressed by the presence of sugar as an attractant (Arnold and Hill, 1972).

Organic acids. There is some evidence that both cattle and sheep respond to the levels of particular organic acids present in temperate grasses used as fodder. Jones and Barnes (1967) have reported a positive correlation between the levels of citric and shikimic acids and the feeding preferences of ruminants. Acidity is, therefore, a recognizable component of the make-up of the plant tissues fed upon by farm creatures.

Tannins. High tannin content has been shown to be a significant deterrent to cattle browsing on the herbage of the legume plant Sericea (*Lespedeza cuneata*). A drop in voluntary intake of 70% was observed when the tannin content of Sericea rose from 4·8 to 12% dry wt. There is also much circumstantial evidence indicating that cattle and deer find a high tannin content in plants distasteful (see e.g. Cooper-Driver and Swain, 1976). As with insects (p. 119) so with ruminants, tannin in quantity will depress the digestion and nutritive quality of plant protein.

Ironically, it may be noted in passing that tannin content of forage crops may actually be beneficial to ruminants under some circumstances. Presence/absence of tannin in legume species seems to be correlated with the incidence of bloat, a metabolic disorder caused by the abnormal accumulation of gases in the rumen. Bloat foams are due, at least in part, to fractions within the leaf proteins which are responsible for the production of stable foams. This is largely prevented in those legumes which contain appreciable tannin, due to the precipitation of the deleterious protein by the tannin (Reid, 1973).

Coumarins. The pleasant sweetness of new mown hay is due to coumarin. It has a bitter taste and is apparently objectionable to sheep, who reject clover containing 0·5 to 1·0% of this compound. However, the substance is volatile and rapidly lost by evaporation, so that its effects wear off within an hour or two. It therefore only reduces palatability for a short period. It is doubtful whether coumarin, released whenever grasses containing the necessary precursor are cut, is a significant feeding deterrent in the long run. The precursor of coumarin, a glucoside of *o*-hydroxycinnamic acid, occurring in *Melilotus,* is some danger to sheep and cattle. However, this is because it can be converted to dicoumarol, a substance which becomes an anti-clotting factor if it reaches the blood (Ramwell *et al.*, 1964).

Cyanogenic glycosides. Recent studies of feeding on bracken, in which cyanogenesis is a polymorphic character, indicate that herbivores select the acyanogenic forms in natural conditions (Cooper-Driver and Swain, 1976). Cyanogenesis, and specifically the production of the poisonous HCN by this plant, is thus a feeding deterrent. Bracken fronds from areas where the acyanogenic form predominated (up to 98% of individuals in the population) were heavily grazed by both deer and sheep. By contrast, bracken protected by the presence of prunasin and the enzyme needed for the release of HCN was untouched by the same herbivores. These results are in line with earlier reports of cyanogenesis acting as a deterrent to rabbits and voles feeding on *Trifolium* and *Lotus* (Jones 1972; see also p. 73).

Essential oils. Although many species of plant that are browsed on by ruminants contain essential oils, there is rather little evidence that the presence of these volatile terpenes has a significant effect on choice of plant. It is well known that in the case of cows, some of the essential oils of plants can appear in the milk and taint it. For example, the Australian umbellifer *Apium leptophyllum* has an oil reminiscent of wild carrot and the milk of cows feeding on it in Queensland pastures smell strongly of carrot (Park and Sutherland, 1969). This rather indicates that the cow itself is relatively insensitive to these plant odours.

Oh *et al.* (1967) have examined the effect of different monoterpenes on rumen activity in deer and sheep and have noted that while the hydrocarbons and esters have little activity, the monoterpene alcohols such as linalol and α-terpineol do have a pronounced inhibitory action on the digestive processes. It is not clear, however, whether these effects are related to palatability differences. It is an interesting question whether these ruminants are capable of learning to avoid feeding on plants rich in monoterpene alcohols, while accepting other essential oil-rich plants into their diet.

Isoflavones. As has already been mentioned (p. 87), *Trifolium* species are rich in isoflavones, compounds which are oestrogenic and which have a deleterious effect on the reproductive capacity of mammals feeding in quantity on such clovers. Although isoflavones thus can produce serious disturbance in animal reproduction, there is no evidence of selective preferences for clover lines deficient in isoflavone. Tests show that sheep cannot discriminate between a high isoflavone strain of *Trifolium subterraneum* and a strain essentially lacking these compounds. Presumably isoflavones are not sufficiently repellent in taste to deter feeding so that plants rich in these potentially dangerous compounds are not obviously avoided.

Alkaloids. There is much evidence that alkaloids are significant feeding deterrents to grazing animals, particularly when their presence, as in most cases, is associated with a bitter taste. Ragwort, *Senecio jacobaea,* which is rich in pyrrolizidine alkaloids (see p. 78), is notably avoided by cattle and sheep and is one of the few weeds, other than thistles and nettles, to survive uneaten in English meadows. In the genus *Lupinus*, there is a species *L. angustifolius* in which there are alkaloid-rich (up to 2·5% dry wt alkaloid) and alkaloid-free strains. These differ by a single gene. It has been shown that sheep, when presented with a choice of "bitter" and "sweet" strains, avoid feeding on the alkaloid-containing strain if at all possible but readily graze on the alkaloid-free variety.

Other alkaloidal plants in which feeding experiments have been attempted (Arnold and Hill, 1972) are *Phalaris tuberosa* and *P. arundinacea*, two grasses containing the tryptamine-based alkaloids, gramine and hordenine. Experiments with sheep indicate that gramine at low levels (0·01%) actually stimulates feeding while higher levels (up to 1%) lead to rejection.

C. Feeding Preferences

One can conclude from the limited data available, then, that ruminants respond to a range of chemical stimuli as a guide to feeding. These animals show a significant preference for sweetness, but also exhibit some requirement for a balanced taste involving the sourness of organic acids. They clearly avoid alkaloid, cyanogen and tannin-containing plants whenever they can. Domestic cattle, however, will not have learnt to avoid all poisonous or dangerous plants present in wild pastures and will obviously not be able to survive unscathed when exposed to unfamiliar grazing lands. Not surprisingly, cattle death due to plant toxins is a familiar agricultural hazard, especially where a wide range of potentially dangerous wild species are present in the native flora (as in the South African veldt or the North American prairies). Some of the symptoms of toxicity have already been mentioned earlier in Chapter 3.

Detailed knowledge of the response of ruminants to the chemical composition of their foods and especially of their response to nutritional factors is still largely unavailable. Much work is needed in the future to analyse with more refined techniques the behavioural responses of farm animals to the plants they ingest.

III. WILD ANIMALS

What applies to sheep and cattle does not necessarily apply to wild animals and their feeding preferences may be determined by other factors than those mentioned so far. Wild animals in desert habitats, for example, may be guided in their feeding largely by an unending search for water in an otherwise arid environment and they will learn to feed on almost any succulent plant tissue that offers itself. This is true of the antelope-like oryx, which lives in Southern

Arabia on *Tamarix,* the root parasites *Cynomorium* and *Orobanche, Tribulus* and a sweet grass (*Aristida* sp.) (Shepherd, 1965).

Wild herbivores are probably better adapted to plant toxins than domestic animals and may be able to feed on many potentially toxic plants which are also nutritious. Evidence of such adaptation to cardiac glycoside poisoning is shown in the behaviour of the hyrax (*Procavia*) and of gazelles which feed on leaves of oleander, *Nerium oleander,* without tragic consequences. Other toxic plants eaten by the hyrax include *Phytolacca dodecandra* (rich in saponin), leaves of figs and various Euphorbiaceae (with toxic compounds in the latex) and members of the Solanaceae (an alkaloid-rich family) (Rothschild, 1972).

With such wild animals as the hyrax and the mountain goat, which is also rather unselective in its choice of plant, one may wonder whether angiosperms offer any serious barrier to mammalian feeding. Probably, in extreme situations where alternative food plants are not available, such animals may be

Table 6.2 Food plants of the mountain gorilla

Family and species	Family and species
Boraginaceae *Cynoglossum geometricum* *C. amplifolium*	Polygonaceae *Rumex afromontanus*
	Rosaceae *Hagenia abyssinica*[a]
Compositae *Carduus afromontanus* *Helichrysum* sp.[a] *Senecio erici-rosenii*[a] *Vernonia adolfifrederici*[a]	*Pygenum africanum*[a] *Rubus runssorensis*[a]
	Rubiaceae *Galium sinense*
Ericaceae *Erica arborea*[a]	Umbelliferae *Peucedanum kerstenii*[a]
Gramineae *Arundinaria alpina*[a]	*P. linderi*[a]
Hypericaceae *Hypericum lanceolatum*[a]	Urticaceae *Laportea alatipes*[a]
	Droquetia iners Zingiberaceae
Moraceae *Myrianthus arboreus*	*Afromomum* sp.
Polypodiaceae *Polypodium* sp.	Family uncertain *Xymalos monospora*

Data from Schaller (1963).

[a] Plant parts which are bitter to man.

able to adapt to any toxin that may be present in a plant. More useful information on feeding preferences of mammals can probably be obtained by considering species which have a wide choice of plants available to them in a habitat of high rainfall. Such an animal is the mountain gorilla of the African Congo and much is known about its feeding habits from the studies of Schaller (1963).

These gorillas are vegetarians, with an enormous daily capacity to eat leaves, stems and roots, topped up with fruits and seeds. Presented with a range of literally hundreds of different angiosperm species to feed on, the gorillas ignore most of them and concentrate on only some 29 species (Table 6.2). What is remarkable about these 29 species, however, is the fact that a significant number of them contain what appear to be effective feeding deterrents and yet they are still consumed. Up to 30% of them are significantly bitter in taste, at least to man, and they are still eaten. One of them, namely *Laportea alatipes,* is covered with viciously stinging hairs. As Schaller writes: "The virulence of (these) nettles was such that they readily burned through two layers of clothing ... yet gorillas handled them without hesitation and fed on stems and leaves that bristled with white hairs—the animals were apparently insensitive to them".

The question may be asked: what determines the choice by the gorilla of these 29 plant species out of the several hundred it could choose from? If normal barriers to feeding such as bitterness and stinging hairs fail to deter gorilla appetites, what can be present in other plants of the Congo which restricts the gorilla to such a small selection of taxa? The answer to this question is one that can only be inferred; experimental proof is still required. However, as Bate-Smith (1972) has pointed out, the plants eaten by this animal, while they come from over a dozen families, have one thing in common—they are essentially lacking in condensed tannins. The only exceptions are two species of Rosaceae, where the bark, rather than the leaf or stem, is consumed. By contrast, the vast majority of plants avoided by the gorilla are probably woody angiosperms, a major feature of which are large quantities of tannin in the leaf tissues (Bate-Smith and Metcalfe, 1957).

One may hypothesize then, that the gorilla makes its basic choice of plants simply on the level of tannin present, significant quantities being deterrent. This choice is determined by taste, by the astringency of the tannin-containing plants, but it may well be motivated by the unconscious recognition that such plants are nutritionally inadequate, in that, when eaten, the protein will be complexed with the tannin and thus be partly or wholly indigestible (see p. 120). Its main choice then decided, the gorilla then eats almost all other plants open to it and, among these, develops a "taste" for a number which have bitter constituents. In this case, as in human feeding responses, familiarity leads to acceptability and even liking, so that a basically repellent character becomes an attractive one. Finally, the gorilla's ability to cope with stinging hairs is proof that obvious physical barriers to feeding can be successfully circumvented.

IV. MAN

A. The Choice of Plant Foods

Early man chose to eat from a wide range of plants. This is apparent from the plant remains found at the dwelling sites of Neolithic man. It is also apparent from the sort of plants eaten by primitive tribes today, e.g. the Bushman of Africa and the Veddhas of Ceylon. It is only in relatively recent times, as a result of civilization and urbanization, that the choice of food plants has become restricted. The limited basis of present-day diets is reflected in the small number of staple crops of agriculture; in the U.K., for example, there are less than a dozen major crop plants grown for human consumption.

Two major refinements have had a profound effect on man's choice of food—the cultivation of plants and the cooking of foods. Human selection among wild species for favourable strains to cultivate has meant that many deleterious chemicals have disappeared or been reduced in quantity from plant tissues. Wild potato tubers, for example, are often bitter and toxic partly because of the high alkaloid content. This characteristic was bred out by the South American Indians who first cultivated the crop and is almost completely absent from modern cultivars. By contrast, favourable properties of plants have been enhanced by breeding and selection and cultivated fruits such as the apple, pear and strawberry have a much higher sugar content and are more attractively coloured than the wild relatives.

The effect of cooking on diet has also been important in changing the taste properties of plant tissues and also their acceptability. The potato, already mentioned above, would hardly have become such a staple item of the diet if it was eaten raw, since its starch tends to be indigestible before cooking. Again, cooking and other processing of plants has meant that many toxic components are destroyed or removed, so that a wider range of plants become available for eating. The trypsin inhibitors, an undesirable feature of raw soya beans, are destroyed by cooking. Fruits of quinoa, *Chenopodium quinoa,* contain a toxic saponin, but this can be leached out by steeping overnight in water, and the seed so treated can then be milled into flour for baking bread.

Given freedom of choice, then, man's selection of food among plants would be guided by a variety of qualities, such as colour, shape, smell, flavour, taste and texture. As with other animals, sweetness of taste and aroma is highly attractive to man's palate, while sharpness, bitterness and astringency are general repellents. However, some degree of acidity, bitterness or astringency in the presence of sugar increases the acceptability of otherwise insipid foods.

A taste for bitterness can be developed—witness the increasing preference among habitual beer drinkers for bitter rather than mild beers. Bitterness here is due to the hop constituents, the hupulones and lupulones, which were originally added to beer only in order to improve the keeping qualities of the brew.

While much could be written on the biochemical basis of human response to flavours, there is a gap in our knowledge when it comes to the selection of plants as food, since we know so little about the detailed chemical make-up of plants in relation to palatability. Here, three areas of this subject are considered in more detail: the chemistry of flavour, the chemical basis of sweetness and the flavour potentiators.

B. The Chemistry of Flavours

Much progress has been made in recent years in the chemical analysis of food flavours. Some typical results are shown in Table 6.3. The identification of plant volatiles has been enormously aided by modern instrumentation particularly gas liquid chromatography, which is ideal for the rapid and sensitive separation of components of smell. Nevertheless, there are still experimental problems when characterizing an active agent which is often only present in plants as a trace constituent. It was necessary, for example, to extract 5 tons of celery in order to identify its flavour volatiles.

Table 6.3 Chemical components of fruit and vegetable flavours

Plant	Components identified as flavour principles
FRUITS	
Apple	Ethyl 2-methylbutyrate
Banana	Amyl acetate, amyl propionate and eugenol
Coconut	α-Nonalactone
Lemon	Citral
Mandarin orange	Methyl N-methyl anthranilate and thymol
Peach	Undecalactone
Pear	Ethyl *trans*-2,*cis*-4-decadienoate
Raspberry	1-(*p*-Hydroxyphenyl)-3-butanone
Vanilla	Vanillin
VEGETABLES	
Celery	Alkylidene phthalates, diacetyl and *cis*-hex-3-enyl pyruvate
Cucumber	$CH_3CH_2CH=CHCH_2CH_2CH=CHCHO$
Garlic	Di-2-propenyldisulphide
Onion	Dipropyl disulphide, propanethiol
Mushroom	Lenthionine

It must also be remembered that the ultimate identification of a particular flavour principle depends on the subjective judgement of the human subject. Only the human nose can detect and the human brain record that a particular chemical or mixture of chemicals has the smell of raspberry, blackcurrant or peach. Much care has to be given to the selection of taste panels and to the use of organoleptic controls in flavour research. Special descriptive terms have to be adopted in order to standardize procedures. Several classifications of chemical odours have been attempted and a comprehensive survey of odour descriptions is available (Harper *et al.*, 1968b; see also Harper, 1975).

As will be seen from Table 6.3 and Fig. 6.2, many fruit flavours have now been identified (see also Nursten, 1970). A few are probably given by single

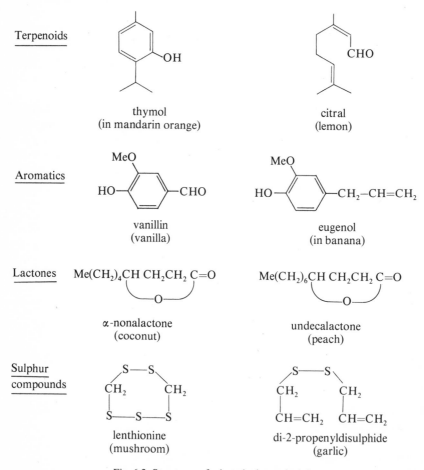

Fig. 6.2 Structures of selected odour principles

compounds, e.g. apple, peach, coconut and pear. Others are provided by several components; e.g. banana essence is composed of the aliphatic esters and the aromatic phenol, eugenol. Yet others are more complex; some ten monoterpenes are apparently active in the flavour principle of apricots.

Two fruits which have so far defied analysis are blackcurrants and strawberries. In both cases, over a hundred volatiles have been isolated from them but the aroma principles remain unknown. In the case of strawberry, a purely synthetic compound, ethyl 1-methyl-2-phenylglycidate, is available for use in artificial strawberry essence. Other failures have been with coffee and chocolate, which have yielded over 700 compounds on analysis. It is not known, however, which, if any, of these components are responsible for flavour or whether as yet undetected substances are the real odour principles.

It is clear from this and other work that trace components are often important and indeed they may contribute more to the characteristic flavour than the major volatiles present. This is true of lemon, in which limonene makes up 70% of the oil; it is the content of citral (less than 5% of the oil) which gives the lemon flavour. The effectiveness of some volatile odour principles is exemplified by the case of cucumber smell, which is due to the aldehyde, nona-2,6-dienal (Table 6.3). This substance has an odour threshold of 0·0001 ppm!

The relationship between odour and chemical structure is hardly a straightforward one. Who would suspect that two such similar structures as undecalactone and α-nonalactone (Fig. 6.2) actually provide the odours of peach and coconut respectively? How is it that the simple difference in the number of exocyclic methylene groups should change the odour so profoundly? Another remarkable relationship in odour character can be seen in the molecules responsible for the vanilla and ginger principles. Vanillin, the vanilla pod essence, has a pleasant sweet aromatic odour. Condensation of vanillin with acetone gives zingerone, a compound which is now hot and pungent!

Analysis of the root of ginger, *Zingiber officinale*, has, in fact, shown that zingerone is an artifact derived from the true natural principles, gingerol and paradol, which are also hot and pungent in flavour. Related structures which provide pungency in *Curcuma longa* (also Zingiberaceae), in the pepper and in the capsicum are illustrated in Fig. 6.3. Some relationships between degrees of pungency and structure are apparent here. Pepper is less pungent than capsicum, which is in keeping with the hypothesis that a 4-hydroxy-3-methoxy-phenyl group, present in zingerone and capsaicin, contributes to pungent properties. Replacement by a 3,4-methylenedioxyphenyl group, as in piperine, reduces pungency.

In any discussion of food flavours, the contribution of sulphur compounds to plant volatiles must be mentioned. The mustard oils, of acrid flavour in mustard and other crucifers, have already been described as repellents in

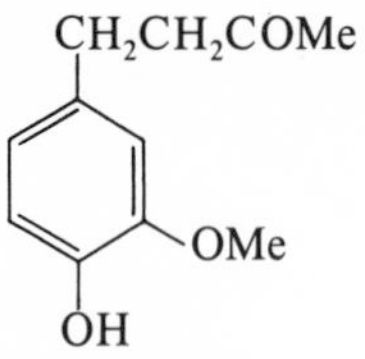
CH2CH2COMe
OMe
OH

zingerone

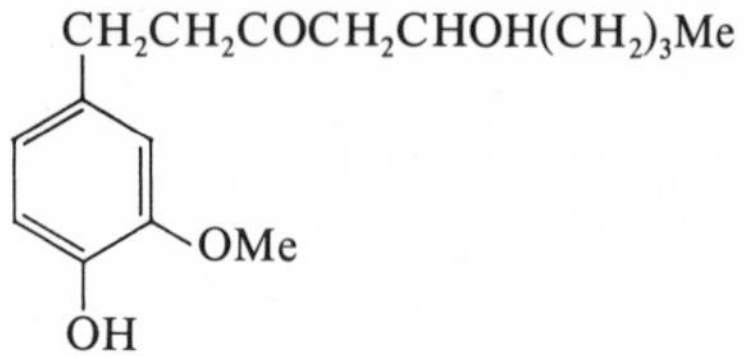
CH2CH2COCH2CHOH(CH2)3Me
OMe
OH

gingerol
(*Zingiber officinale*)

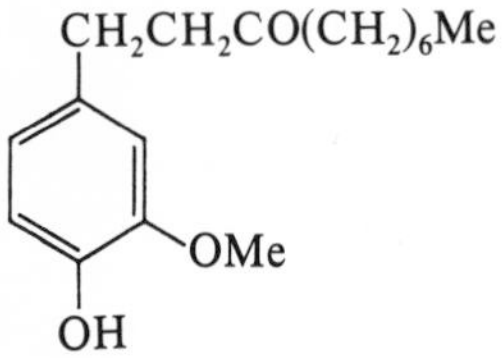
CH2CH2CO(CH2)6Me
OMe
OH

paradol
(*Zingiber officinale*)

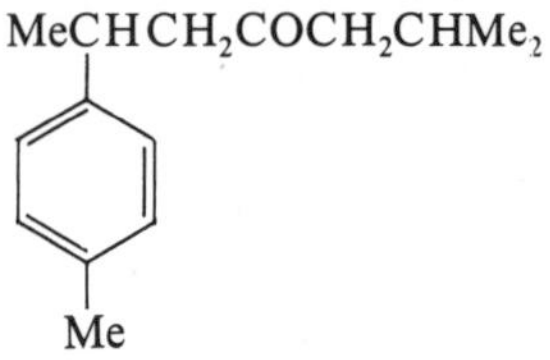
MeCHCH2COCH2CHMe2
Me

ar-turmerine
(*Curcuma longa*)

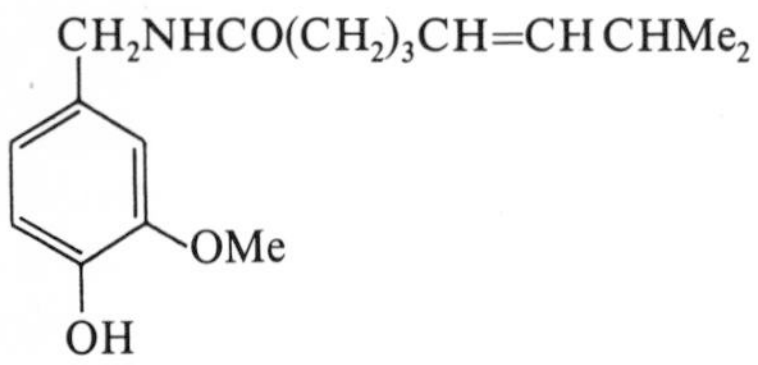
CH2NHCO(CH2)3CH=CHCHMe2
OMe
OH

capsaicin
(*Capsicum annuum*)

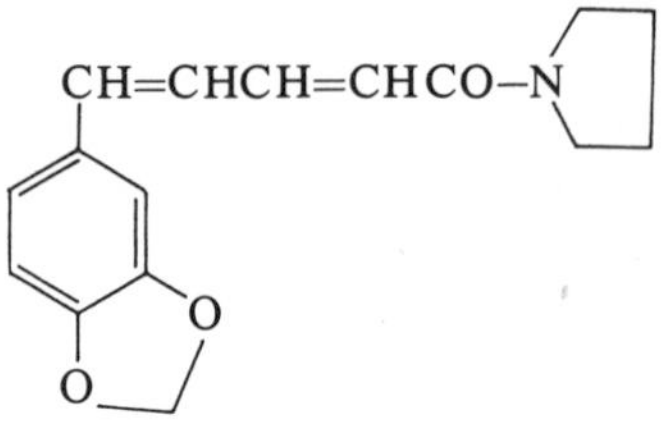
CH=CHCH=CHCO–N
O
O

piperine
(*Piper nigrum*)

Fig. 6.3 Structures of pungent principles in plants

relation to insect feeding (p. 113). While attractive to man in trace amounts, as a garnish to meat, mustard is clearly a repellent when taken in any quantity. Other vegetables containing sulphur components are the onion and garlic, the principles of which are mainly aliphatic disulphides (Table 6.3; see also Johnson *et al.*, 1971). Again, the flavour is two-edged, being attractive to some but objectionable to others. Finally, one remarkable sulphur-containing principle, which has no undesirable flavour qualities, is the compound lenthionine, the structure of which includes five sulphur atoms joined in a ring system with two methylene groups (Table 6.3). This substance is the delectable and highly prized aroma principle of the Japanese mushroom, *Lentinus edodes*.

C. The Chemistry of Sweetness

Sweetness in plant tissues is usually provided by a mixture, in varying proportions, of the three common sugars, glucose, fructose and sucrose. The disaccharide sucrose probably predominates in most plants; it is a major storage form of sugar and accumulates, sometimes in massive quantity as in the stems of sugar-cane and the roots of sugar-beet. As far as man is concerned, sucrose is used as the standard for sweetness, and all other sweet compounds are compared with it in solution on a molar basis. As indicated in Table 6.4, its two component sugars differ in sweetness from it, glucose being less sweet and fructose sweeter. Other naturally occurring monosaccharides and oligosaccharides are also usually sweet to taste, although this is not invariably so. While the disaccharides maltose, gentiobiose and lactose are all sweet, the trisaccharide raffinose is tasteless.

Sweetness, however, is not a unique property of plant sugars and, as is well known, some purely synthetic compounds have considerably greater sweetness than sucrose. Two of the most familiar—cyclamate and saccharin—are 30 and 500 times as sweet. Synthetic sweeteners have certain dietary disadvantages. Not only may they differ from sucrose in having an aftertaste (as does saccharin), but also they are "suspect molecules" in that their intake in quantity over a period of years could conceivably cause cancer in humans. Although the evidence of suspected carcinogenicity is very weak, cyclamate has already been banned in some countries as a food additive and even the use of saccharin has fallen under some suspicion. Use of synthetic sweeteners in foods and drinks, of course, is artificial in the sense that it meets man's craving for sweetness without burdening him with the calorific content of sugar. The

Table 6.4 Relative sweetness of organic molecules

Compound	Sweetness, on a molar basis, relative to sucrose
Glucose	0·70
Sucrose	1·0
Fructose	1·3
Cyclamate	30
Glycyrrhizin	50
Stevioside	300
Saccharin	500
Naringenin dihydrochalcone	500
Neohesperidin dihydrochalcone	1,000
Serendip protein	3,000
Thaumatin protein	5,000

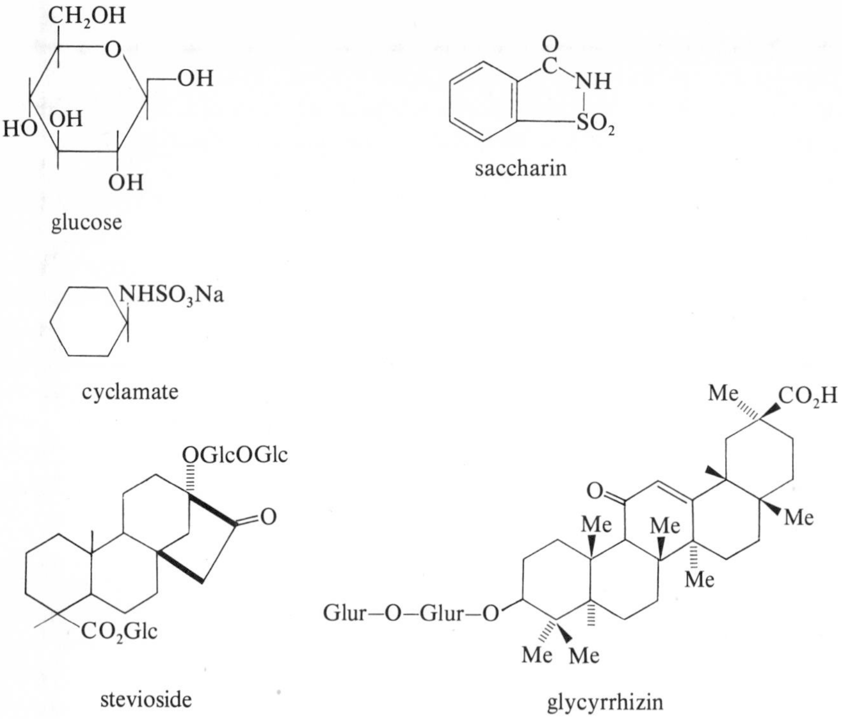

CH₂OH

OH

HO OH

OH

glucose

saccharin

cyclamate

OGlcOGlc

stevioside

glycyrrhizin

Fig. 6.4 Structures of some sweet compounds

dangers of over-consumption of sugars in man's diet has been emphasized in recent years, notably by Yudkin (1972). There is also a more justifiable use of artificial sweeteners in the diet of diabetics.

For these various reasons, the search for natural plant sweeteners has been intensified in recent years and several such compounds are now being developed for commercial application. The fact that certain plant molecules other than carbohydrates have intense sweetness has been known for some time. One of the best known is stevioside, a diterpenoid glycoside which occurs in the leaves of *Stevia rebaudiana* (Compositae). Another is glycyrrhizin, a triterpenoid glucuronide from liquorice root, which has the disadvantage of a liquorice-like aftertaste. The structures of these and other sweet molecules are shown in Fig. 6.4 and their sweetness ratings are given in Table 6.4.

The most remarkable discovery of natural sweeteners has been of proteins occurring in the fruits of two West African plants: *Dioscoreophyllum cumminsii* (Menispermaceae) and *Thaumatococcus daniellii* (Marantaceae).

The enormously intense sweetness of these fruits is reflected in their wide use in native cultures and their common names: serendipity berry and the miraculous fruit of the Sudan, respectively. Although first thought to be glycoproteins (see Inglett, 1975), the purified sweeteners are, in fact, simple proteins. They have been variously called monellin, serendip and thaumatins I and II. On hydrolysis, they give all the standard amino acids, with the notable exception of histidine. The simple dipeptide, aspartylphenylalanine methyl ester, is known to be sweet so that the sweetness of these proteins could reside within a small part of the total amino acid sequence.

The secondary and tertiary structure of the protein must also be involved in sweetness, since the taste is lost when monellin is denatured by heating in solution at 70–75°. Indeed, sequence analysis has shown that monellin consists of two subunits of 50 and 42 amino acids, and their separation causes the sweetness to disappear (Bohak and Li, 1976). There is evidence that cysteine and methionine residues occur at adjacent sites in that part of the molecule responsible for sweetness.

Finally, one other type of natural sweetener has been discovered in an unexpected way, initially from the study of bitterness in *Citrus* fruits (Horowitz, 1964). The water-soluble bitter compound was determined as

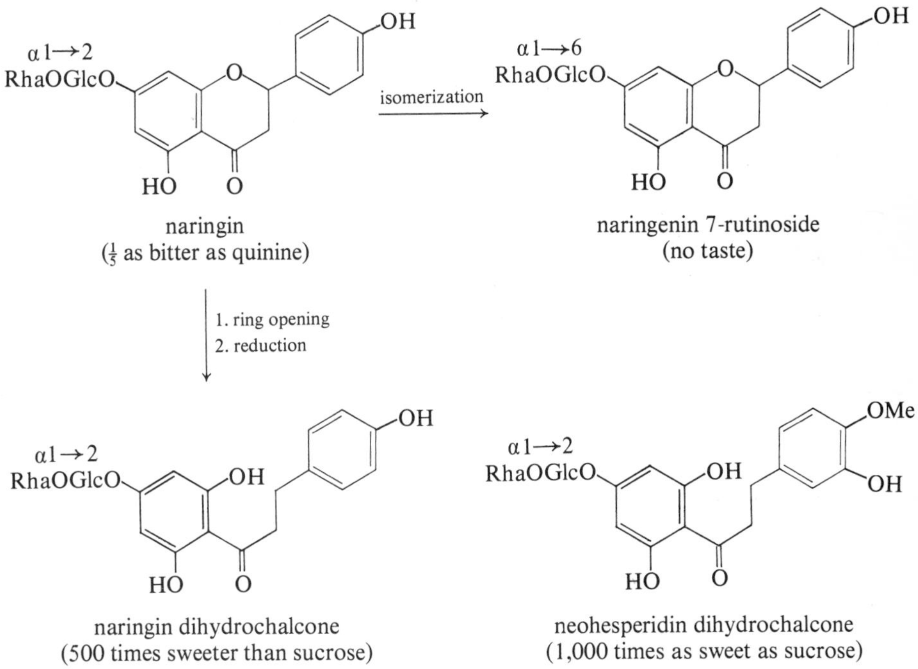

Fig. 6.5 Reversal of bitterness to sweetness in the flavonoid series

naringin, the 7-neohesperidoside of naringenin, the formula of which is shown in Fig. 6.5. The structural requirements for bitterness were found to be highly specific, depending on the association of the flavanone nucleus with a disaccharide of glucose and rhamnose in which the inter-sugar linkage is precisely defined as $\alpha 1 \rightarrow 2$. A change in the mode of this linkage, as reflected in the structure of naringenin 7-rutinoside (rhamnose-glucose linkage $\alpha 1 \rightarrow 6$), another natural constituent of *Citrus*, destroys all bitterness and the substance is quite tasteless. The more important discovery came when the bitter naringin was chemically modified by opening of the central pyran ring and reduction of the isolated double bond. The molecule so produced—a dihydro-chalcone—was found to be intensely sweet. Simple chemical manipulation can thus convert a molecule from being very bitter to great sweetness. As with bitterness, the structural requirement for sweet taste in this series is very specific and the special sugar moiety neohesperidose (Rha $\alpha 1 \rightarrow 2$ Glc) is essential for maximum sweetness. There are several naturally occurring dihydrochalcones known, but these only have glucose *or* rhamnose as the sugar moieties and they are only slightly sweet or bitter-sweet. By contrast, the dihydrochalcone derived from naringin is 500 times as sweet as sucrose, while that derived from neohesperidin (see Fig. 6.5) is a 1,000 times as sweet on a molar basis. This latter compound is the sweetest dihydrochalcone known and it is being developed in the United States as a commercial sweetener.

The fact that it is possible to convert a bitter compound such as naringin, by simple rearrangement of the molecule, to a sweet compound does suggest that the sites of perception of sweetness and bitterness are related to each other. This is also apparent in the facts that some sugars (e.g. mannose) are bitter-sweet and that certain modified sugars (e.g. penta-acetyl glucose) are actually bitter (see Birch and Lee, 1974). Recent tasting experiments with methyl α-D-mannoside and other model sugars have indicated that the sweet and bitter receptor sites on the tongue are very close to each other, indeed within 3 to 4 Å of each other (Birch and Mylvaganan, 1976). These authors suggest that sugar

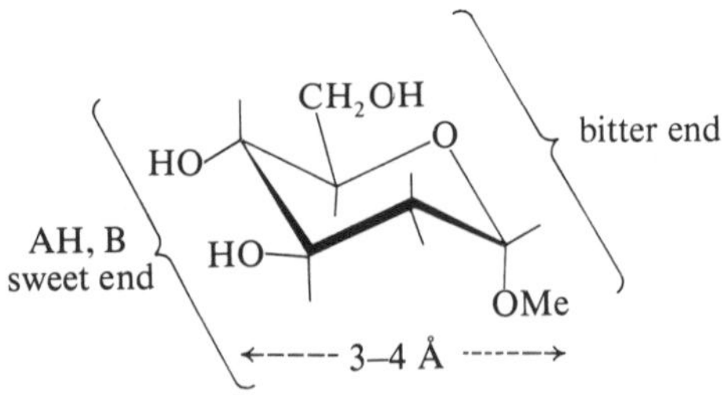

methyl α-D-mannoside

Fig. 6.6 Structural requirements for sweet and bitter receptor sites in man.

molecules are polarized on taste receptors and fit on as indicated in Fig. 6.6. Interaction at the two sites was observed when attachment by presaturation with either sweet or bitter molecules lowered the subsequent response to either bitterness or sweetness respectively.

D. Flavour Potentiators and Modifiers

Finally in this chapter, some mention is appropriate of flavour potentiators, since such compounds occur naturally and they could significantly influence the palatability of plant tissues to both insects and higher animals. Flavour potentiators are simply molecules which on their own have little effect but with other taste molecules, they enhance the flavour. They are added to food to bring out the natural flavour or aroma. The most familiar potentiator is sodium chloride, a substance which has to be used judiciously in small amounts because of its own salty taste. In recent years, an amino acid mono-sodium glutamate and a purine base 6-hydroxypurine 5'-mononucleotide have been used in the food industry as excellent flavour enhancers. Both are naturally occurring, the latter compound being isolated in the first instance from bonito fish.

A more unusual flavour potentiator or modifier is the glycoprotein miracularin, of molecular weight 44,000, which occurs in miracle fruit *Synsepalum dulcificum* (Sapindaceae). This has the property of eliminating sourness or acidity, without disturbing the sweet response. Its most amazing effect can be seen when sour lemons full of citrate are eaten, following the chewing of the berries of this plant. The lemons taste as sweet as oranges! The effect is limited and wears off within an hour or so. In its action, it is assumed that the taste membrane is physically bound to this glycoprotein so that it is completely ineffective in responding to sourness.

Another equally remarkable modification in taste is due to a mixture of pentacyclic triterpenes, the gymnemins, which occur in the leaves of *Gymnema sylvestre* (Asclepiadaceae). Here, the effect is on the sweetness receptor; after these leaves are chewed, any food eaten lacks all sweetness and even bitterness is partly repressed. Thus it has the general property of dulling some of the most important taste sensations. The ability to remove sweetness, of course, which is a main attractant to eating, could be of value to plants in their battle of survival against being eaten. Indeed, the effect of gymnemins in repelling herbivores of the plant in which they occur has been investigated by Granish et al. (1974). They found that gymnemic acids do act as feeding deterrents to the caterpillar of *Prodenia eridania*. Deterrence operates even with a sugar-free diet, so that it does not apparently modify the insect's taste responses. Presumably, the sweetness receptor sites in insects and mammals differ in some fundamental way.

One can conclude that the gymnemic acids have a dual action as defensive chemicals, acting as simple biting deterrents to insects but having a more profound effect on taste responses of mammalian feeders. These substances may only be the first of a series of such complex chemical agents to be implicated as deterrents in plant–animal interactions.

The above flavour modifiers exert gustatory effects not only in man, but also in the monkey *Cercopithecus aethiops*. However, gymnemic acid and miracularin have less effect in the dog or rabbit and apparently do not modify sweetness and sourness respectively when tested in the pig, rat and guinea-pig (Hellekant, 1976). The same author has also noted that the sweet proteins monellin and thaumatin are no longer sweet when tasted by the dog, hamster, pig and rabbit. Evidence is thus accumulating that the nature of the sweet receptor site varies significantly within the mammalian kingdom.

BIBLIOGRAPHY

Books and Review Articles

Arnold, G. W. and Hill, J. L. (1972). Chemical factors affecting selection of food plants by ruminants. In: Harborne, J. B. (ed.), "Phytochemical Ecology", pp. 72–102. Academic Press, London.

Bate-Smith, E. C. (1972). Attractants and repellents in higher animals. In: Harborne, J. B. (ed.), "Phytochemical Ecology", pp. 45–56. Academic Press, London.

Birch, G. G. and Lee, C. K. (1971). The chemical basis of sweetness in model sugars. In: Birch, G. G., Green, L. F. and Coulson, C. B. (eds.), "Sweetness and Sweeteners", pp. 95–111. Applied Science, London.

Harper, R., Bate-Smith, E. C. and Land, D. G. (1968a). "Odour Description and Odour Classification", 191 pp. J. & A. Churchill, Ltd., London.

Horowitz, R. M. (1964). Relations between the taste and structure of some phenolic glycosides. In: Harborne, J. B. (ed.), "Biochemistry of Phenolic Compounds", pp. 545–572. Academic Press, London.

Inglett, G. E. (1975). Protein sweeteners. In: Harborne, J. B. and Van Sumere, C. F. (eds.), "The Chemistry and Biochemistry of Plant Proteins", pp. 265–280. Academic Press, London.

Johnson, A. E., Nursten, H. E. and Williams, A. A. (1971). Vegetable volatiles: a survey of components identified. *Chem. Ind.* 556–565, 1212–1224.

Moncrieff, R. W. (1967). "The Chemical Senses", 3rd edn., 760 pp. Leonard Hill, London.

Nursten, H. E. (1970). Volatile compounds: the aroma of fruits. In: Hulme, A. C. (ed.), "The Biochemistry of Fruits and Their Products", Vol. I, pp. 239–268. Academic Press, London.

Ramwell, P. W., Sherratt, H. S. A. and Leonard, B. E. (1964). The physiology and pharmacology of phenolic compounds in animals. In: Harborne, J. B. (ed.), "Biochemistry of Phenolic Compounds", pp. 457–510. Academic Press, London.

Rohan, T. A. (1972). The chemistry of flavour. In: Harborne, J. B. (ed.), "Phytochemical Ecology", pp. 57–71. Academic Press, London.

Rothschild, M. (1972). Some observations on the relationship between plants, toxic insects and birds. In: Harborne, J. B. (ed.), "Phytochemical Ecology", pp. 1–12. Academic Press, London.

Schaller, G. B. (1963). "The Mountain Gorilla." University of Chicago Press, Chicago and London.

Shepherd, A. (1965). "The Flight of the Unicorns." Elek Books, London.

Yudkin, J. (1972). "Pure, White and Deadly—the Problem of Sugar." Davis-Poynter, London.

Literature References

Amoore, J. E. and Forrester, L. J. (1976). *J. Chem. Ecol.* **2**, 49–56.

Bate-Smith, E. C. and Metcalfe, C. R. (1957). *J. Linn. Soc. (Bot.)* **55**, 669–705.

Birch, G. G. and Mylvaganan, A. R. (1976). *Nature (Lond.)* **260**, 632–634.

Bohak, Z. and Li, S. L. (1976). *Biochem. Biophys. Acta* **427**, 153–170.

Cooper-Driver, G. and Swain, T. (1976). *Nature (Lond.)* **260**, 604.

Granich, M. S., Halpeon, B. P. and Eisner, T. (1974). *J. Insect Physiol.* **20**, 435–439.

Harper, R. (1975). *Chemical Senses and Flavour* **1**, 353–357.

Harper, R., Bate-Smith, E. C., Land, D. G. and Griffiths, N. M. (1968b). *Perfumery and Essential Oil Record,* 1–16.

Hellekant, G. (1976). *Chem. Senses Flavor* **2**, 85–95, 97–106.

Jones, D. A. (1972). *Genetica* **43**, 394–406.

Jones, E. C. and Barnes, R. J. (1967). *J. Sci. Fd. Agr.* **18**, 321–324.

Oh, H. K., Sakai, T., Jones, M. B. and Langhurst, W. M. (1967). *Appl. Microbiol.* **15**, 777–784.

Park, R. J. and Sutherland, M. D. (1969). *Aust. J. Chem.* **22**, 495–496.

Reid, C. S. W. (1973). In: Butler, G. W. and Bailey, R. W. (eds.), "Chemistry and Biochemistry of Herbage", Vol. 3, pp. 215–261. Academic Press, London.

Swain, T. (1974). *Observer,* London, 3rd February.

7 | Animal Pheromones and Defense Substances

I. INTRODUCTION

The paramount importance of chemical communication in biological systems is now widely appreciated. Together with aural and visual modes of communication, olfactory signals play a vital role in most groups of animals. Examples have already been given in previous chapters where insect behaviour in pollination and feeding is controlled by such chemical signals. It is the purpose in this chapter to consider these phenomena in more detail, with especial emphasis on the chemical structures involved.

Chemical signals in their widest sense are a universal attribute of life. In some form, they exist within cells and within and between all organisms. In lower plants, for example, there is clear evidence of such interaction. Two chemical agents in fungi are sirenin, which acts as a sex pheromone in the water mould *Allomyces* and cyclic AMP which acts as an aggregation pheromone in the slime mould *Dictyostelium discoideum*. In higher plants too, volatile chemicals are involved in interactions between organisms; for example, detrimental effects involving monoterpenoids and other compounds occur between one higher plant and another, a phenomenon called allelopathy (see Chapter 8). It is, however, only in the animal kingdom that chemical signals of an olfactory type are generally present, to serve an enormous variety of different purposes. Such signals are used in relation to an animal's need for food, reproduction and protection from predation. They are also important, in the case of social animals, for communication between individuals of the same species. Volatile chemicals used for communication *within* species are termed "pheromones", while chemicals used *between* different species are called "allomones". The distinction between the two classes of pheromone is sometimes blurred, since the same compound may occasionally serve both purposes.

Although pheromones are known throughout the animal kingdom, most of our information on these substances is derived from work on insects. This is partly because with insect pheromones it is relatively easy to monitor their activities; it is more difficult to do this with mammalian pheromones. It is also partly because there has been a practical incentive for the study of insect pheromones, since their identification at once provides a means of monitoring populations and thus, in the case of agricultural pests, of pest control.

The existence of pheromonal interactions in mammals, is, however, also now well documented. Obvious examples occur in the sexual life of animals living in groups, e.g. caged mice and rats. An odorant in the urine of male mice, for example, induces and accelerates the oestrus cycle in the female. This effect is more pronounced in those females whose cycles have been suppressed by grouping them together in the absence of a male, another pheromonal response. In humans, this can be seen in the effect on the menstrual cycle in female students living together in University dormitories; their cycles eventually become synchronized in such a way that most members of the group eventually menstruate at the same time. Although such pheromonal interactions in mammals are now well accepted, the chemicals concerned are often unknown and further discussion must await the time when the molecular basis of these signals is better understood.

In insects, pheromones are secreted in exocrine glands and are transmitted to other members of the species in vapour form. The effectiveness of some insect sex pheromones is proverbial. Only a few molecules are apparently needed to produce a response and the same few molecules can be effective over considerable distances. The great signalling power of sex pheromones is reflected in the fact that the release of less than 1 μg/sec by the female can attract the male gypsy or silkworm moth; the male begins to react when the molecular concentration is as low as 100 molecules/ml of air. A single female moth releasing its pheromone downwind from a particular site will produce what Wilson (1972) has called "an active air space" several kilometres long and over a hundred metres in diameter. Any male entering this active space will then turn upwind and fly towards the female. The size of the active space will vary with the wind velocity, an increase in velocity decreasing its volume. For a chemical to be active in such a system, it must be highly volatile and of a relatively low molecular weight. Indeed, most sex pheromones fall into this category in being hydrocarbon derivatives of carbon number between C_5 and C_{20} and of molecular weight between 80 and 300.

By contrast to such airborne pheromones, those used by aquatic organisms clearly have to be less volatile, of a higher molecular weight and presumably water-soluble. Their effectiveness must depend on their rate of diffusion in water, this being speeded up if they are placed in natural or artificially produced currents. In keeping with these ideas, it should be noted that some waterborne pheromones are protein in nature. This is true of the female substance produced in *Volvox* (Chlorophyta) (Starr, 1968) and of the substance controlling the attraction and settling of larvae of barnacles *Balanus balanoides* (Crisp and Meadows, 1962). Other water-borne signals are steroidal in nature. Thus, an oestrogen is released from the female to attract the male in the fish *Lebistes reticulatus* (Amouriq, 1965).

To the biochemist, one of the most intriguing aspects of animal pheromones is their biosynthetic origin. In the case of insects, it is probable that many are synthesized *de novo* within the animal body from simple starting materials. Others could, however, be obtained from plant sources and used directly or modified biochemically before use. In the case of animal defense compounds (allomones), there are many examples where arthropods have taken over plant chemicals and used them for protection. The very fact that animals make use of plant toxins in this way argues in favour of a function for these substances in the plants themselves. Animals are hardly going to borrow or adapt chemical defenses from plants, unless they have already proved of value as a defensive barrier in the plant to herbivore attack.

One particularly interesting group of plant substances used by animals are the alkaloids, compounds well known for their physiological activities in animals. There is good evidence that plant alkaloids are used by some animals for defense, e.g. the *Senecio*-feeding cinnabar moth protects itself from avian predators by accumulating alkaloids at the larval stage in its tissues (see p. 77). Another example discussed in this chapter concerns aristolochic acid, which is used by the butterfly *Pachlioptera aristolochiae* for the same purpose. Even more remarkable is the fact that certain animals appear to mimic plants in synthesizing their own alkaloids as defensive agents. This is true of millipedes, ants, ladybirds and water-beetles.

One other group of defensive substances which may be both of dietary origin and the subject of direct synthesis are terpenoids. The larvae of the saw-fly, for example, has the disconcerting habit of discharging at its predators an oily effluent of dietary-derived monoterpenes, previously stored in a pouch of the foregut. By contrast, the meloid beetle *Lytta vesicatoria* in order to discourage its attackers exudes a terpenoid toxin, synthesized *de novo*, by bleeding at its knee joints. One final group of defense compounds, discussed later in this chapter, are quinones which are, like the toxin of the meloid beetle, synthesized by the animals. These substances are produced as "hot secretions" by the bombardier beetle in special reactor glands, as the need arises.

Information on pheromones and defense substances has accumulated rapidly over the last 20 years, so much so that it is impossible in the space available to present a completely comprehensive account. It is only possible to illustrate the situation here with selected examples. More detailed information on insect pheromones is available in the books of Jacobson (1972) and Beroza (1970) and the review of Law and Regnier (1971). Mammalian pheromones are discussed by Albone (1977) and Stoddart (1977). Defense substances are reviewed by Weatherston and Percy (1970), Schildknecht (1971), Eisner (1972) and Tursch *et al.* (1976).

II. INSECT PHEROMONES

A. Sex Pheromones

The term sex pheromone refers to a compound liberated by a female, with the dual purpose of both attracting the male from a distance and also of inciting it to copulation when at close quarters. The same term also applies to substances produced by the males to excite females. Such compounds are sometimes referred to as aphrodisiacs, although this term strictly speaking applies to drugs which excite venereal desires in man. Sex pheromones are probably the most widely studied group of insect allelochemics and they have now been recognized and characterized in many different species. In the case of the Lepidoptera alone, female pheromones have been recognized in over 200 species and male-releasing attractants in at least a further 60 species.

In terms of chemical structure, the simplest sex attractant is valeric acid, the female pheromone from the sugar-beet wireworm. The majority, however, are long chain unsaturated alcohols, acetates or carboxylic acids (see Table 7.1). One of the best known is undoubtedly 9-ketodecenoic acid, or the queen-bee substance, which attracts the male drones to mate with the queen-bee. It is, however, only one of 32 compounds of similar structure present in the head of the queen-bee. The related 9-hydroxydecenoic acid, for example, is also an active compound, causing clustering and stabilization of the worker swarms.

Aliphatic cyclic compounds occasionally act as pheromones, as for example, the compounds frontalin and exobrevicomin, pheromones in the beetles of the genera *Brevicomis* and *Ips* (see p. 98). Also cyclohexane derivatives are pheromones in the boll weevil, *Anthonomus grandis*. There are a few aromatic

Table 7.1 Structures of some typical insect sex pheromones

Structure and name	Sex	Organism
$CH_3(CH_2)_3CO_2H$ valeric acid	♀	Sugar-beet wireworm *Limonius cakfornicus*
$CH_3CO(CH_2)_5CH=CHCO_2H$ *trans*-9-keto-2-decenoic acid	♀	Honey-bee *Apis mellifera*
$CH_3(CH_2)_3CH=CH(CH_2)_6OAc$ *cis*-7-dodecenyl acetate	♀	Cabbage looper *Trichoplusia ni*
$CH_3(CH_2)_2CH=OH(CH_2)_7OAc$ *cis*-8-dodecenyl acetate	♀	Oriental fruit-fly *Grapholitha molesta*
$CH_3CH_2CH=CH(CH_2)_{10}OAc$ *cis*-11-tetradecenyl acetate *trans*-11-tetradecenyl acetate	♀	Oak leaf roller-moth *Archips semiferanus*
$CH_3(CH_2)_{15}OAc$ hexadecanyl acetate $CH_3(CH_2)_4CH=CH(CH_2)_{10}OAc$ *cis*-11-octadecenyl acetate	♂	Butterfly *Lycorea ceres ceres*
$CH_3(CH_2)_9CO(CH_2)_3CH=CH(CH_2)_4CH_3$ *cis*-6-heneicosen-11-one	♀	Douglas fir tussock-moth *Orygia pseudotsugata*

pheromones. Phenol itself is a female pheromone in the grass grub beetle, presumably derived from tyrosine of dietary origin. Benzaldehyde is a pheromone in the moth *Leucania impuris*. The only alkaloidal pheromones are those produced by *Danaus* male butterflies in the wing pencils, the origins of which have already been discussed in an earlier chapter (p. 78).

Pheromones occur in very low concentration in insects and many specimens may be needed when isolating and identifying them. Each female Douglas fir tussock-moth contains about 40 ng of pheromone in the abdominal tip and 6,000 insects were required in order to isolate enough material for characterization. In the case of the pink Bollworm moth, nearly a million virgin female moths were extracted to yield 1·5 mg of its pheromone.

In any one insect, the chemical structure of the main pheromone is usually very specific and small changes in the molecule normally destroys or diminishes the activity. In the case of most hydrocarbon pheromones, there is a single isolated double bond in the structure; its position and stereochemistry (*cis*- or *trans*-) is vital to activity. This has been demonstrated in the case of the female pheromone of the cabbage looper *Trichoplusia ni* where a range of synthetic analogues have been tested (Fig. 7.1); none has as much activity as the natural compound and most are completely inactive (Jacobson *et al.*, 1970). While the natural pheromone is the *cis*-7-alkenol acetate, the synthetic *trans*-7-isomer shows some activity and it seems to be fairly general that, as

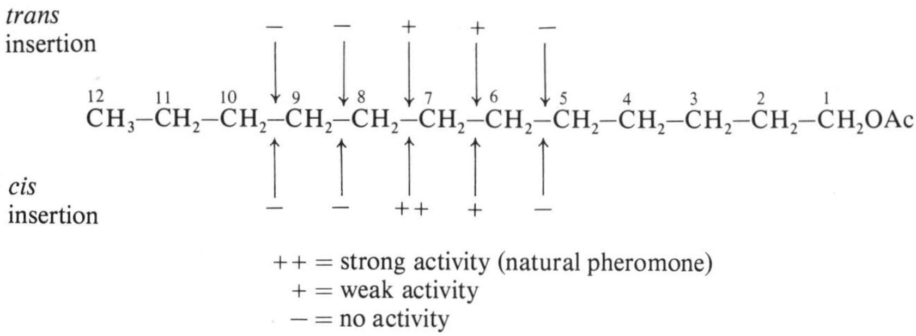

Fig. 7.1 Effect of position of double bond on the sexual attraction of C_{12} alcohol acetates to cabbage looper males

long as the double bond is in the right position in the molecule, some activity is shown by both the *cis*- and *trans*- forms. In the case of the oak leaf roller, the natural pheromone of the female is unusual in actually being a 2:1 mixture of *trans*- and *cis*- isomers. With the Douglas fir tussock-moth, the natural compound is pure *cis*-6-heneicosen-11-one, but synthetic *trans*- material is as effective as the *cis*- in attracting the male moths (Smith *et al.*, 1975).

Although the structural requirements for sex pheromonal activity are relatively rigid, it is possible that completely unrelated compounds can produce the same signal. Evidence of this has been obtained with the male of the American cockroach *Periplaneta americana,* which is sexually excited by compounds present in plant extracts as well as by the natural female pheromone (Bowers and Bodenstein, 1971). One such active substance, present in gymnosperms, was identified as D-bornyl acetate (for structure, see Fig. 7.2), which is active at a concentration of 0·07 mg/cm². It is noteworthy that the L-

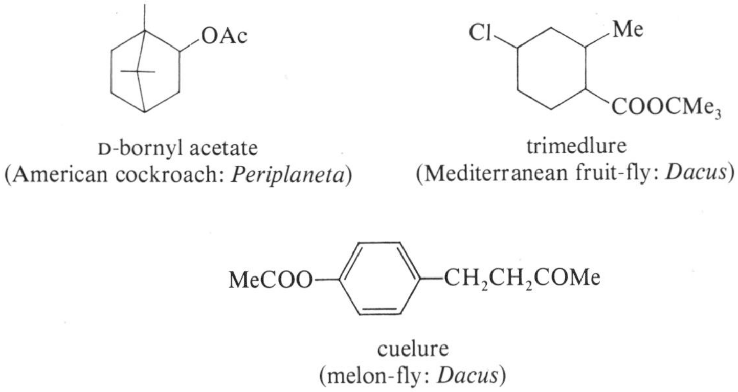

D-bornyl acetate
(American cockroach: *Periplaneta*)

trimedlure
(Mediterranean fruit-fly: *Dacus*)

cuelure
(melon-fly: *Dacus*)

Fig. 7.2 Structures of some sex pheromone mimetic compounds

derivative has only a hundredth of the activity of the D-isomer, so that stereo-chemistry is in this case very important. Angiosperm species also give volatile compounds with pheromonal effects on this cockroach—a survey of 100 such species showed eight with unknown active constituents. Purely synthetic organic substances can also sometimes mimic the activity of the natural pheromones and two which have been used commercially are trimedlure, which is active in the Mediterranean fruit-fly, and cuelure, which attracts males of the melon-fly *Dacus cucurbitae*. The structures of these two latter molecules are shown in Fig. 7.2.

A more specific role for the plants on which insects live and breed has been discovered in the chemistry of sex attraction in certain instances. Thus, Riddiford and Williams (1967) have found that polyphemus moths *Antherea polyphemus* can only mate in the presence of leaves of the red oak *Quercus rubra*. Analysis showed that a leaf emanation, consisting of the volatile hydro-carbon *trans*-2-hexenal, impinges on the sensory receptors of the female's antennae, triggering the release of her pheromone which then activates the male to copulate. A similar situation is probably present in a number of other insect species. It is presumably true of the sugar-cane weevil, *Rhabdoscelum obscurus* which will not release its own sex attractant until it has been fed on sugar-cane (Chang and Curtis, 1972); some unidentified plant compound specific to sugar-cane is presumably the trigger in this case.

Evidence that host plants actually provide the insect with their sex pheromones directly through the diet has come from the recent studies of Hendry *et al.* (1975, 1976), on the oak leaf roller. This moth is a highly destructive pest in oak forests of the North-east United States and methods of control are continually being sought. The pheromones are well characterized (Table 7.1); they are produced by the female and consist of a mixture of tetra-decenyl acetates. Hendry *et al.* found these same compounds to be present as such in the host plant of this pest. The first sign that this was so was in the curious behaviour of the male moths in that they actually tried to copulate with oak leaves which had been damaged by larval feeding. Extraction of the leaves showed indeed the presence of precisely the same substances as make up the natural pheromonal secretion, in low concentrations. There is a clear implication here that the female oak leaf roller larvae absorbs the pheromonal compounds from the plant during feeding and does not need to synthesize them *de novo* from simple starting materials. The tetradecenyl acetates were found to occur in the leaves of a range of oak species, but were absent from leaves of two non-host plants, the red maple and the white pine.

It is clearly economical for the leaf roller to use a pheromone of direct dietary origin. There is also another advantage in that the chemical messenger being present in the leaves of the host plant will attract males to the general location of the female insect. At this point, the female can then emit from her abdomen a higher concentration of the pheromone in order to draw the male to copulation point. The ratio of the *cis*- and *trans*-isomers in the volatiles emitted by the female could also have an effect on the subsequent behaviour of the male.

While Hendry *et al.* (1976) have put forward a case for the view that sex pheromones can be of dietary origin, there are still some points of this complex interaction needing further investigation (see Miller *et al.*, 1976; Hindenlang and Wichmann, 1977) and only the future will show what the true biosynthetic origin of these active molecules is.

The practical application of sex pheromones to the problems of pest control have been developed widely, especially in the U.S. Broadly, there are two approaches, one is to set up traps for the males of the species by releasing quantities of the female pheromone in areas where pest control is needed. This effectively prevents the males orientating themselves to the natural pheromone released by females and thus arrests mating. The quantities of pheromone needed in traps may be quite small. Field trials show that for the cabbage looper, 17 mg samples placed in 100 positions within a 27 m³ plot prevents males from orientating themselves to living females. An alternative approach is to release more unspecific volatile chemicals which mask the effect of the pheromone and interfere with the signal.

While theoretically some insect pests could be completely eliminated by trapping procedures, in practice there are many factors limiting the effectiveness of sexual lures. The most widespread use of synthetic attractants to date has been in trapping insect samples for detecting the build-up of infestations and the size of a given insect population. This information can then be used to determine what control measures are to be taken, such as spraying the area with conventional pesticides.

B. Trail Pheromones

Trail pheromones, as the name implies, are used by social insects to lay down an odour trail which other members of the species can follow to guide them from the nest to a food source and back again. They are characteristically employed by ants, bees and termites, who produce them in a variety of special glandular tissues.

Chemically, trail pheromones are of a variety of structures (Fig. 7.3). That produced by the leaf-cutting ant *Atta texana* is the highly active substance, methyl 4-methylpyrrole 2-carboxylate (Tomlinson *et al.*, 1971). This compound is detected by ants at a concentration of 0·08 pg/cm which is equivalent to $3·48 \times 10^8$ molecules/cm. On this basis, it is possible to calculate that 0·33 mg of the substance would be enough to draw a detectable trail completely around the world! The biosynthetic origin of this very active pheromone is not

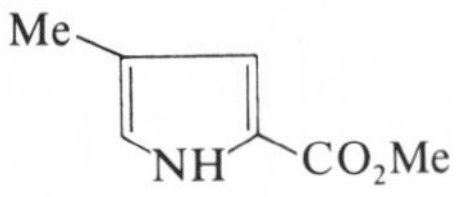

methyl 4-methylpyrrole 2-carboxylate
(leaf cutting ants: *Atta*)

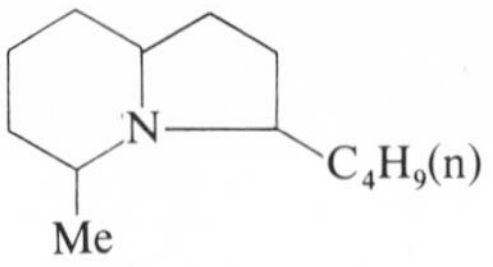

bicyclic alkaloid
(tropical ants: *Monomorium*)

$$CH_3(CH_2)_2(CH=CH)_2CH_2CH=CH(CH_2)_2OH$$

3-*cis*-6-*trans*-8-dodecatriene-1-ol
(termites: *Reticulitermes*)

Fig. 7.3 Insect trail pheromones

yet clear but it could conceivably be formed by bacterial action in the gut on dietary tryptophane.

The same pyrrole has been identified as a trail pheromone in a second species *Atta cephalotes* and it may well be present in other ants of the tribe Attini. Thus all but one of 12 such ant species tested (Robinson *et al.*, 1974) followed a trail of this substance, while non-attine ants completely ignored it.

The biochemistry of leaf-cutting ants is also of great interest from other points of view (Martin, 1970). Besides producing these interesting trail pheromones, ants also synthesize three hormonal substances which they use to control the growth of the fungal colony which they supply with plant material and on which they ultimately feed. One chemical, indoleacetic acid, the auxin of higher plants, is supplied by the ant to encourage the growth of the fungus. A second substance, myrmicacin, $CH_3(CH_2)_6CHOHCH_2CO_2H$, is used to prevent the growth of undesirable (i.e. foreign) fungal spores. A third chemical phenylacetic acid, $PhCH_2CO_2H$, is employed to keep the plot free from bacteria. All three control substances are synthesized in the metathoracic glands and are sprayed by the ant continuously onto the fungus and distributed over the whole nest. In this remarkable symbiotic association between the insect and the fungus, the ant uses chemical herbicides to control the growth of other undesirable micro-organisms on its fungal colony.

A trail pheromone of an alkaloidal structure has been identified in another group of ants. The tropical ant *Monomorium pharaonis* uses a bicyclic alkaloid (for structure, see Fig. 7.3) for laying its odour trails (Ritter *et al.*, 1973). This substance again could be biosynthetically modified from a plant alkaloid of dietary origin.

One insect which undoubtedly obtains its trail pheromone directly from plants is the honey-bee *Apis mellifera* which uses the monoterpene geraniol as a trail substance. Geraniol is collected from flower scents, concentrated within the bee's body and then exuded when required as a food guide. Another compound, possibly of plant origin, is similarly used by bees of the genus *Trigona* and is benzaldehyde, which may be derived from the cyanogenic glycoside prunasin. This aldehyde, with its familiar almond-like odour, is an almost ideal pheromone for food trails, since it loses its potency after a time due to oxidation to benzoic acid, which is inactive. Unless reinforced, benzaldehyde trails can be timed to decay in potency and fade just as the food source for which they are a guide is used up by the insect.

Termites also use odour trails and a pheromone of *Reticulitermes virginicus* has been characterized as 3-*cis*-6-*trans*-8-dodecatriene-1-ol. This alcohol occurs in the fungus-infected wood that the termites feed on, so it seems likely that they obtain it from their food source, channelling it to the sternal gland where they secrete it for trail laying. Whether the alcohol is a wood product or a fungal metabolite is not known and it is still possible that the termite actually synthesizes its own pheromone, although the fact that the same substance occurs in its diet is too coincidental to be ignored.

C. Alarm Pheromones

Most insect alarm pheromones are produced and delivered from the mandibular or anal glands or from the sting apparatus. Production is often related to that of defense substances. In combat among social insects, the contents of the mandibular glands are discharged through the mandibles onto the enemy which is thus "tagged" as an aggressor. Alarm is communicated to other members of the society by diffusion of the pheromonal vapours in the air.

The sting apparatus of bees and wasps contains several glands that produce alarm pheromones. The poison gland itself often produces alarm chemicals which are discharged with the venom. Wasps of the genus *Vespa* spray venom containing an alarm substance while honey-bees leave traces of isoamyl acetate at the sting site, which induces other bees to sting at the same location. In some insects, the same substance can function both for alarm and in defense. This is true of the formic acid produced by ants of the genus *Formica*.

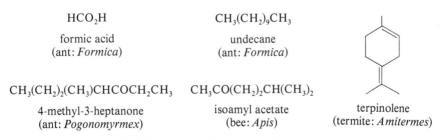

HCO₂H

formic acid
(ant: *Formica*)

$CH_3(CH_2)_9CH_3$

undecane
(ant: *Formica*)

$CH_3(CH_2)_2(CH_3)CHCOCH_2CH_3$

4-methyl-3-heptanone
(ant: *Pogonomyrmex*)

$CH_3CO(CH_2)_2CH(CH_3)_2$

isoamyl acetate
(bee: *Apis*)

terpinolene
(termite: *Amitermes*)

Fig. 7.4 Structures of insect alarm pheromones

Most alarm pheromones identified in insects are of a relatively simple structure (Fig. 7.4). In certain ants, they consist of simple hydrocarbons, such as undecane, tridecane and pentadecane. In other species, the same hydrocarbons occur with aldehyde or ketonic functions. Essential oil components, including citronellol, citral, α-pinene, terpinolene and limonene, have been implicated as alarm odours in species of the Formicinae, Hymenoptera, Isoptera and Myrmicinae.

Alarm pheromones appear to be the least specific of the various volatile hormones in insects. Thus different species of the same genus or even species in different genera may employ the same alarm signal. Nevertheless, ants have a high degree of olfactory acuity and display considerable sensitivity to their own alarm pheromones, closely related chemicals having little effect. The myrmicine ant *Pogonomyrmex babbatus* for example is 10,000 times less sensitive to 2-methyl-3-heptanone, an isomer of the natural pheromone 4-methyl-3-heptanone, than to the natural compound itself.

III. MAMMALIAN PHEROMONES

A classic response to danger is shown by the skunk *Mephitis mephitis,* which, when frightened, releases a secretion of scent from the anal glands while in a hand-stand posture. The resulting stink not only acts as a warning of danger to other skunks in the neighbourhood, but is also an important antipredator mechanism. It is, for example, highly effective in driving away human predators. The active principles of the revolting skunk odour include three sulphur compounds, crotyl and isopentyl mercaptan and methylcrotyl-sulphide. The release of scent during stress situations is only one of many examples where, in the animal kingdom, chemical communication occurs via olfactory means. The sulphur components of the skunk gland are both pheromones and allomones, and are similar in many ways with the odours produced in insects, already discussed in the previous section. Unlike the situation in insects, however, our knowledge of the chemistry of mammalian pheromones is still relatively primitive and in many cases we can only guess at the nature of the chemicals involved.

Other mammals besides the skunk produce strong odours from scent glands when under stress, e.g. the striped hyaena *Hyaena hyaena,* the house shrew *Suncus murinus* and the black-tailed deer *Odocoileus hemionus.* When threatened with danger, urine and faeces are often excreted, sometimes as an automatic response but occasionally as a controlled response. Chinchillas and guinea-pigs, for example, deliberately squirt urine at human handlers when disturbed. Practically all chemical signals in animals in fact originate either from the urine or faeces or else from anal glandular exudates. Special glands may be employed for the manufacture of the volatile pheromone, as in the case of the skunk, or the odours are produced in sex accessory glands or in the glands of the skin.

The range of chemical signals used in mammalian communication is very considerable and new examples are regularly being discovered (for review, see Eisenberg and Kleiman, 1972). One of the advantages of an olfactory signal over an auditory or visual one is that the odour persists for sometime after the sender has moved on. This is valuable in relation both to warning signals and also in scent marking of territorial rights. The persistence of olfactory signals is probably also advantageous in sexual arousal and in the preparation of both partners for mating.

Some of the complexities of mammalian odour signals used to transmit information concerning sex, age, identity and mood have been learnt from studies of the black-tailed deer. In this animal, six specialized gland areas are involved, the secretions being spread by the sender on another part of its own body or the substances being deposited on specific loci within its chosen environment. The secretions on the body of the sender diffuse into the air and are received by other deer of the same herd. The tarsal gland secretion of this animal has been characterized as a γ-lactone (see Fig. 7.5) (Brownlee *et al.*, 1969) but in general the chemistry that provides the basis of these various signals still remain to be elucidated.

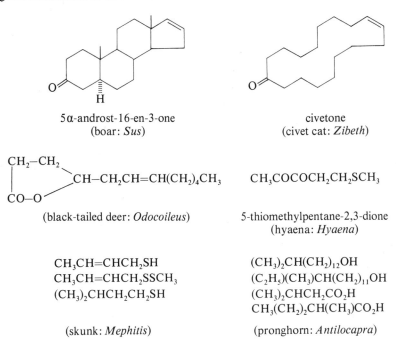

5α-androst-16-en-3-one
(boar: *Sus*)

civetone
(civet cat: *Zibeth*)

(black-tailed deer: *Odocoileus*)

$CH_3COCOCH_2CH_2SCH_3$

5-thiomethylpentane-2,3-dione
(hyaena: *Hyaena*)

$CH_3CH=CHCH_2SH$
$CH_3CH=CHCH_2SSCH_3$
$(CH_3)_2CHCH_2CH_2SH$

(skunk: *Mephitis*)

$(CH_3)_2CH(CH_2)_{12}OH$
$(C_2H_5)(CH_3)CH(CH_2)_{11}OH$
$(CH_3)_2CHCH_2CO_2H$
$CH_3(CH_2)_2CH(CH_3)CO_2H$

(pronghorn: *Antilocapra*)

Fig. 7.5 Structures of some mammalian odours

Most mammals use a similar range of odour signals in their social and sexual life. In sheep, the ram can detect when ewes are ready for mounting by changes in the odour of their urine. This is presumably related to the excretion of increasing amounts of oestrogen at the time of oestrus. In the pronghorn deer *Antilocapra americana,* the male secretes a series of long chain alcohols and short chain organic acids (e.g. isovaleric) in the subauricular glands and uses them for marking vegetation within its territory (Muller-Schwartze *et al.,* 1974). A similar scent marking pheromone in the male Mongolian gerbil *Meriones unguiculatus* has been identified as phenylacetic acid $PhCH_2CO_2H$ (Thiessen *et al.,* 1974).

One of the few cases where chemical signals of sexual arousal have been fully identified is that of the boar. The nature of boar odours indeed was determined some years ago as a mixture of 5α-androst-16-en-3α-ol and the related 3-ketone (for formula, see Fig. 7.5). These two compounds, which are closely related in structure to the male sex hormones androsterone and testosterone, have a strong musky odour. Presumably there is a parallel here with the glandular secretions of the civet cat, civetone, and of the musk ox, muscone, both of which are also musky to smell. Indeed, the structural resemblance is clearly apparent if the civetone molecule is drawn on the same steroid template as that of the boar odour compounds (Fig. 7.5).

The effectiveness of boar odour in arousing sows can be gauged from experiments where the chemical odour remaining in a pen after removal of the boar was found to be sufficient to induce 81% of females in oestrus to assume the mating stance. The boar odour occasionally taints the meat produced from them and it is significant that this musky taint is much more apparent to women eating the meat than to men. Indeed, it is possible that in human sexual contacts, there are pheromonal interactions based on the excretion of the appropriate male or female steroid hormones from the skin or the sexual organs. It is known, at least, that human males and females have recognizably different body odours.

Table 7.2 Female sex pheromones of primates

Chemical structure	Organic acid	Percentages in Rhesus monkey ♀	*Homo sapiens* ♀
CH_3CO_2H	Acetic	36	66
$CH_3CH_2CO_2H$	Propanoic	12	19
$(CH_3)_2CHCO_2H$	Methylpropanoic	3	2
$CH_3CH_2CH_2CO_2H$	Butanoic	38	8
$(CH_3)_2CHCH_2CO_2H$	Methylbutanoic	6	4
$(CH_3)_2CH(CH_2)_2CO_2H$	Methylpentanoic	5	1

Besides steroids or steroidal-like compounds, the only other mammalian pheromones to have been fully characterized are those given off by female primates to arouse the male. These are remarkably simple mixtures of short chain organic acids, secreted in the vagina (Table 7.2). These acids have been detected as trace constituents in vaginal secretions of rhesus monkey, anubis baboon, patas monkey, pigtail monkey, crab-eating monkey and monkey squirrel. They are thus almost certainly a general feature of primate sex life. Sexual excitation and activity can be induced in male rhesus monkeys by means of these olfactory cues. The same organic acids, in different concentrations, have been detected in vaginal discharges of the human female. Here, the amounts vary at different stages of the menstrual cycle, being greater at the time of maximum libido (Michael et al., 1974). The apocryphal tale of Napoleon writing, before returning from one of his military campaigns, to his mistress Josephine commanding her not to have a bath before he returned may thus have a sound scientific basis. The destruction of these pheromones by over-zealous washing of the female parts by women clearly could have a disastrous effect on their olfactory attractiveness to the opposite sex.

One last group of odoriferous substances which may be of significance in mammalian interactions are various amines. For example, trimethylamine, NMe_3, which has a strong fishy odour has been identified as a component of both human menstrual blood and the anal gland secretion of the red fox Vulpes vulpes (see Amoore and Forrester, 1976). Curiously, the same compound occurs to the extent of 400 ppm (Cromwell and Richardson, 1956) in the aptly named plant: stinking goosefoot. Chenopodium vulvaria. Indeed Linnaeus (1756) who named the plant, clearly recognized the odour and also recorded the fact that dogs become very excited when they approach this plant. In the case of the anal sac secretions of the red fox, two diamines, putrescine and cadaverine, are also present, together with volatile fatty acids (Albone and Perry, 1976). It is possible that all these compounds are formed in the fox from non-volatile precursors by microbial action within the gland. Their value as pheromones in foxes has not yet been fully clarified but they may be sex attractants or factors in group "recognition".

IV. DEFENSE SUBSTANCES

A. Distribution

Chemical defense is well known to operate as a form of protection against predation in many animals. A variety of defense mechanisms have been recognized and many chemical substances have been implicated in such interactions (Table 7.3). In the case of arthropods which have been most widely studied in recent years, the chemicals may be either synthesized de novo by the

Table 7.3 Chemical defense substances in animals

Class	Examples	Typical toxins
Fish -	Puffer fish	Alkaloids
Amphibia	Frogs, toads, salamanders	Cardiac toxins, peptides, neuro-toxins
Reptilia	Snakes	Peptide venom
Arthropoda		
Diplopoda	Millipedes	Alkaloids, quinones, cyanogens
Chilopoda	Centipedes	
Arachnida	Whipscorpions	Acetic acid, peptides
Insecta	Cockroaches	Aliphatic aldehydes
	Termites	Terpenes, quinones
	Beetles	Steroids, quinones
	Moths, butterflies	Cardiac glycosides, alkaloids
	Ants	Formic acid, terpenes

animal or adapted from dietary sources. Some of the toxins are elaborated in special exocrine glands and others are contained in the blood or gut. Some glandular secretions are ejected with some force, others are sprayed onto the enemy and yet others simply ooze out of the creature. Most of the toxins have a broad spectrum of activity against many different kinds of predator.

From the viewpoint of the phytochemist, the most interesting aspect of arthropod defensive secretions is that, with few exceptions, the compounds present are of the same type known to occur in plants as secondary metabolites. Some of the substances used, such as *trans*-2-hexenal, benzaldehyde, salicylaldehyde, citral and citronellal are in fact widely distributed in plants. Even the mechanism of release may be the same. In plants, HCN is generated by hydrolysis of cyanohydrin glycosides (see p. 69); in larvae of certain chrysomelid beetles, the cyanogenic secretion contains both benzaldehyde and glucose, so that a similar mechanism probably operates (Moore, 1967).

The subject of arthropod defense against predation has been well reviewed recently (see especially: Weatherston and Percy, 1970; Schildknecht, 1971; Eisher, 1972). Here only a selection of typical examples will be considered under four chemical headings: terpenoids, alkaloids, phenols and quinones.

B. Terpenoids

The lower terpenoids are relatively non-specific toxicants produced in defensive secretions of many insects (Fig. 7.6). Because of their volatility and powerful smell, their odours may be sufficient to deter the attacker. The vapours may

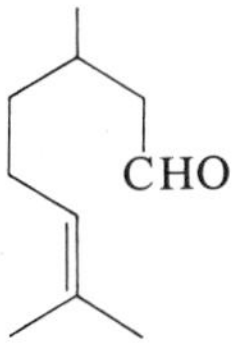

citronellal
(ants: *Acanthomyops*)

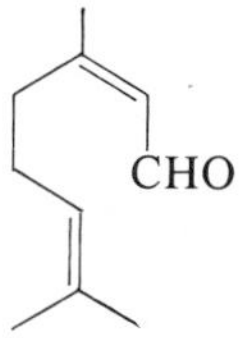

citral
(ants: *Acanthomyops*)

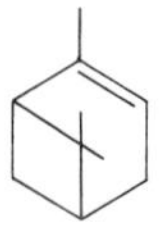

α-pinene
(termites, sawflies: *Neodipridion*)

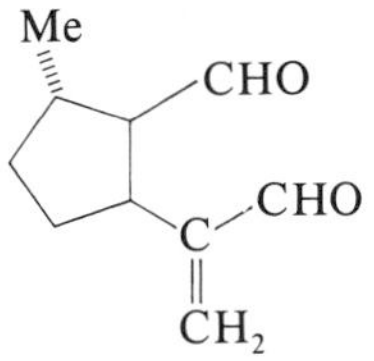

dolichodial
(stick insects: *Anisomorpha*)

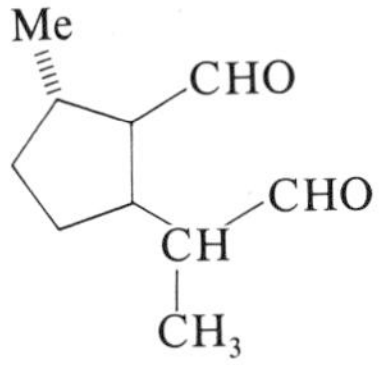

iridodial
(devil's coach horse: *Staphylinus*)

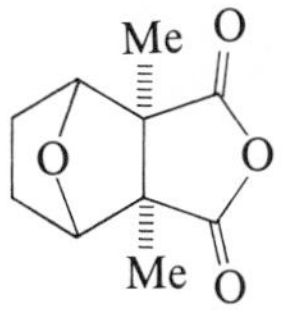

cantharidin
(meloid beetles: *Lytta*)

Fig. 7.6 Lower terpenes as defense compounds in arthropods

have an irritating effect and the oil once arriving on the predator's skin may cause burning and itching. A good example of the use of simple terpenoids in defense is the case of the larvae of the sawfly *Neodipridion setifer* (Hymenoptera) (Eisner *et al.*, 1974). When disturbed, this insect discharges an oily effluent identical chemically in every way with the terpenoid resin of its host plant, *Pinus sylvestris*. What happens is that the larvae sequester the resin constituents during feeding and store them in two compressible diverticular pouches of the foregut. When approached by a predator, the fluid is discharged and is effective in repelling the majority of such attackers.

Analysis has shown that the same mixture of mono- and diterpenes occur both in the pine resin and in the insect secretion. Compounds present include α- and β-pinene, pinifolic acid, pimaric acid, palustric acid, dehydroabietic acid, abietic acid, neoabietic acid and (−)-pimaric acid. In this mixture, α- and β-pinene are probably the major deterrents, since these compounds are known to be highly obnoxious to most arthropods. The various diterpene acids present in the insect secretion presumably act mainly as a fixative for the two more volatile components. The pine resin is an important defensive secretion of the tree and this saw-fly has clearly "crashed" through the chemical defense of the host plant, at the same time appropriating the very same materials for its own purposes.

The sawfly, by adapting the plant toxins directly for its use in this way, might be regarded as an evolutionary advanced insect, since it is clearly economical not to have to synthesize defensive toxins *de novo*. Most other insects utilizing mono- and sesquiterpenes for defense appear to make their own toxins from simple starting materials. Thus, it has been shown by radioactive precursor feeding experiments that the walking stick insect *Anisomorpha buprestoides* and the ant *Acanthomyops claviger* produce their terpenes from acetate through mevalonate, according to the usual biosynthetic pathway. The former makes dolichodial, while the latter uses citronellal and citral as defense agents. These three compounds (Fig. 7.6) are typical plant terpenes and, although today they are made by the insects, they are substances which could have been obtained from dietary sources at some earlier stage in the evolutionary history of these insects.

One of the few insect terpenoid defense compounds, not known in the plant kingdom, is cantharidin, and experiments have shown that it is indeed synthesized *de novo* in the animal body from acetate precursor. Cantharidin occurs in the blood of the meloid beetle *Lytta vesicatoria,* but curiously although present in both adult sexes, is only synthesized by the adult male. The adult female thus must depend on manufacturing it during the larval stage and storing it for subsequent use during adult life.

Cantharidin is a highly irritating material and is, in fact, the basis of the well-known "aphrodisiac" Spanish fly. Its effect on human sexual performance is entirely due to its vesicant properties, causing marked irritation to the urogenital tract during its excretion. To use it is quite hazardous, since it is significantly poisonous in man, the lethal dose being about $0 \cdot 5$ mg/kg body wt.

In the beetle, cantharidin is released by reflex bleeding from the knee joints and it appears to act as a feeding deterrent to predaceous insects, largely because of its unpleasant taste. The amount present in meloid beetles ($0 \cdot 2$ to $2 \cdot 3$% body wt) however is enough to cause toxic effects when swallowed by vertebrates. Pederin, a second terpenoid more complex in structure than cantharidin, occurs in the blood of staphylinid beetles of the genus *Paederus*. Besides being a vesicant like cantharidin, pederin is also a cytotoxin, being effective in concentrations of $1 \cdot 5$ ng/ml (Eisner, 1972).

Finally, it should be pointed out that some arthropods may use mixtures of compounds of different biosynthetic origin in their defense secretions. The devil's coach horse beetle *Staphylinus olens* secretes the terpenoid iridodial, together with 4-methylhexan-3-one, a ketone of fatty acid origin (Fish and Pattenden, 1975). This funereal-coloured beetle defends itself chemically by exuding the foetid-smelling mixture of the above two compounds from glands near the anus; at the same time, it holds its mandibles apart and snaps vigorously at any passing object. As with most arthropods, it combines chemical with physical means of defense.

Iridodial of the devil's coach horse and dolichodial, the defense substance of stick insects, both belong to a group of cyclopentanoid monoterpenes which have their analogues among plant constituents. One such plant compound is nepetalactone, a constituent of the mint *Nepeta cataria*, well known for its peculiar ability to excite cats and other felids (Hill *et al.*, 1976). Clearly the function of nepetalactone in *Nepeta* cannot lie alone in its ability to attract cats to the plant. On the other hand, from its close structural resemblance to the above two insect defense compounds, its *raison d'être* could well be its ability to repel insects attacking the plant. This argument has been tested by Eisner (1964) who indeed was able to show that a majority of insects tested (17 out of 24) were repelled by a pure solution of nepetalactone. More work is obviously needed to prove that it has this function in the living plant.

The defensive role of higher terpenoids in insect–plant interactions has already been discussed under other headings in earlier chapters. There are, for example, the phytoecdysones, insect moulting hormones of plant origin, which can interfere with insect metamorphosis and which are thus potentially dangerous to insects (see p. 90). More directly relevant here are the cardiac glycosides which again are of plant origin but are used by insects, especially by Monarch butterflies, to protect themselves from bird predation (p. 75). A range of other insects, it should be emphasized, use the same toxins of dietary origin in their defense. The grasshopper *Poekilocerus bufonius*, like the Monarch butterfly, feeds on milkweed and accumulates the cardenolides. Unlike the Monarch butterfly which makes only passive use of the toxins, this grasshopper, when attacked by a bird, ejects the cardenolide material as a noxious foam from special dorsally situated poison glands.

It is worth noting here that a number of animal toxins are closely related in structure to the plant cardenolides. There are the bufogenins, steroidal toxins which also act on the hearts of vertebrates and which are used by frogs and toads as defense agents. Bufotalin (Fig. 7.7) for example is the bufogenin of the common toad *Bufo vulgaris* and is quite similar in structure to the cardenolide aglycone of milkweed (see p. 76). A not unrelated structure, samandarin, is in the defensive secretions in the skin of the salamander. However, unlike the bufogenins and the cardiac glycosides, it acts on the nerves and not on the heart. Another neurotoxin of steroidal structure is holothurin, a compound synthesized by sea cucumbers to deter their predators, especially fish.

Finally, returning to the arthropods, remarkably rich sources of steroidal defense compounds have been encountered in water-beetles of the sub-families Colymbetinae and Dytiscinae (Schildknecht, 1971). These particular beetles store up their toxins as a poisonous milk in the prothoracic glands. The activity of the toxin is not appreciated by the predator until it has actually swallowed a beetle. Within a few minutes, it sickens and disgorges its prey. Predatory fish, feeding on the same beetles, fall into a narcotic state and learn from this to avoid future feeding on water-beetles.

The water-beetle toxins are pregnane derivatives; at least fifteen structures

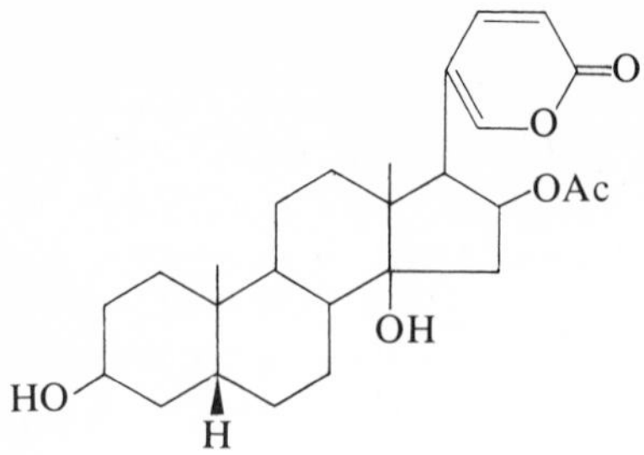

bufotalin
(common toad: *Bufo*)

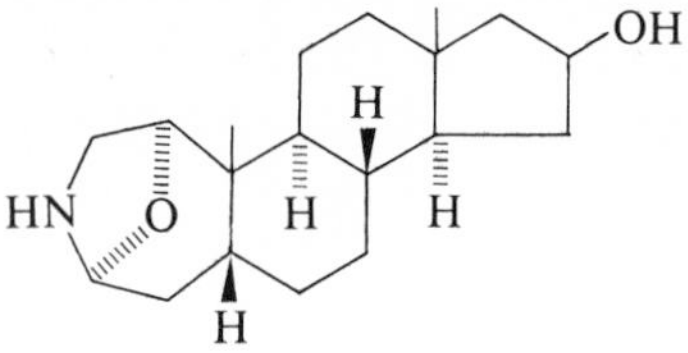

samandarin
(salamander toxin: *Salamandra*)

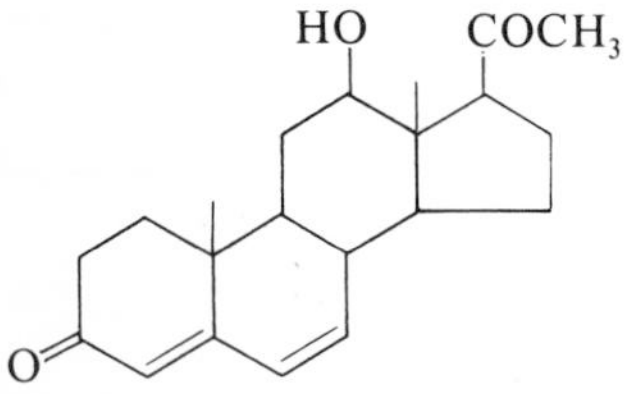

12-hydroxy-4,6-pregnadien-3,20-dione
(Mexican water-beetle: *Cybister*)

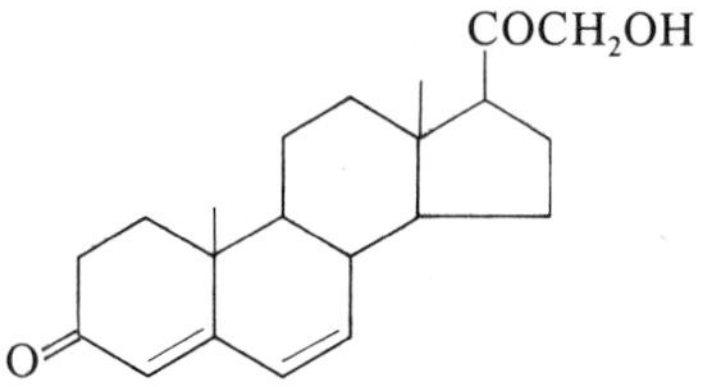

cortexone
(*Cybister*)

Fig. 7.7 Steroids as defense compounds in animals

have been identified variously in a similar number of beetle species. Each Mexican water-beetle, *Cybister tripunctatus*, contains as much as 1 mg of 12-hydroxy-4,6-pregnadien-3,20-dione poison, while each *C. limbatus* beetle contains the same amount of cortexone (Fig. 7.7). In addition to having these pregnane derivatives, one further genus of water-beetle *Ilybius*, is remarkable in secreting mammalian sex hormones, namely testosterone, dehydro-testosterone, oestradiol and oestrone. Whether these serve a purpose as deterrents in upsetting hormonal balance in mammalian predators is not yet known.

C. Alkaloids

Until recently, alkaloids were considered to be exclusively plant products, part of the richness and variety of secondary metabolism in the plant kingdom. However, the identification of alkaloids not only in several marine organisms (Scheuer, 1975) but also in a number of arthropods (Tursch *et al.*, 1976) shows quite clearly that the capacity for alkaloid synthesis is not confined to plants. In considering the contribution of alkaloids to animal defense mechanisms, however, it is probably true that plant alkaloids, accumulated following dietary origin, make a major contribution to protection in insects, especially in Lepidoptera.

The best known case is that of the cinnabar and tiger moths which feed on *Senecio*, accumulate pyrrolizidine alkaloids (e.g. senecionine) and are hence highly toxic to their predators (see p. 77). At least four other insects feeding on alkaloid-containing plants have been shown to accumulate alkaloids (Rothschild, 1973). Another related example is that of insects feeding on *Aristolochia clamatis* or *A. rotundo* which accumulate the nitro compound, aristolochic acid. The butterfly *Pachlioptera aristolochiae* has been particularly investigated but six other species feeding on Aristolochiaceae do the same thing. Indeed, there is evidence from the work of Rothschild (1973) that ingestion of plant alkaloids or cardiac glycosides is a widespread protective device among Lepidoptera, Hemiptera, Coleoptera and Orthoptera.

Turning now to alkaloids apparently of animal origin, i.e. bases synthesized *de novo* by the insect, these have been reported variously in millipedes, fire-ants, ladybirds and water-beetles (Tursch *et al.*, 1976). Some of the structures of these animal alkaloids are illustrated in Fig. 7.8. Two produced by the European millipede *Glomeris marginata* are the quinazolinones glomerin and homoglomerin. Their effectiveness as toxins is shown by the fact that ingestion of the millipede causes death in mice and paralysis in spiders. There is good evidence that these two compounds are synthesized by the millipede, since feeding radioactive anthranilic acid to the insect produced labelled alkaloids. Another millipede with an alkaloid as defense is the species *Polyzonium rosalbum*. This substance, polyzonimine, acts as a topical irritant to predating insects, causing cockroaches to scratch themselves.

The potency of the red fire-ant is due to its venom which has haemolytic, insecticidal and antibiotic properties. The major principles of the venom have been characterized as a series of 2,6-dialkylpiperidines of which the simplest is the 2-methyl-6-nonyl derivative (Fig. 7.8). Such compounds have been identified in the venom of all seven species of the genus *Solenopsis* so far studied. A structural relationship of these ant compounds with the highly poisonous plant alkaloid coniine (2-propylpiperidine) of the hemlock *Conium maculatum* is clear. The substances are unique in the animal kingdom as the first examples of venom constituents which are not peptides.

Ladybirds (Coccinellidae), when molested, emit haemolymph droplets at their joints (like the cantharidin-producing beetles, p. 168), a mechanism which is an efficient protection against their predators. That the droplets have a bitter taste has been known since the eighteenth century; the fact that alkaloids are present was not firmly established until 1971 (see Tursch *et al.*, 1976). A major component was identified as the alkaloid N-oxide coccinelline and a number of related structures were subsequently found in similar secretions.

Coccinelline (Fig. 7.8) is a representative of a new class of alkaloid and a type not known in plants. Biosynthesis has been shown to be endogenous. By feeding the ladybird with labelled $1\text{-}^{14}C$-acetate and $2\text{-}^{14}C$-acetate, labelled coccinelline was produced. In laboratory tests, this alkaloid was shown to be

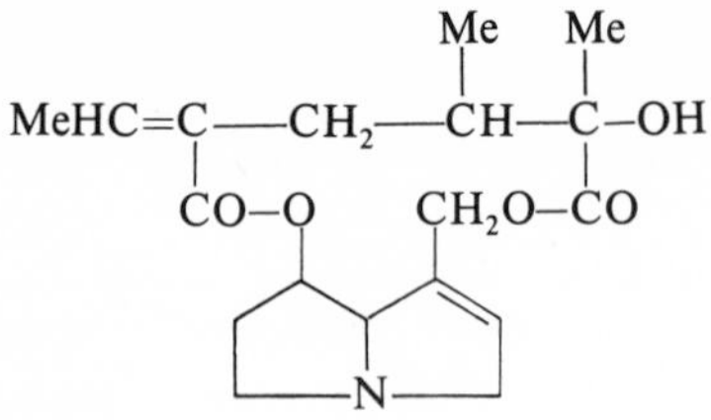

sekenecionine
senecionine
(cinnabar moth: *Tyria*)

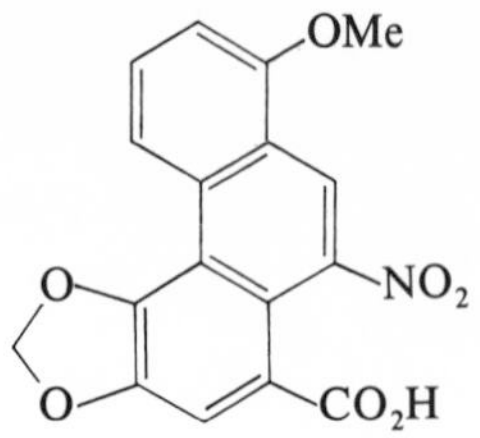

aristolochic acid
(butterfly: *Pachlioptera*)

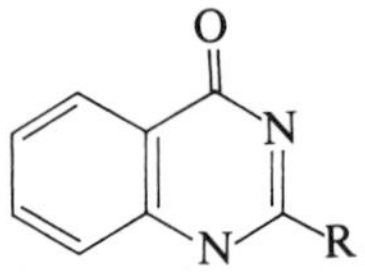

glomerin, R = Me
homoglomerin, R = Et
(millipede: *Glomeris*)

polyzonimine
(millipede: *Polyzonium*)

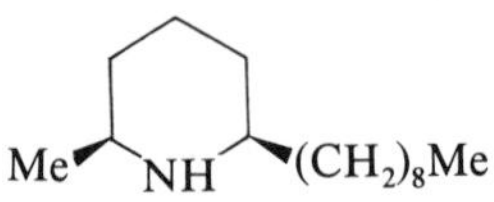

2-methyl-6-nonyl
piperidine
(ant: *Solenopsis*)

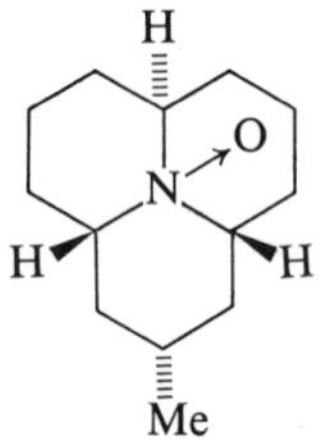

coccinelline
(ladybird: *Coccinella*)

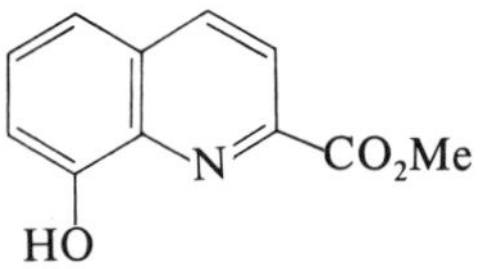

8-hydroxyquinoline
2-carboxylate
(water-beetle: *Ilybius*)

Fig. 7.8 Alkaloid defenses of arthropods

effective protection against attack by ants and quails. Most ladybirds are brightly coloured and the occurrence of these alkaloids was found to be correlated with the distribution of aposematic (warning) coloration in these insects.

Although the defensive chemistry of water-beetles mainly involves steroids (see p. 169), one particular species *Ilybius fenestratus* diversifies in its defensive secretion by synthesizing an alkaloid. This compound is methyl 8-hydroxy-quinoline 2-carboxylate (Schildknecht, 1971). Its function as a toxin has not been proved conclusively, but it does appear to operate in defense. While it is not toxic to amphibians or fish, it produces clonic spasms in mice, so it could provide a defense against land animals. It is also a powerful antiseptic, so it could additionally protect the water-beetle from penetration by micro-organisms (a topic which is considered in more detail in the next section).

D. Phenols and Quinones

The most remarkable use of phenols in the chemistry of animal defense is that exhibited by the bombardier beetle, *Brachynus,* a creature commonly found on chalkland in Europe. This animal, when endangered, discharges a hot explosive cloud of toxin in the direction of the attacker. This unique system of defense, involving the production of secretions as hot as 100°C, is due to the beetle initiating at the moment of discharge a reaction between a phenol substrate, hydroquinone, H_2O_2 and the enzyme catalase (Fig. 7.9). A highly exothermic reaction occurs, with the phenol hydroquinone being oxidized to benzo-quinone, the major product of defense. The reaction can occur with explosive force, the noise produced having been likened to the report of a pistol. Benzo-quinone has a highly irritating vapour, producing damaging effects on eye tissue, so it is a simple but effective weapon.

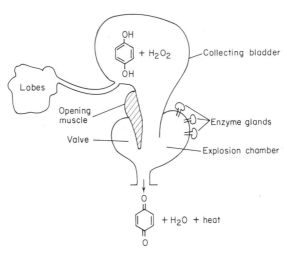

Fig. 7.9 The defensive organ of the bombardier beetle

The use of "hot" quinones in this way is not restricted only to the bombardier beetle and certain other carabid beetles not related to *Brachynus* have glands for producing these explosive discharges. Quinones, produced by more conventional means, also occur quite widely in defense secretions of arthropods and through their persistent and disagreeable odours provide repellency to attackers. In the case of black beetles (Tenebrionidae), quinones are invariably present. They also occur variously in arachnids, millipedes, earwigs and termites. Besides quinone itself, seven other simply substituted derivatives are present, including 2-methyl,2,3-dimethyl and 2,3,5-trimethyl-benzoquinones. In a recent survey of 147 species of beetles from 55 genera, Tschinkel (1975) reported that all contained 2-methyl and 2-ethylbenzo-quinone, while rather few contained quinone itself, the major weapon of the bombardier beetle.

Phenols, from which quinones can be produced by enzymic oxidation, are themselves relatively toxic molecules and undoubtedly provide a degree of protection to arthropods from predators. Indeed, simple phenols such as *m*- and *p*-cresol and salicylaldehyde have been detected in some defense secretions (Fig. 7.10). The biosynthetic origin of these phenols is not known, but they could be obtained from the diet, since phenolic derivatives are widespread in plants. It is indicative that 2,5-dichlorophenol was found in the defense secretion of a grasshopper, a compound clearly derived from ingested herbicide (Eisner *et al.*, 1971).

p-cresol
(ground-beetle: *Calasoma*)

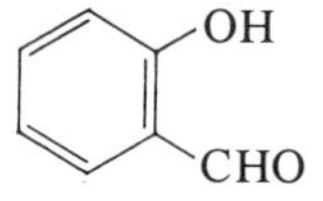

salicylaldehyde
(water-boatman: *Notonecta*)

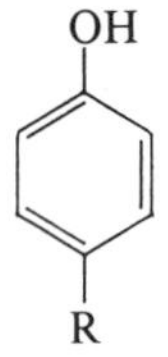

hydroquinone, R = OH
p-hydroxybenzoic acid, R = CO_2H
(water-beetle: *Dytiscus*)

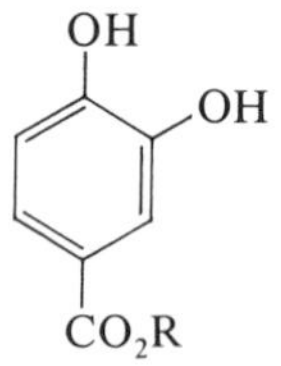

protocatechuic acid methyl
(R = Me) and ethyl (R = Et) esters
(water-beetle: *Dytiscus*)

Fig. 7.10 Simple phenols as defensive agents in arthropods

Phenols are also highly toxic to micro-organisms and one of the more specialized uses of phenols as defensive agents relates to their production in the pygidial defense bladders of water-beetles of the Dytiscinae and Colymbetinae, creatures whose defense mechanisms have already been commented on earlier (p. 173). In these beetles, bodily hygiene is essential to life since although they are at home in water, they have to project their posteriors above the water surface from time to time to replace their air (Schildknecht, 1971). This is only possible as long as their chitin covering does not become wet. If algae, fungi or bacteria become attached to the beetle, water no longer flows off and the subsequent change in surface tension prevents the beetle suspending itself by its steering legs. The air cavity under the wings, essential for respiration, fills up with water and the luckless beetle then suffocates.

The need for an effective means of keeping the body clean is therefore self-evident and fortunately these beetles are excellently equipped for this cleaning operation. Using their rear legs as brushes, they distribute over their rear ends droplets of a secretion from the pygidial glands which are located on either side of the terminal intestine. Injurious micro-organisms are killed by the phenolic compounds (Fig. 7.10) present in the secretion; at the same time they are embedded in a glycoprotein network which is formed as cysteine also present in the secretion polymerizes on contact with air. When the beetle springs back into the water, the solidified secretion crumbles away; the beetle is clear of any debris and it can breathe freely once more.

BIBLIOGRAPHY

Books and Review Articles

Albone, E. (1977). Ecology of mammals—a new focus for chemical research. *Chem. in Britain* **13**, 92–99.

Beroza, M. (ed.) (1970). "Chemicals Controlling Insect Behaviour", 170 pp. Academic Press, New York.

Eisenberg, J. F. and Kleiman, D. G. (1972). Olfactory communication in mammals. *Ann. Rev. Ecol. System.* **3**, 1–32.

Eisner, T. (1972). Chemical defense against predation in arthropods. In: Sondheimer, E. and Simeone, K. (eds.), "Chemical Ecology", pp. 157–218. Academic Press, New York.

Jacobson, M. (1972). "Insect Sex Pheromones", 382 pp. Academic Press, New York.

Jacobson, M., Green, N., Warthen, D., Harding, C. and Toba, H. H. (1970). Sex pheromones of the Lepidoptera. Structure–activity relationships. In: Beroza, M. (ed.), "Chemicals Controlling Insect Behaviour", pp. 3–20. Academic Press, New York.

Law, J. H. and Regnier, F. E. (1971). Pheromones. *Ann. Rev. Biochem.* **40**, 533–548.

Martin, M. M. (1970). Biochemical basis of the fungus-attine ant symbiosis. *Science* **169**, 16–19.

Rothschild, M. (1973). Secondary plant substances and warning coloration in insects. In: van Emden, H. F. (ed.), "Insect–Plant Relationships", pp. 59–83. Oxford Univ. Press.

Scheuer, P. J. (1975). Recent developments in the chemistry of marine toxins. *Lloydia* **38**, 1–7.

Schildknecht, H. (1971). Evolutionary peaks in the defensive chemistry of insects. *Endeavour* **30**, 136–141.

Stoddart, D. M. (1977). "Mammalian odours and pheromones", 64 pp. Edward Arnold, London.

Tursch, B., Braekman, J. C. and Daloze, D. (1976). Arthropod alkaloids. *Experientia* **32**, 401–407.

Weatherston, J. and Percy, J. E. (1970). Arthropod defensive secretions. In: Beroza, M. (ed.), "Chemicals Controlling Insect Behaviour", pp. 95–144.

Wilson, E. O. (1972). Chemical communication within animal species. In: Sondheimer, E. and Simeone, J. B. (eds.), "Chemical Ecology", pp. 133–156. Academic Press, New York.

Literature References

Albone, E. S. and Perry, G. C. (1976). *J. Chem. Ecol.* **2**, 101–111.

Amoore, J. E. and Forrester, L. J. (1976). *J. Chem. Ecol.* **2**, 49–56.

Amouriq, L. (1965). *Compt. Rend.* **260**, 2334–2335.

Bowers, W. S. and Bodenstein, W. G. (1971). *Nature (Lond.)* **232**, 259–261.

Brownlee, R. G., Silverstein, R. M., Muller-Schwarze, D. and Singer, A. G. (1969). *Nature (Lond.)* **221**, 284–285.

Chang, V. C. S. and Curtis, G. A. (1972). *Environ. Entomol.* **1**, 476.

Crisp, D. J. and Meadows, P. S. (1962). *Proc. Roy. Soc.* **156B**, 500–520.

Cromwell, B. T. and Richardson, M. (1956). *Phytochemistry* **5**, 735–746.

Eisner, T. (1964). *Science* **146**, 1318–1320.

Eisner, T., Hendry, L. B., Peakall, D. B. and Meinwald, J. (1971). *Science* **172**, 277–279.

Eisner, T., Johnessee, J. S., Carvell, J., Hendry, L. B. and Meinwald, J. (1974). *Science* **184**, 996–999.

Fish, L. J. and Pattenden, G. (1975). *J. Insect Physiol.* **21**, 741–744.

Hendry, L. B., Wichmann, J. K., Kindenlang, D. M. and Mumma, R. O. (1975). *Science* **188**, 59–62.

Hendry, L. B., Wichmann, J. K., Kindenlang, D. M. and Mumma, R. O. (1976). *Science* **192**, 143–145.

Hill, J. O., Parlik, E. J., Smith, G. L., Burghardt, G. M. and Coulson, P. B. (1976). *J. Chem. Ecol.* **2**, 239–253.

Hindenlang, D. M. and Wichmann, J. K. (1977). *Science* **195**, 86–89.

Linnaeus, C. (1756). *Amoenitates Academicae* **3**, p. 200.

Michael, R. P., Bonsall, R. W. and Warner, P. (1974). *Science* **186**, 1217.

Miller, J. R., Baker, T. C., Cardé, R. T. and Roelufs, W. L. (1976). *Science* **192**, 140–143.

Moore, B. P. (1967). *J. Australian Entomol. Soc.* **6**, 36–38.

Muller-Schwarze, D. and C., Singer, A. G. and Silverstein, R. M. (1974). *Science* **183**, 860–862.

Riddiford, L. M. and Williams, C. M. (1967). *Science* **155**, 589; **156**, 541.

Ritter, F. J., Rotgans, I. E. M., Talman, E., Verwiel, P. E. J. and Stein, F. (1973). *Experientia* **29**, 530–531.

Robinson, S. W., Moser, J. C., Blum, M. S. and Amante, E. (1974). *Insectes Soc.* **21**, 87–94.

Smith, R. G., Daterman, G. E. and Daves, G. D. (1975). *Science* **188**, 63–64.

Starr, R. C. (1968). *Proc. Natl. Acad. Sci. U.S.* **59**, 1082–1088.

Thiessen, D. D., Regnier, F. E., Rice, M., Goodwin, M., Isaaks, N. and Lawson, N. (1974). *Science* **184**, 83–85.

Tomlinson, J. H., Silverstein, R. M., Moser, J. C., Brownlee, R. G. and Ruth, J. M. (1971). *Nature (Lond.)* **234**, 348–349.

Tschinkel, W. R. (1975). *J. Insect Physiol.* **21**, 753–783.

8 | Biochemical Interactions Between Higher Plants

I. INTRODUCTION

As part of the Darwinian struggle for survival, higher plants compete with each other for moisture, light and soil nutrients in the ecosystem. In the course of this struggle, they have developed various means of defense against their neighbours; whenever this defense is chemical in nature, it is referred to as allelopathy. Thus, allelopathy represents chemical competition between plants and the phenomenon may be regarded as yet another phase of chemical ecology, the interference caused by one higher plant on another in the natural environment.

Molisch (1937) was the first to define the word allelopathy, using it in the widest sense to refer to "biochemical interactions between all types of plant" and including both deleterious and advantageous interactions. Rice (1974), in a recent monograph on the subject, defines allelopathy as "the harmful effect by one plant on another through the production of chemical compounds that escape into the environment". Like Molisch, Rice regards it as an all embracing term to cover most types of biochemical interactions, including those between higher plants and micro-organisms. By contrast, Muller (1970), one of the chief pioneers in the modern development of the topic, prefers to restrict the term allelopathy to higher plant–higher plant interactions and this restriction is

178

kept here, biochemical interactions between higher and lower plants being reserved for Chapter 9. While it is convenient from many points of view to make such a distinction, it is worth pointing out that lower plants are indirectly involved in higher plant–higher plant interactions, in that the effectiveness of the chemical substances produced by one higher plant to influence another may depend on the speed with which soil micro-organisms are able to detoxify and further metabolize such compounds.

The chemicals concerned in higher plant interactions, called allelopathic substances or toxins, are typical secondary constituents and appear to be mainly low molecular weight compounds of relatively simple structure. Most of those that have been positively identified are either volatile terpenes or else phenolic compounds. Whittaker (1972), among others, has suggested that because of their chemical nature allelopathic substances may only be secondarily functional in plants, have arisen initially in plants in response to herbivore pressures. This theory assumes that the evolution of feeding deterrents has led to the occasional production of compounds that leak out of the plant, are excreted from the leaves, stems or roots and enter the environment. Such substances may thus have become accidentally caught up in the interaction of one higher plant with another and because of the beneficial effects in terms of reduced plant competition, such plants have continued to synthesize them.

Chemical defense mechanisms are most frequently invoked when one type of plant, e.g. a shrub or tree, competes with another type, e.g. a herb or grass, and some of the best examples of allelopathy have arisen from such studies. Competition between plants of the same general type, e.g. herbs, may also, however, include allelopathic effects (see Newman and Rovira, 1975). Allelopathic effects, in addition, may be exerted between individuals of the same species, particularly when lack of moisture or soil nutrients is limiting growth; the term "auto-toxicity" is sometimes used in such cases. Competition for the standard biological variables is most acute in extreme climates and some of the first recorded examples of allelopathy were demonstrated between desert plants. However, the effect has also been observed in plants growing in a range of other habitats from open grasslands to humid rain forests, so that allelopathy may take place in almost any climate.

Historically, the taxonomist de Candolle (1832) was one of the first to record situations in which chemical interactions between higher plant species appeared to be taking place. He noted, for example, that thistles growing in cornfields had an injurious effect on oat plants and similarly that *Euphorbia* harmed the growth of flax. De Candolle also described experiments in which bean plants, dipped in water containing matter exuded from the roots of other individuals of the same species, languished and died. Many other miscellaneous observations of a similar nature accumulated in the botanical literature up to about 1925. In this year, Massey provided one of the first clear cut demonstrations of allelopathy between trees and herbs, when he set up a series of experiments to show that the black walnut *Juglans nigra* produced chemicals which killed tomato and alfalfa plants grown in its vicinity.

The study of allelopathy was advanced during the 1939–1945 war period by the largely accidental discoveries, made by plant physiologists working on war projects, of allelopathic interactions in plants growing in the Californian desert, especially in the shrubs *Encelia farinosa* and *Parthenium argentatum*. However, it was not until the pioneering efforts of Muller and his colleagues (summarized in Muller and Chou, 1972) with their work on the Californian chaparral and of Rice (1974) on chemical factors in field succession that the concept of plant allelopathy became really established. Most of our information on allelopathy at present derives from a series of papers published over a 20-year period by Muller and his coworkers at Santa Barbara, California.

Even today, not all plant ecologists accept the concept of allelopathy as a significant factor in competition in plant communities. The extreme view against the idea of chemical competition between plants is expressed by Harper (1975) in a review of Rice's recent textbook (1974) on the subject. There is clearly a problem in that conclusive proof of allelopathy occurring in any given ecological situation is extremely difficult to obtain and even after careful experimentation, as has been carried out by Muller and his associates, there are still many facets of the interaction which require further study. Having said this, one can still point to a large body of circumstantial evidence, most of which is mentioned in Rice's book, which supports the view that chemical interactions do occur between higher plants. Indeed, considering the enormous capacity of angiosperms to synthesize such a wide range of generalized highly toxic compounds, it would be very surprising if no such interactions ever occurred. A failure to appreciate the chemical versatility of higher plants, the plethora of chemical structures produced and their considerable physiological activities, may rest behind some of the criticisms of allelopathy expressed in the past.

Muller himself has always been very careful not to overstress the case for allelopathy occurring in plants. As he says (Muller and Chou, 1972): "it is one of several basic ecological processes whose chemical cause is but another major factor in the environmental complex. The chemical variable takes no precedence over light, temperature, moisture and mineral nutrients ... and shares with each of them a part in determining the plant environment. However, it also shares in the potential for becoming a limiting factor and thus exerting control".

In the present short account of allelopathy, emphasis will be given to the examples where the allelopathic substances have been chemically characterized. In general, the many recent reports by ecologists of allelopathic effects exerted by so far unidentified toxins (see e.g. Grover, 1975; Turner and Quarterman, 1974; Putnam and Duke, 1974) will be omitted from present consideration. Most of the major references on allelopathy can be found in Rice (1974), but see also Muller and Chou (1972), Went (1972), Whittaker (1972), Whittaker and Feeny (1971) and references given in Harper (1975).

II. THE WALNUT TREE

The concept of allelopathy has been unconsciously recognized for many years in the observations of gardeners and farmers that while some plants thrive when grown together in close proximity others do not. One tree which has been known for a long time, indeed since the time of Pliny (AD 23–79), to exert an allelopathic effect on other species if they are grown near it is the walnut, *Juglans nigra.* The antagonistic effects of walnut have been recorded on such diverse plants as pine trees, potatoes and cereals. There are even reports that the walnut toxin will kill apple trees if they are planted too close (Schneiderhan, 1927). Most observations on walnut refer to the North American black walnut, *J. nigra,* grown as timber, but the effect may well be true for the European *Juglans regia,* grown for its nuts, and for other species in the genus.

The first direct evidence of the reasons underlying the fatal consequences of the walnut toxin on herbs was obtained by Massey (1925) who planted tomato and alfalfa plants in a region up to 27 m from the trunk of a walnut tree and found that many plants died as a result (see Fig. 8.1). The position at which the tomato plants remained unaffected by the allelopathy (Fig. 8.1) coincided with

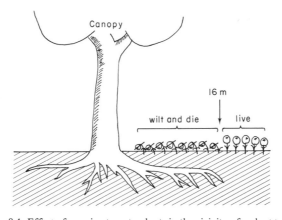

Fig. 8.1 Effect of growing tomato plants in the vicinity of walnut trees

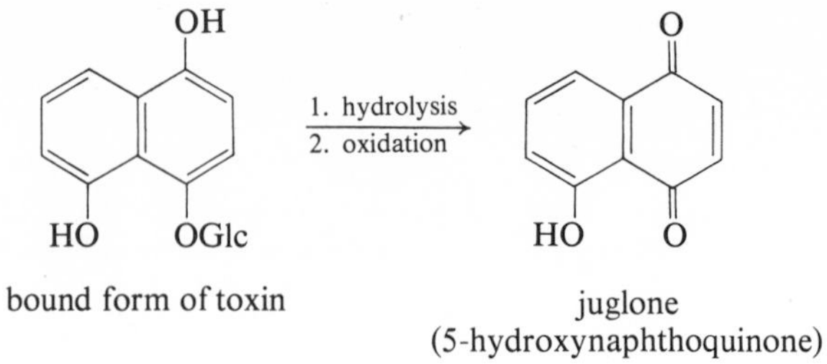

Fig. 8.2 Release of juglone from bound form

the extent of root growth of the tree and Massey assumed at that time that the plants were killed by the exudation of toxin from the roots.

Later work by Bode (1958) indicated that this simple view of root exudation might be incorrect and that the toxic effects were actually due to leaching from the walnut leaves, stems and branches of a bound toxin, which underwent hydrolysis and oxidation in the soil with the release of the true toxin, which then killed any annual species growing in the vicinity. The area of toxicity was therefore determined by the leaf area of the tree and the ability of the leachate to saturate the surrounding soil. Our own preliminary experiments on this topic at Reading University suggest that leachates from *both* roots and leaves may actually be involved.

The bound toxin has been identified as the 4-glucoside of 1,4,5-trihydroxy-naphthalene, which on hydrolysis and oxidation is converted to the naphtho-quinone, juglone (Fig. 8.2). Juglone is a water-soluble yellow pigment and much of the characteristic brown staining of the hands caused by handling walnuts is due to the release of this compound. It is strictly limited in its occurrence to green parts of the tree and is lost from dead tissue and from the ripe nuts. Its considerable toxicity has been widely recognized. Many plants (e.g. tomato, alfalfa) are killed if juglone is injected into them via the petiole. It is also an important inhibitor of seed germination and may be conveniently bioassayed by such means. Thus, juglone at a concentration of 0·002% will completely prevent germination of lettuce seed treated with such a solution.

The walnut story is of especial interest because the toxin occurs in the plant in a safe, non-toxic bound form and it is only after leaching from the leaves and stems into the soil that it becomes active and can exert its effect. Clearly, to be a useful ecological agent, juglone must persist for a reasonable length of time in the soil around the tree and its concentration must presumably be regularly renewed by rainfall carrying down fresh supplies into the soil area. Little information seems to be available on the rate of turnover of juglone and which soil micro-organisms are capable of detoxifying it or otherwise inactivating it in the ecosystem. There is, therefore, still a gap in our knowledge in relation to the importance of juglone in the natural environment.

One final point should be stressed: in this case of allelopathy, as in most others, the toxin is effective against many but by no means all competing plant species. Thus, while many broad-leaved herbs and ericaceous shrubs are excluded by the walnut toxin, *Rubus* and Kentucky blue-grass *Poa pratensis* are able to tolerate it and grow tolerably well under walnuts (Brooks, 1951).

III. DESERT PLANTS

In desert plants, it might be expected that the considerable competition for the limited water available in the soil would result in the development of many competitive effects including allelopathy which are exemplified in those plants able to survive in these harsh conditions. Indeed, evidence that allelopathy is one important factor comes from the fact that some, but not all, shrubs are found with bare patches of soil underneath their canopies and around them, with zones where annuals do not appear to flourish. One such plant, investigated by Went (1942), is the shrub *Encelia farinosa* (Compositae) which grows for example in the Mohave desert of Central California. By inhibiting the growth of annuals, it thus ensures for itself the available moisture within a metre or so of its site of growth.

Went (1942) suggested that the effect in *Encelia* was due to a root exudate having a toxic effect on the growth of annuals such as *Malacothrix* but Gray and Bonner (1948) were later able to isolate from the leaves a toxin that was not self-inhibitory but caused pronounced inhibition in many other plants. The substance was identified as 3-acetyl-6-methoxybenzaldehyde (Fig. 8.3), a simple benzene derivative with two carbonyl functions. While primarily produced in the leaves, this toxin is released when the leaves fall to the ground and decompose, and remains persistent in the soil, at least until it is washed away by heavy rainfall. Acetophenones of related structure to the *Encelia* toxin have been identified in a number of other composite semishrubs (Hegnauer, 1977) so it is possible that a similar isolating mechanism occurs in other species.

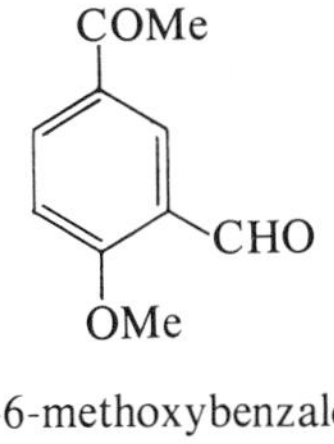

3-acetyl-6-methoxybenzaldehyde
Encelia farinosa

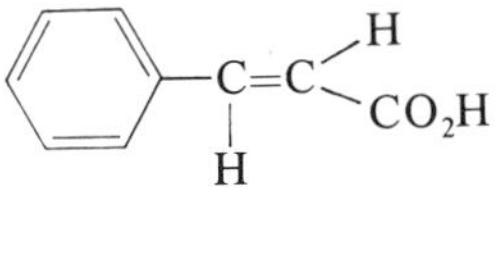

trans-cinnamic acid
Parthenium argentatum

Fig. 8.3 Toxins of desert shrubs

The role of toxins in desert shrub communities has also been examined in some detail by Muller and Muller (1953, 1956) who found that two other shrubs *Franseria dumosa* (Compositae) and *Thamnosma montana* (Rutaceae) were capable of producing water soluble toxins and yet did not exert any allelopathic effect on neighbouring annuals. Bioassays indicated a degree of toxicity, when tested with tomato seedlings, greater than in the case of *Encelia*. The role of toxins in controlling the development of an annual flora in the desert is thus a complex one, and other factors, including the build-up of organic litter in the soil around the shrubs, could account for the presence/absence of annuals. A further factor may be the ability of soil micro-organisms to differentially detoxify some allelopathic compounds and not others. The *Encelia* aldehyde may be resistant to breakdown while the toxins of other shrubs may be much more rapidly lost in the soil. While the *Franseria* toxin does not appear to have been identified, that of *Thamnosma* is a mixture of furanocoumarins (Bennett and Bonner, 1953) which could conceivably be turned over quickly by micro-organisms. Detailed information on the metabolism of these toxins in the soils, however, waits further investigation.

One of the few examples of growth inhibition caused by a root, instead of a leaf, toxin is that of the rubber plant guayule, *Parthenium argentatum*

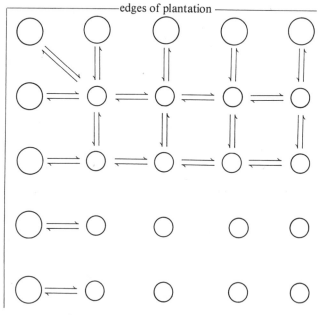

====⇀ toxic effects exerted by root exudates

Fig. 8.4 Effect of self inhibition in plantations of *Parthenium argentatum*

(Compositae). Significantly in this case the substance produced in the root causes self inhibition and does not appear to affect other species. The toxin was discovered during experiments devised to develop new plant sources of rubber. It was found that in regular plantations of *Parthenium* plants, individuals on the edge of the plot always grew better than those in the middle (Fig. 8.4). These differences could not be eliminated by extra watering or mineral application. Furthermore, roots of adjacent plants did not intermingle but grew separately. In addition, while seedlings never became established under larger *Parthenium* plants, they grew successfully under the canopy of other shrubs.

Subsequent experiments showed that a specific toxin was present in root exudates of *Parthenium* and this was identified as the simple aromatic compound, *trans*-cinnamic acid (Fig. 8.3). The leachate from 20,000 roots eventually yielded 1·6 grams of toxic material (Bonner and Galston, 1944). *Trans*-cinnamic acid is toxic to *Parthenium* growth at a concentration of 0·0001%, whereas tomato seedlings are only affected if treated with a solution containing a 100 times this concentration.

Cinnamic acid is effective in restricting growth when applied to the soil in pot cultures, but it does not persist very long so it must be continuously produced by the root in order to exert an allelopathic effect. It is not yet clear whether this compound has any importance in natural stands of *Parthenium argentatum* but presumably its production might ensure that the plants are so widely spaced that inhibition of growth is not normally observed. It could conceivably affect the growth of native competitors of *Parthenium* and thus have a dual role in reducing competition both from other members of the same species and also from plants of other species.

IV. ALLELOPATHY IN THE CALIFORNIAN CHAPARRAL

A. Volatile Terpenes and the Fire Cycle

The Californian chaparral is a vegetational area of relatively low Mediter-ranean rainfall, along the coastal strip of Southern California and this is adjacent to areas of natural, uncultivated grassland. One of the most striking natural phenomena of this shrubby grassland area is the zonation of herbs around the thickets of shrubs which dominate this flora. Two of the more important of these shrubs are the labiate *Salvia leucophylla* (Sagebrush) and the composite *Artemisia californica*. Immediately surrounding each shrub or clump of shrubs there are bare zones of soil from one to two metres in width. Beyond the bare zones, there are areas of stunted growth where a few herbs show limited development. Finally, one reaches the grassland, where *Avena,* *Bromus* and *Festuca* species flourish and grow. These effects of zonation are

Fig. 8.5 Photograph of allelopathic effects of shrub versus herb in the Californian chaparral

most clearly revealed by aerial photographs (see Muller, 1966) but are also perfectly apparent in snapshots of the local vegetation (Fig. 8.5).

The explanation for this remarkable inhibitory effect of shrubs on surrounding herbs has been shown by Muller and his coworkers to be due to terpene toxins. Careful study of other ecological parameters showed clearly that biological factors were not responsible for these effects. Thus, shade, soil drought, nutrient conditions, slope of ground, root competition, insect and animal predation and water soluble components were all, in turn, ruled out. The possible role of animals, especially birds and rodents, in producing the bare zones was experimentally investigated by Muller (1970) and independently by Bartholomew (1970), but no convincing evidence that they play a causal role could be established in numerous experiments.

The case in favour of volatile constituents of the shrubs, namely simple terpenes, being the major agents responsible for these allelopathic effects has been cogently argued by Muller (1970). This role for the terpenes was established from observations of their presence in all the various phases of the interaction. Thus terpenes (1) are richly present in the leaves; (2) are constantly "turned over" by the shrubs and a vapour cloud of volatile essence hangs around the plants; (3) occur in the soil surrounding the plants; (4) remain in the dry soil until rains bring into activity soil micro-organisms which degrade

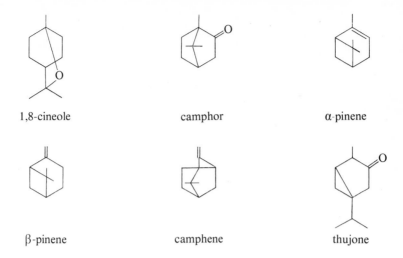

| 1,8-cineole | camphor | α-pinene |

| β-pinene | camphene | thujone |

Fig. 8.6 Formulae of terpenes concerned in plant allelopathy

them; (5) can be transported into plant cells through the waxy coatings of seeds or roots; and (6) have a significant effect on the germination of seeds of those annuals (e.g. *Avena fatua*) which grow in the adjacent grassland area.

The terpenes present in the two shrubs have been fully characterized and identified and identical compounds have been isolated from the appropriate soil samples. These same compounds have been tested and shown to inhibit plant growth and seed germination. Of the various terpenes of the sagebrush, *Salvia leucophylla*, the two most effective toxins are 1,8-cineole and camphor. Also present are α- and β-pinene and camphene (Fig. 8.6). *Artemisia californica* is remarkably similar in that its two most potent terpenes are again 1,8-cineole and camphor. Other volatile agents of *Artemisia* include artemisiaketone, α-thujone and isothujone (Halligan, 1975).

The chemical ecology of the Californian chaparral is complicated by the fact that the vegetation undergoes cyclical change as a result of natural fires which occur on average about every 25 years. The destruction of the shrubs by fire is followed by several years in which the annual herbs and grasses dominate the landscape. However, slowly but inexorably, the shrubs grow again and begin to exert their allelopathic effects. Finally, the characteristic tell-tale bare patches of soil develop around the shrubs some 6 or 7 years after the fire and remain until the next fire occurs. The cycle then repeats itself. The terpenes fit into this fire cycle perfectly, since they are hydrocarbon in nature and are rapidly volatilized and burnt off the soil during the period of the fire. As a result, the soil is no longer contaminated with them and annuals are able to grow and multiply for several years following a fire (Fig. 8.7). It is only

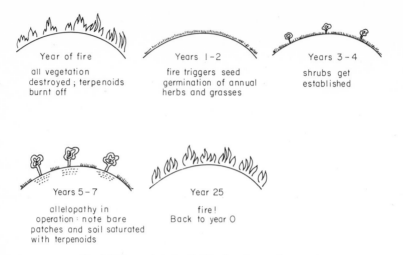

Year of fire

all vegetation
destroyed ; terpenoids
burnt off

Years 1 – 2

fire triggers seed
germination of annual
herbs and grasses

Years 3 – 4

shrubs get
established

Years 5 – 7

allelopathy in
operation : note bare
patches and soil saturated
with terpenoids

Year 25

fire !
Back to year 0

Fig. 8.7 Fire cycle in the Californian chaparral vegetation

when the shrub flora has developed sufficiently to synthesize terpenes in quantity that the influence of these toxins is again felt and the characteristic zonation appears.

If terpenes are so effective in reducing plant competition in sagebrush and *Artemisia,* one might ask the question whether other plant species make use of these toxins in a similar fashion. In fact, volatile mono- and sesquiterpenes are present in abundance in a wide range of angiosperms, particularly in many species of Myrtaceae, Labiatae and Rutaceae. They are also richly present in most gymnosperms. It is thus possible that these terpenes may be allelopathic substances in other plants, although their effects on surrounding vegetation may not be necessarily as dramatic as in the case of sagebrush. Indeed tests have been made on a number of chaparral shrubs and it is likely that similar limitations on annual species occur in these cases too. Plants in which terpenoids have been identified as effective allelopathic agents include *Eucalyptus globosus* (Baker, 1966), *E. camaldulensis* (Myrtaceae) (Del Moral and Muller, 1970), *Artemisia absinthium* and *Sassafras albidum* (Lauraceae) (Gant and Clebsch, 1975).

B. Water-Soluble Inhibitors

Two other dominant shrubs in the Californian chaparral are chamise *Adenostoma fasciculatum* (Rosaceae) and *Arctostaphylos glandulosa* (Ericaceae). Both are widespread and exert allelopathic effects on herbs similar to those observed for sagebrush. *Adenostoma,* for example, grows in pure stands on dry exposed slopes; even though the soil is fully exposed to the sun and receives ample rain, no herbs grow in the vicinity of the lower slopes. Yet adjacent roadsides produce a heavy crop of annuals. If allelopathy is responsible for this situation, then toxins other than terpenoids must be responsible, since neither *Adenostoma* nor *Arctostaphylos* has any significant quantity of terpenes in the leaves.

Indeed, experiments of McPherson and Muller (1969) have shown that, in both these plants, substances responsible for the observed allelopathic effects are water-soluble and water-borne. As with the terpene toxins, there is a particular cycle of events which ensures that the chemical factors are effective in this particular ecological situation. One of the major climatic features of this vegetation is coastal fog, even in the summer months, and although rainfall is only moderate, there is as a result of both forms of precipitation, a constant drip of moisture on to the leaves of these shrubs and hence onto the surrounding soil (del Moral and Muller, 1969). This can be sufficient to carry a regular supply of water-soluble inhibitor from leaf to the soil, where they remain in sufficient concentration to prevent the growth of any annual species that spreads its seeds near these shrubs.

The leaves of both *Adenostoma* and *Arctostaphylos* are relatively rich in water-soluble phenolic compounds and it was therefore no surprise when McPherson and Muller found that the inhibitors turned out to be varying mixtures of phenols and phenolic acids. A similar but not identical range of phenolics were isolated (a) by leaching the foliage of the shrubs and (b) by extracting the surrounding soil with alkaline ethanol. The major compounds obtained in these treatments are shown in Table 8.1. Differences in phenolic

Table 8.1 Phenolics identified as water-borne inhibitors in shrubs of the Californian chaparral

Class	Compound	*Adenostoma* Foliage	*Adenostoma* Soil	*Arctostaphylos* Foliage	*Arctostaphylos* Soil
Neutral phenols	Hydroquinone	+	−	+	−
	Phloridzin	+	−	−	−
	Umbelliferone	+	−	−	−
Hydroxybenzoic acids	*p*-Hydroxybenzoic	+	+	+	+
	Protocatechuic	−	−	+	−
	Vanillic	+	+	+	+
	Syringic	+	+	−	+
	Gallic	−	−	+	−
Hydroxy-cinnamic acids	Ferulic	+	+	+	+
	p-Coumaric	+	+	−	+
	o-Coumaric	−	−	−	+

Data from Muller and Chou (1972).

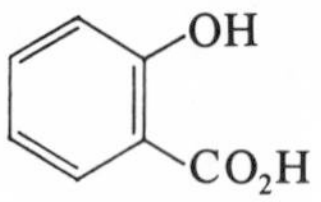

salicylic acid

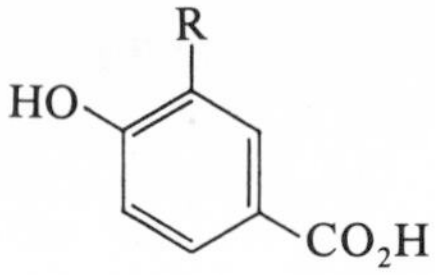

p-OH benzoic acid, R = H
vanillic acid, R = OMe

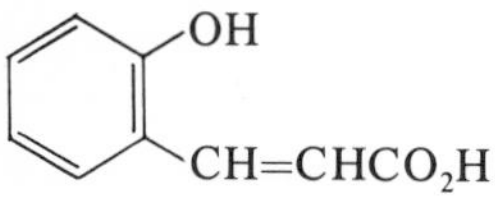

o-coumaric acid

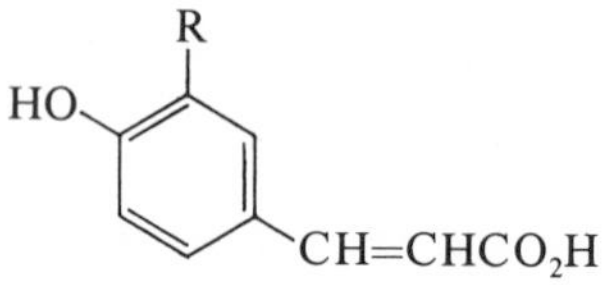

p-OH cinnamic, R = H
ferulic acid, R = OMe

Fig. 8.8 Some water-soluble allelopathic agents in plants

content between leachate and soil are probably due to the fact that some leachate compounds either become irreversibly bound to soil particles or else are metabolized by micro-organisms so rapidly that they are lost in the ecosystem.

Of the phenolic compounds isolated, those most effective in inhibiting the seed germination of grasses and other herbs are the hydroxybenzoic and hydroxycinnamic acids (Fig. 8.8) and it is just these compounds which are found in the soils as well as in the leachates.

Phenolic substances are normally present in leaf tissue mainly in bound form but they are known to be turned over within the plant tissue so that the fact that the leachate contains significant amounts of free as well as bound phenolics is perfectly reasonable. There are, however, problems regarding the isolation of phenolics from soil. While undoubtedly the concentration of such phenols could be reinforced by this drip mechanism, it is also true that the same acidic phenols could arise in the soil by the microbial decomposition of leaf-litter of some antiquity. The rate of turnover of these compounds in the soil is also not completely known, so that there are technical problems concerning the effectiveness of these phenolics as germination inhibitors. Nevertheless, the argument in favour of water-soluble toxins providing an ecological effect in these shrubs is clear. Further work is however needed, on the identification of leachate constituents and their fate in the soils into which they are deposited.

The study of water-borne inhibitors has been extended to other habitats and it is possible that this may be a general phenomenon in any climate where the right humid conditions exist for regular leaching of organic material from plant leaves. In the subhumid deciduous forests of South Carolina, for example, two trees, *Quercus falcata* (Fagaceae) and *Liquidambar styraciflua* (Altingiaceae), have been observed to inhibit undergrowth within the dripline of the foliar crowns. In these conditions, there is a high rainfall, an abundance of mineral nutrients and the lack of shading phenomena; there is therefore, the likelihood of allelopathic effects operating (Muller and Chou, 1972). Indeed, in the case of *Quercus falcata,* salicylic acid has been isolated from the leaf leachate and shown to be toxic in bioassays. In tropical rain forests, other situations may be found. For example, Webb *et al.* (1967) explored the factors limiting the size of pure stands of *Grevillea robusta* growing in Queensland and found evidence that root exudates were self inhibitory in this species. Such exudates were found to be highly toxic to seedlings of the same species and were presumably exerting such an effect in the natural environment.

V. ECOLOGICAL IMPORTANCE OF ALLELOPATHY

The importance of chemical interactions between higher plants is undoubtedly underrated by ecologists but this is largely because of the scarcity of information relating to allelopathic effects in natural plant communities. One could argue that the chaparral vegetation studied by Muller and his colleagues has a number of special features associated with it, especially an unusual climate and the hazard of fire, which makes it impossible to extrapolate these results to the more equable conditions of temperate grasslands. Other hazards in interpreting the importance of particular chemicals in allelopathic situations are the physico-chemical complexity of the soil, its ability or otherwise to bind organic molecules and also the presence in the soil of micro-organisms which can either convert a particular plant product to a more toxic agent or else destroy it so that it can no longer have any effect on higher plant tissue.

A series of allelopathic experiments, which at least remove the problem of microbial involvement from the situation, have been carried out by Newman and Rovira (1975). These authors suggest that chemical interactions may occur commonly between herbs and grasses present in British meadows. Plants of eight species were grown in buckets of sand together with sterilized soil from the natural habitat. Leachates of these individual pots (and of control pots lacking plants) were then applied to all the other species in turn and the influence on growth rates examined after a period of some weeks.

The leachates from three species *Holcus lanatus, Hypochoeris radicata* and *Trifolium repens* consistently depressed the yield of the other five species. Of these, *Anthoxanthum odoratum* was the most sensitive, but this species was exceptional in that it grew faster in the presence of its own leachate than under any other conditions (including the control). The other four species affected by leachates of the first three were *Cynosarus cristatus, Lolium perenne, Plantago lanceolata* and *Rumex acetosa*. These results not only suggest that some species may compete with others in temperate grasslands by exerting allelopathic effects; equally they indicate that self-stimulation may be important in the attainment of dominance within a sward. These data are further significant in that they indicate allelopathic effects may occur in situations when zonation is absent and where no obvious chemical interaction would be suspected.

One ecological situation where allelopathic effects are likely to be more pronounced than in a stable pastureland is in field succession, where farming has removed the natural flora and has extensively altered the potentiality of the land in terms of mineral and organic matter content. Any such field, left fallow, will undergo a series of successive invasions of plant species before a more stable plant community becomes established. Rice (1974) has discussed in detail the possible role of allelopathy in such plant communities and its effect on the sequence of succession. He has listed five possible effects as follows: (1) the speeding up of the replacement of one species by another due to allelopathic self-toxicity (e.g. as in *Helianthus rigidus*); (2) the direct allelopathic suppression of the first species by the second via root or leaf exudates; (3) the slowing down of species replacement by the direct allelopathic effects of a dominant species on all potential invaders; (4) the indirect effect of a species through its decay products (shown in *Sorghum halepense*) or through its inhibition of nitrogen-fixing bacteria (shown by *Euphorbia supina*); and (5) allelopathic effects which determine what other species can invade the community and which cannot.

Clearly, many practical problems may arise in agriculture and horticulture from the effects of allelopathy. Thus weeds growing among crop plants, besides competing in the expected fashion for soil nutrients and light, may also exert a deleterious effect on the latter plants through the release of toxins. Again, the ploughing in, instead of burning, of cereal stubble causes the release of considerable quantities of phenolic acids during the breakdown of the cell-walls and these could have an inhibitory effect on growth of certain crop plants grown subsequently. The quality of the microbial flora and its ability to further detoxify the phenolics are also important factors in such situations (Guenzi and McCalla, 1966). Similarly, trees which produce toxic substances in the roots and which cause self toxicity to the seedlings are at a disadvantage when replanted in the same soil and may not thrive. Such effects have been encountered in rosaceous fruit trees; in the case of the apple, the phenolic compound phloridzin is thought to be responsible for such effects (Börner, 1959). Other cases where allelopathic activities may interfere with crop rotation and with the establishment of nitrogen fixation in legumes are recorded by Rice (1974). It should, however, be pointed out that in almost all instances critical experimental data are lacking and much of the evidence of allelopathy is still circumstantial.

VI. CONCLUSION

Sufficient experiments have now been carried out to indicate that allelopathic effects are exerted between one higher plant and another in a reasonable number of cases. The chemicals involved are generally secondary constituents, some of which are widely if not universally distributed in plants. It is therefore possible that allelopathy is a general phenomenon and could occur in many different ecological situations. How often allelopathy has a *controlling effect* in a particular case of plant competition is more difficult to predict and clearly all the biological aspects of the situation have to be fully investigated before the influence of chemical control can be considered as established.

The toxins involved in allelopathy generally occur in leaves and stems, although root constituents have a place in such interactions. How far compounds in other plant parts (e.g. flower, fruit) are deleterious to higher plant growth is not clear because these substances have rarely been studied as allelopathic agents. It is, however, well known that the seed coats of many plants contain chemicals which inhibit seed germination. These substances, besides contributing to the internal control of dormancy, may eventually leak out into the environment and have a deleterious effect on other species, before being degraded to harmless materials. Such possible allelopathic effects, however, need further study.

The method of release into the environment of the toxins can take one of several pathways. Extraction of phenolics from the living leaf is clearly effective, but depends on regular rainfall to accomplish the leaching. Volatilization from the leaf surface seems to be important in more arid climates and is the way that essential oils are released into the atmosphere and into the soil. Other volatile toxins, not yet fully implicated in allelopathy but which could be equally effective, are the mustard oils (glucosinolates) of the Cruciferae and the cyanogens of *Prunus, Trifolium* and many other plants.

Exudation of toxin from the root would seem to be the method *par excellence* for producing a harmful effect on a neighbouring species. However, of the situations studied, such exudations seem to occur in a minority of cases. However, a number of crop plants such as wheat, oats, guayule, cucumber and tomato are known to exude root toxins so that such root emanations may be important agriculturally. Finally, toxins may be released from plants during the decay of leaf material and these besides producing self-toxicity, may be effective against a range of other species. Here, microbial activity may be partly or wholly responsible for the interactions observed, so that such effects pass out of the realm of allelopathy proper into that of microbial ecology.

The sorts of secondary compound so far implicated in allelopathy are either terpenoids (mono- or sesquiterpenes) or phenolics (phenols, phenolic acids, cinnamic acids, hydroxyquinones). This is a limited range of natural products and it is perhaps surprising that alkaloids, the most important group of plant constituents from the viewpoint of toxicity to animals, have not yet been assigned a role in higher plant–higher plant interactions. This may be because of their low concentrations in plants or else to their possible rapid turnover in the soil. Another group of substances which could be important are the condensed tannins and their relatively slow turnover in the ecosystem would ensure the persistency of their effects. They have, of course, the disadvantage of relative immobility within the plant. Future work will no doubt show whether these or other as yet undescribed structures also have a role as toxins in the chemical competition between higher plants.

BIBLIOGRAPHY

Books and Review Articles

Molisch, H. (1937). "Der Einfluss einer Pflanze auf die andere-Allelopathie." Fischer, Jena.
Muller, C. H. (1970). Phytotoxins as plant habitat variables. *Recent Advanc. Phytochem.* **3**, 106–121.
Muller, C. H. and Chou, C. H. (1972). Phytotoxins: an ecological phase of phytochemistry. In: Harborne, J. B. (ed.), "Phytochemical Ecology", pp. 201–216. Academic Press, London.
Rice, E. L. (1974). "Allelopathy", 353 pp. Academic Press, New York.
Went, F. W. (1972). Plants and the chemical environment. In: Sondheimer, E. and Simeone, J. B. (eds.), "Chemical Ecology", pp. 71–82.
Whittaker, R. H. (1972). The Biochemical ecology of higher plants. In: Sondheimer, E. and Simeone, J. B. (eds.), "Chemical Ecology", pp. 43–70. Academic Press, New York.
Whittaker, R. H. and Feeny, P. P. (1971). Allelochemics: chemical interactions between species. *Science* **171**, 757–770.

Literature References

Baker, H. G. (1966). *Madrone, S. Francisco* **18**, 207–210.
Bartholomew, B. (1970). *Science* **170**, 1210–1212.
Bennett, E. and Bonner, J. (1953). *Amer. J. Bot.* **40**, 29–33.
Bode, H. R. (1958). *Planta* **51**, 440–480.
Börner, H. (1959). *Contrib. Boyce Thompson Inst.* **20**, 39–56.
Bonner, J. and Galston, A. W. (1944). *Bot. Gazz.* **106**, 185–198.
Brooks, M. G. (1951). *West Va. Univ. Agr. Expt. Sta. Bull.* **347**, 1–31.
de Candolle, M. A. P. (1832). "Physiologie Vegetale", Vol. III. Bechet Jenne, Lib. Fac. Med., Paris.
Gant, R. E. and Clebsch, E. E. C. (1975). *Ecology* **56**, 604–615.
Guenzi, W. D. and McCalla, T. M. (1966). *Agron. J.* **58**, 303–304.
Gray, R. and Bonner, J. (1948). *Amer. J. Bot.* **34**, 52–57.
Grover, M. G. (1975). *Bot. Gazz.* **136**, 207–211.

Halligan, J. P. (1975). *Ecology* **56**, 999–1003.
Harper, J. L. (1975). *Quart. Rev. Biol.* **50**, 493–495.
Hegnauer, R. (1977). In: Heywood, V. H., Harborne, J. B. and Turner, B. L., "Biology and Chemistry of the Compositae", in press. Academic Press, London.
Massey, A. B. (1925). *Phytopathology* **15**, 773–784.
del Moral, R. and Muller, C. H. (1969). *Bull. Torrey Bot. Club.* **96**, 467–475.
del Moral, R. and Muller, C. H. (1970). *Amer. Midl. Natur.* **83**, 254–282.
McPherson, J. K. and Muller, C. H. (1969). *Ecol. Monogr.* **39**, 177–198.
Muller, C. H. and Muller, W. H. (1953). *Amer. J. Bot.* **40**, 53–60.
Muller, C. H. and Muller, W. H. (1956). *Amer. J. Bot.* **43**, 354–361.
Muller, C. H. (1966). *Bull. Torrey Bot. Club* **93**, 332–351.
Newman, E. I. and Rovira, R. D. (1975). *J. Ecol.* **63**, 727–737.
Putnam, A. R. and Duke, W. B. (1974). *Science* **185**, 370.
Schneiderhan, F. J. (1927). *Phytopathology* **17**, 529–540.
Turner, B. H. and Quarterman, R. (1975). *Ecology* **56**, 924–932.
Webb, L. J., Tracey, J. G. and Haydock, K. P. (1967). *J. Appl. Ecol.* **4**, 13–25.
Went, F. W. (1942). *Bull. Torrey Bot. Club* **69**, 100–114.

9 | Higher Plant–Lower Plant Interactions: Phytoalexins and Phytotoxins

I. INTRODUCTION

While the interaction between higher and lower plants can take many forms, it is the attack of the micro-organism on the higher plant leading to plant disease that is the major topic of the present chapter. The enormously damaging effect that microbial attack can have on the growth and development of plants is reflected in the common terms used in plant pathology to describe the different diseases. Diseases of the potato plant, for example, range from common scab, black leg, ring rot and skin spot to blight, gangrene and leaf roll. As these descriptive names imply, the symptoms are many and various; if unchecked, the end result of disease is usually the same whatever the invading micro-organism: death of the plant.

It should be emphasized, however, that susceptibility to disease, all too frequently apparent in cultivated plants, is really the exception rather than the rule. In fact, most higher plants especially those growing in natural communities, are either resistant to microbial attack or co-exist in a symbiotic

196

relationship with the parasites without the production of any visible symptoms. Experience shows that even with crop plants, while the cultivars are often highly susceptible to a range of diseases, most of the related wild species are relatively immune. In fact, breeding for disease resistance in cultivars often involves the introduction of genetic material from the disease-free wild relatives.

It is the basis of this resistance to disease or microbial attack which has been of special interest to biochemists and plant pathologists in recent years and which will be considered in some detail in the present chapter. There is also a significant agricultural incentive in developing such studies. Practically all the chemicals used for crop protection have been discovered empirically rather than by design and this is true even of the recently introduced systemic fungicides which control, for example, powdery mildew in cereals (Greenaway and Whatley, 1976). Knowledge of disease resistance factors may help in approaching the problem of disease control in crop plants on a more rational and scientific basis.

Attacking micro-organisms, in order to invade a plant, have to penetrate the surface layers. Obvious barriers to such invasion might be the presence of a waxy coating, numerous surface hairs or a thick cuticle. While much work has been done on the role of the leaf surface in disease, there is little concrete evidence to indicate that the surface layers provide any real protection from invasion. The main effect of the cuticular barriers is to reduce the speed of attack; successful invasion is nevertheless assured.

If there is no impenetrable physical barrier in plants to microbial invasion, one is forced to postulate the existence of a chemical barrier. Indeed, ideas of a chemical basis to disease resistance date back many years. Marshall Ward (1905) in his toxin theory was one of the first to suggest that there were compounds present in plants capable of inhibiting fungal growth. This theory states that: "infection and resistance to infection depend on the power of a fungus to overcome the resistance of the cells of the host plant by means of enzymes or toxins; and reciprocally, on that of the cells of the host to form antibodies or toxins which repel the fungus protoplasm". Among the many types of compound known to be present in plants, one group known as phenolics or polyphenols fit this role rather well. Phenolic compounds are universally distributed among higher plants and are often toxic to micro-organisms *in vitro* at physiological concentrations (10^{-4} to 10^{-6} M). It is, however, not clear, even today, whether such phenolic compounds have a causal role in protecting plants from disease *in vivo*.

A more dynamic view of phenolics and plant disease was developed by Offord (1940) who proposed that one particular class of phenolic—the tannins—were especially important as pre-infective agents in higher plants. He suggested that "the toxic action is initiated and conditioned by enzymes of the fungus; ultimate toxicity depends on the type of phenolic constituent formed by interaction of host and parasite and partly on the quantity and distribution of tannin". Unfortunately for Offord's theory, experimental evidence that tannins are involved in disease resistance is very thin. While it can be shown that tannins prevent the mechanical transmission of plant viruses, they cannot similarly provide control against soil-borne or insect-transmitted disease attack.

The major breakthrough in the study of chemically based disease resistance mechanisms in higher plants came with the enunciation of the phytoalexin theory by Müller and Börger in 1941. This theory proposed that certain chemical substances were produced by plants *de novo* at the time of infection and, they came into action as "compounds warding off ('alexos') disease organisms from the plant ('phytos')" (hence the term phytoalexin). The theory developed from experiments carried out by the two authors on resistant factors in potato to the blight organism *Phytophthora infestans*; but they were unsuccessful themselves in actually demonstrating the existence of a discrete chemical substance in potato with the properties of a phytoalexin. It remained for Cruickshank and Perrin (1960) 20 years later to be the first to isolate and identify a phytoalexin, namely the substance pisatin from *Pisum sativum*. Since then, a large number of phytoalexins have been described from a range of plants and phytoalexin induction is now widely regarded as a major protective device in higher plants. The precise role of phytoalexins in disease situations is still being actively investigated and much remains to be learnt about this. Work on other modes of biochemical resistance have also proceeded recently and the existence of pre-infectional chemical barriers in certain plants is also generally accepted.

While there are clearly chemical barriers to invasion, disease still occurs. Thus virulent strains of a given micro-organism are capable of breaching these defenses. When this happens, a different set of biochemical reactions occur, set off by the invader. A variety of changes in the respiration rate and the primary metabolism occur in the host plant. At the same time, the micro-organism as it multiplies in the cells of the host may secrete substances called pathotoxins, with which it directly "poisons" the host plant. These pathotoxins lead to the typical symptoms of disease susceptibility in the host, for example, the wilting of the leaves as a result of biochemical interference with the plant's water supply. The host plant, in turn, attempts to detoxify the pathotoxins by conjugation or degradation and a battle ensues between the higher plant and the invading micro-organism for ultimate control of the situation. Thus, there is a clearly defined second stage in the biochemical interaction between plant and microbe when the primary defense has broken down and the plant is fighting for its survival and protection from the harmful metabolites synthesized by the microbe.

In the present chapter, biochemical defense mechanisms involving both pre- and post-infectional changes in the host plant will first be considered. Emphasis will be placed on phytoalexin formation. The second part of the chapter will outline the biochemical compounds produced in disease susceptibility and in the eventual mutilation or destruction of the host. For general reviews covering many of the topics discussed here, the reader is especially directed towards four books (Wood, 1967; Wood *et al.*, 1972; Heitefuss and Williams, 1976; Friend and Threlfall, 1976) and the monograph on plant pathogenesis by Wheeler (1975). New advances in the topics discussed here are reported in journals such as *Physiological Plant Pathology, Phytopathology* and *Phytochemistry.*

II. BIOCHEMICAL BASIS OF DISEASE RESISTANCE

A. Pre-Infectional Compounds

As mentioned in the introduction, it is now clear that plants adopt a variety of biochemical defenses to ward off microbial attack. Several attempts have been made to classify these different modes and there is some confusion in nomenclature regarding the chemicals involved. Ingham (1973) has attempted to provide a classification of these compounds, making a primary division between pre-infectional and post-infectional factors (Table 9.1). It should be remembered, however, that there is no sharp division between such factors, since pre-infectional compounds can undergo significant post-infectional changes. While this system is thus to a certain degree an arbitrary one, it is

Table 9.1 A classification of disease resistance factors in higher plants

Class	Description
Pre-infectional compounds	
1. Prohibitins	Metabolites which reduce or completely halt the *in vivo* development of micro-organisms
2. Inhibitins	Metabolites which undergo post-infectional increase in order to express full toxicity
Post-infectional compounds	
1. Post-inhibitins	Metabolites formed by the hydrolysis or oxidation of pre-existing non-toxic substrates
2. Phytoalexins	Metabolites formed *de novo* after invasion by gene derepression or activation of a latent enzyme system

Modified from Ingham (1973).

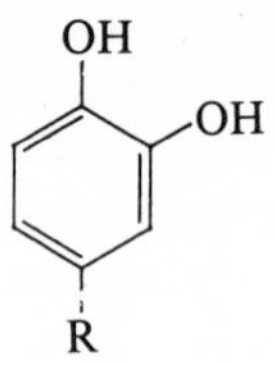

R = H, catechol
R = CO₂H, protocatechuic acid
(onion bulbs, *Allium cepa*)

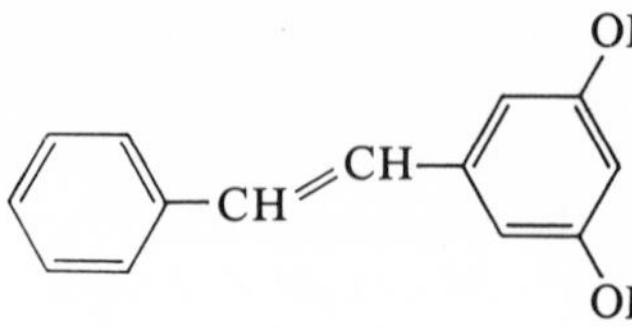

pinosylvin
(*Pinus* heartwood)

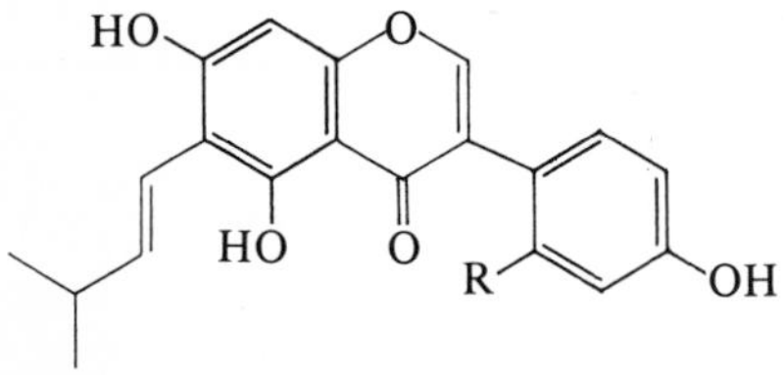

R = OH, luteone
R = H, 2'-deoxyluteone
(lupin leaves, *Lupinus* spp.)

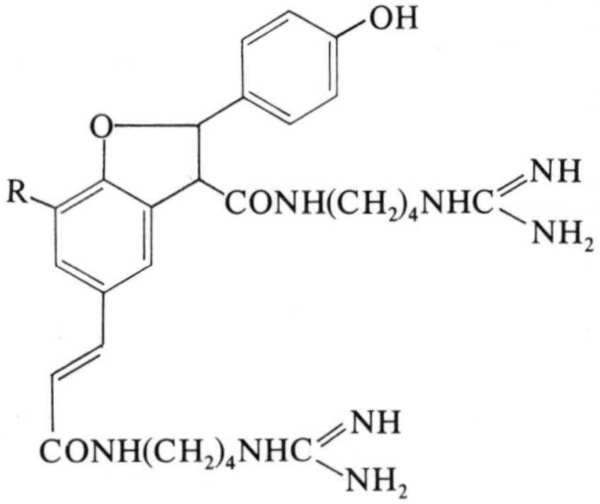

R = H, hordatine A
R = OMe, hordatine B
(barley seedlings, *Hordeum vulgare*)

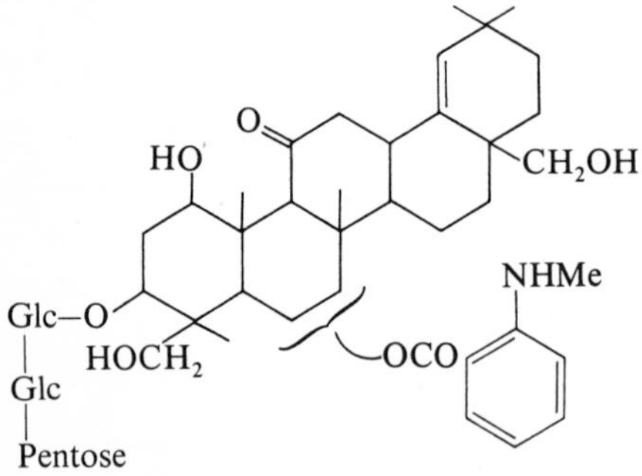

avenacin (partial structure)
(oat roots, *Avena sativa*)

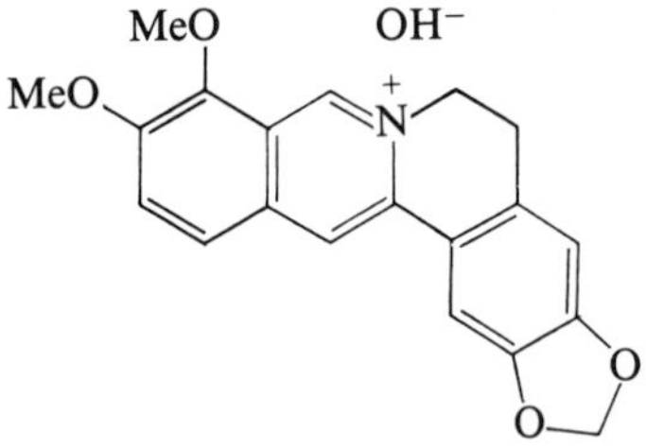

berberine
(*Mahonia trifoliata* roots)

Fig. 9.1 Structures of some pre-infectional compounds present in plants

convenient and will be used here as a framework in which to discuss some of the chemical constituents that have been implicated as disease resistance factors.

The occurrence in plants of substances which will inhibit the germination and/or growth of micro-organisms has been recognized for a long time. Indeed, many of the so-called secondary constituents, especially terpenoids and phenolics, have been demonstrated as having such effects in *in vitro* tests. One of the most striking accumulations of secondary compounds in the plant kingdom is in the heartwood of trees. An enormous profusion of chemical structures, with terpenoid, quinonoid and phenolic skeletons, have been isolated from such tissues, where they frequently occur in considerable quantity (Hillis, 1962). The majority of such tissues are unusually resistant to natural decay (Scheffer and Cowling, 1966) and there have been many suggestions that the role of these heartwood constituents is to provide disease resistance. Among the many groups of compound specifically linked with resistance to fungal attack are the hydroxystilbenes. One such compound is pinosylvin (for structure, see Fig. 9.1) which is widely distributed in *Pinus* and other Pinaceae. Unfortunately, evidence that these compounds are important to the plant is still almost entirely circumstantial, since the experimental difficulties in providing more direct evidence has largely prevented further progress in this field. The occurrence of hydroxystilbenes as pre-infectional compounds in tree heartwoods is supported, at least to some degree, by the recent identification of similar structures as phytoalexins in the leaves of several legumes (see p. 215).

One of the most often quoted examples in the plant pathological literature of pre-infectional compounds apparently providing disease resistance in non-woody plants is the rather exceptional situation of onion bulbs suffering from onion smudge disease, *Colletotrichum circinans* (Walker and Stahmann, 1955). The dead outer scales of resistant onion varieties contain large quantities of protocatechuic acid and catechol (see Fig. 9.1), both of which are highly toxic to spores of *C. circinans*. Extracts of these scales reduce spore germination to below 2% whereas extracts of susceptible onion varieties which lack these agents in quantity allow a germination rate of over 90%. The occurrence of these two phenols in resistant varieties is correlated with anthocyanin colour in the scales, a correlation which is probably purely fortuitous in that other fungi are able to invade both coloured and colourless onion varieties indiscriminately. Anthocyanins based on cyanidin (i.e. with a catechol nucleus in their structures) have the potentiality of being fungitoxic and indeed cyanidin itself has been shown to inhibit germination of *Gloeosporium perennans,* a fungus causing apple rot (Hulme and Edney, 1960). A final point about the onion–phenol interaction is that the actual inhibitor has recently been suggested to be 3,4-dihydroxybenzaldehyde, since this compound has been identified as a fungistatic principle in bananas resistant to *Gloeosporium musarum* (Mulvena *et al.,* 1969). The latter authors found the aldehyde to be extremely readily oxidized to protocatechuic acid and it is possible that, since no special precautions were taken, this oxidation occurred during the isolation of the fungitoxin from onion scales.

Evidence that pre-infectional compounds also have a role in the disease resistance in living tissue, in fresh leaves, has been obtained from recent studies with lupins (Harborne *et al.*, 1976). Whilst examining leaves of white lupin *Lupinus albus* for phytoalexins using the drop diffusate technique (see p. 211), it was found that at least two fungitoxic compounds were present in significant concentration *both* on the leaf surface *and* within the leaf. The compounds were not induced by the microbial spores, since they were present in equal amounts in control droplets which lacked any fungal spores; these two compounds were identified as luteone, an isopentenylisoflavone, and its 2'-deoxy derivative (for structures, see Fig. 9.1). Fungitoxicity was evident from *in vitro* tests in which luteone showed an ED_{50} value of 35–40 µg/ml, when tested against the mycelial growth of *Helminthosporium carbonum*. The ED_{50} is a measure of fungitoxicity and refers to the median effective dose required for the inhibition of mycelial growth of a given fungus. In actual practice, rather higher concentrations will be required for complete (100%) inhibition. The presence of an isopentenyl group in the lupin isoflavones seems to be important for fungitoxicity since comparison of ED_{50} values shows that luteone is ten times more active on a molar basis than isoflavones lacking this terpenoid-based sidechain attachment, e.g. biochanin A and formononetin.

Pre-infectional compounds appear to occur throughout the genus *Lupinus*, since examination of eleven other species besides *L. albus* showed the presence on leaf surfaces of luteone or related isoflavones. Thus, under natural conditions, the isoflavone concentration in the leaf surface moisture film may produce an *in vivo* environment highly unfavourable for fungal development. The toxic effect is probably on fungal spore germination and/or germ tube development rather than on mycelial proliferation. This was evident from histological studies which indicated curled, distorted and highly branched germ tubes when *Helminthosporium carbonum* was allowed to invade lupin leaves; on leaves of its normal host plant, maize, the same organism produced normal, straight germ tubes.

Another group of flavonoids, this time methylated flavones, have been partly implicated in the resistance of citrus leaves to fungal attack. Substances such as nobiletin (5,6,7,8,3',4'-hexamethoxyflavone) are highly fungitoxic and occur in leaves in sufficient amount to ward off attack. However, a quantitative investigation of the relationship between the concentration of nobiletin in the leaves and resistance to the fungus *Deuterophoma tracheiphila* showed no simple correlation (Piatelli and Impellizzari, 1971). Nevertheless, nobiletin has many of the characteristics of a pre-infectional agent and its high lipid solubility and contrasting lack of water solubility suggests that it is most likely to occur on the leaf surface rather than within it. The role of flavonoids as possible pre-infectional agents in disease resistance is further discussed by McClure (1975).

Yet another example of phenolic compounds being involved in disease resistance is the case of the hordatines A and B, which have a protective function in barley seedlings *Hordeum vulgare* attacked by *Helminthosporium sativum* (Stoessl, 1967); these compounds are of an unusual structure, being based on two *p*-coumaric acid residues linked to the amino acid arginine (see Fig. 9.1). An interesting complication in this instance is that the effectiveness of these fungitoxins decreases as the seedlings develop due to the accumulation in the tissues of Ca^{++} and Mg^{++} ions. *In vitro* tests have shown that the two hordatines are inactivated by divalent cations, presumably, due to complex formation.

Evidence that structures other than phenols can act as prohibitins has come from work on root infections in cereals. Resistance of oats *Avena sativa* to the take-all fungus *Ophiobolus graminis* has been ascribed to a highly fluorescent "root tip glycoside" (Turner, 1960). This compound has been partly characterized as a pentacyclic triterpene glycoside, avenacin, the blue fluorescence being due to the presence of an anthranilic acid moiety (Burkhardt *et al.*, 1964). Curiously, this fungitoxin is largely detoxified by the enzymic removal of the terminal pentose sugar (for structure, see Fig. 9.1). An enzyme, avenacinase, is produced by the fungus *O. graminis* var. *avenae* which will catalyse this hydrolysis so that the ability of oats to resist fungal infection is limited by this enzymic activity. A similar system involving a different triterpenoid, avenacoside A, and the enzymic removal of a 26-glucose residue appears to operate in oat leaves when infected with the fungus *Drechslera avenacea* (Lüning and Schlösser, 1976). Another example of a non-phenolic prohibitin is that of the alkaloid berberine which is thought to provide resistance in roots of *Mahonia trifoliata* to invasion by the fungus *Phymatotrichum omnivorum* (Greathouse and Watkins, 1938).

In summary then, there is evidence that a small number of plants have a disease resistance mechanism based in part on the presence of preformed fungitoxins which are sufficient in themselves in preventing microbial invasion. The compounds are mainly phenolic in nature but other types of chemical structures, especially triterpenoids and alkaloids, have also been implicated in this type of defense mechanism.

A second class of pre-infectional compounds thought to be involved in disease resistance in plants are the inhibitins, metabolites which undergo post-infectional increases in order to express their toxic potential (Ingham, 1973). This group of compounds has been proposed on the basis of the general observation that infection in many plants by micro-organisms leads to the accumulation of various aromatic compounds, especially coumarin derivatives near the site of infection. One of the most striking examples of this is in blight-

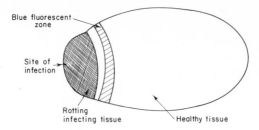

Fig. 9.2 Formation of inhibitory zone of coumarin in potato infected with blight

infected potatoes, where an intensely blue fluorescent zone can be seen in the tuber near the edge of the infection (Fig. 9.2). If Majestic potatoes are inoculated at one end with spores of *Phytophthora infestans,* incubated for 14 days at 18° and then sliced longitudinally in half, the potato will appear as shown in Fig. 9.2. The intense blue fluorescent zone appears between the infected area and the healthy tissue and gives the appearance of being formed as a protective zone between the two types of tissue. Comparison of phenolic constituents in healthy tissue and in the blue fluorescent zone shows that in this zone, there are large increases in the synthesis of two particular phenolics. One, the fluorescent coumarin scopolin increases 10–20-fold whilst the other, chlorogenic acid, of weaker fluorescence, increases 2–3-fold (Hughes and Swain, 1960). Both coumarins and hydroxycinnamic acids such as chlorogenic are known to be significantly toxic when tested *in vitro* against a range of micro-organisms (cf. Jurd *et al.,* 1971).

Such changes in phenolic metabolites (for structures, see Fig. 9.3), may be purely incidental to the effect of infection on the normal metabolism in the tissue. The increased synthesis of these substances may not be directly related to disease resistance, but may simply be a symptom of the disease. It may, however, be mentioned that similar increases in scopolin, scopoletin or chlorogenic acid levels occur in other plants besides the potato, e.g. in tobacco *Nicotiana tabacum* and sweet potato *Ipomoea batatis*. One plant where an increase in as yet unidentified blue fluorescent compounds has been correlated with disease resistance is apple, when the leaves are infected with the scab

R = H, scopoletin
R = Glc, scopolin   chlorogenic acid

Fig. 9.3 Some phenolic inhibitins

organism *Venturia inaequalis* (Hunter *et al.,* 1968). Here, there are three compounds which inhibit conidial germination of *V. inaequalis* and which are present in healthy leaves but increase to inhibitory levels as a result of infection. On the assumption that the blue fluorescent components are hydroxycinnamic acid derivatives of some novel type, various synthetic acids (e.g. isobutyl *o*-coumarate) have successfully been applied as a spray on leaves of susceptible apple varieties to enhance their resistance to the scab disease (Kirkham and Hunter, 1964). However, in spite of this success, it is clear that much further work is needed to establish whether substances which increase in amount after infection really have a significant role in plant protection.

B. Post-Infectional Compounds: Post-Inhibitins

The concept of plants storing in an inactive form within their tissues toxins needed for their protection is now a familiar one. It applies to toxins produced to deter herbivores (Chapter 3) and toxins serving as allelopathic agents (Chapter 8). There is also evidence that disease resistance in plants is afforded by a similar mechanism. The toxins involved are described in Ingham's classification (Table 9.1) as post-inhibitins. They are present in healthy tissues as inactive glycosides, the active toxin being released by enzymic hydrolysis or oxidation following microbial invasion.

The simplest example of this type of mechanism involves the cyanogenic glycosides, which are not toxic as such, but which release prussic acid when hydrolyzed by a specific β-glucosidase, the intermediate cyanohydrin formed breaking down spontaneously to aldehyde or ketone and HCN (see Fig. 9.4). The HCN so produced then serves to protect the plant from further fungal colonization. Release of cyanide occurs, for example, when leaves of birdsfoot trefoil *Lotus corniculatus*, are invaded by the leaf pathogen *Stemphylium loti* (Millar and Higgins, 1970). In this example, the pathogen is relatively tolerant to HCN and can readily adapt to cyanide when cultured in its presence by producing the enzyme formamide hydro-lyase, which detoxifies HCN by conversion to formamide $HCONH_2$. With *Stemphylium* infection, the HCN produced is relatively ineffective in halting fungal invasion. The value of HCN under field conditions is that a number of fungi with the potential to attack birdsfoot trefoil lack the ability to produce a detoxifying enzyme and hence are unable to become established within the tissue of this plant.

A parallel example to the cyanogenic glycosides are the glucosinolates of the Cruciferae, which have been shown to be involved in the resistance of wild and cultivated *Brassicas* to downy mildew (Greenhalgh and Mitchell, 1976). In these plants, tissue damage releases significant amounts of the volatile oil, allyl isothiocyanate, formed by enzymic hydrolysis of the glucoside sinigrin by myrosinase (Fig. 9.4). This isothiocyanate, which is one of the major flavour

HYDROLYSIS
(a) birdsfoot trefoil

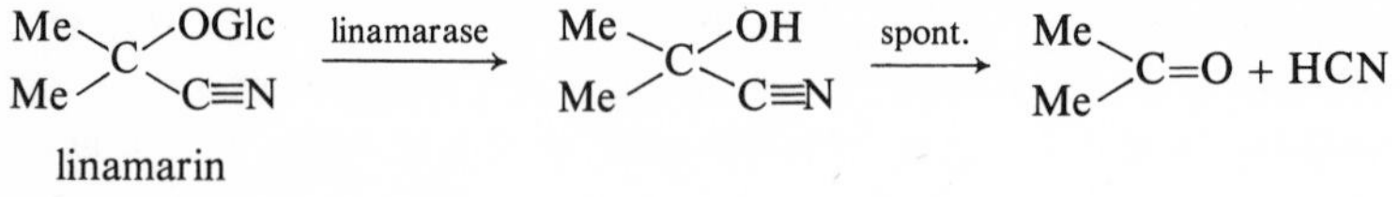

$$\begin{array}{c} Me \\ Me \end{array}\!\!\!C\!\!\begin{array}{c} OGlc \\ C\equiv N \end{array} \xrightarrow{\text{linamarase}} \begin{array}{c} Me \\ Me \end{array}\!\!\!C\!\!\begin{array}{c} OH \\ C\equiv N \end{array} \xrightarrow{\text{spont.}} \begin{array}{c} Me \\ Me \end{array}\!\!\!C\!\!=\!\!O + HCN$$

linamarin

(b) cabbage

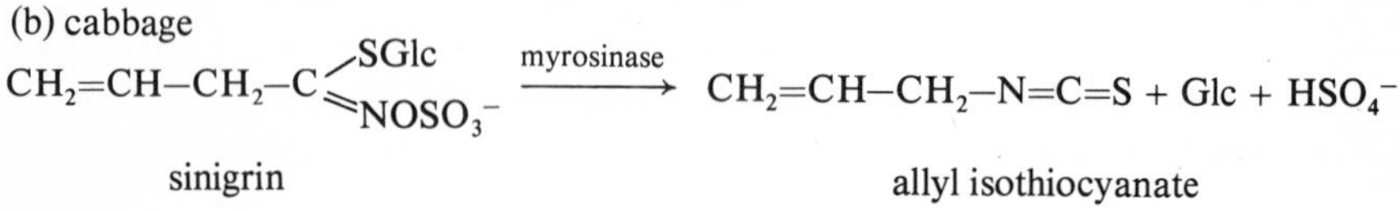

$$CH_2\!\!=\!\!CH\!\!-\!\!CH_2\!\!-\!\!C\!\!\begin{array}{c} SGlc \\ NOSO_3^- \end{array} \xrightarrow{\text{myrosinase}} CH_2\!\!=\!\!CH\!\!-\!\!CH_2\!\!-\!\!N\!\!=\!\!C\!\!=\!\!S + Glc + HSO_4^-$$

sinigrin   allyl isothiocyanate

(c) tulip

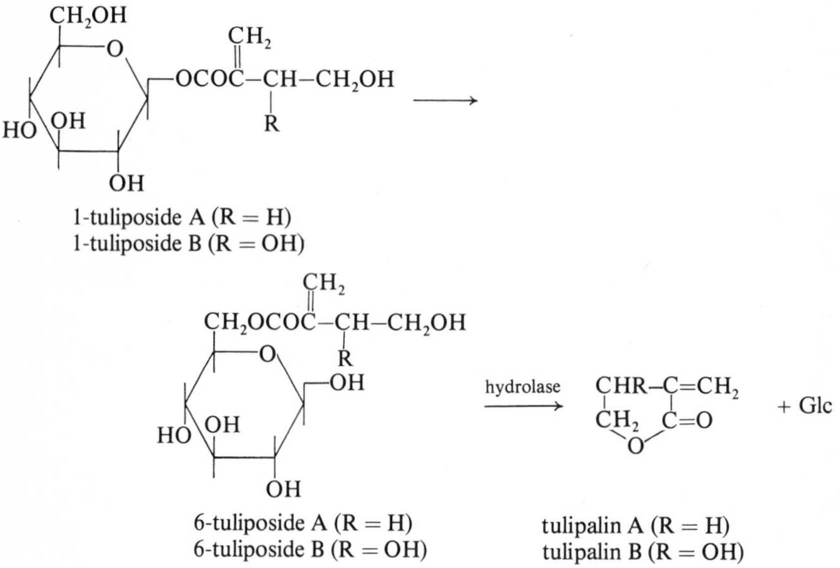

1-tuliposide A (R = H)
1-tuliposide B (R = OH)

6-tuliposide A (R = H)   tulipalin A (R = H)
6-tuliposide B (R = OH)   tulipalin B (R = OH)

OXIDATION
apple

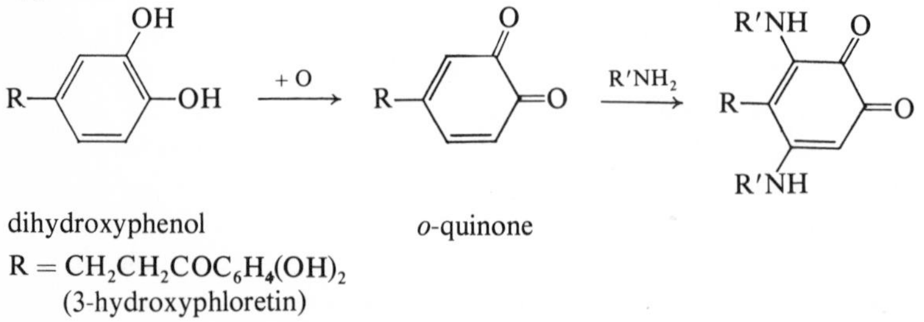

dihydroxyphenol   o-quinone
R = $CH_2CH_2COC_6H_4(OH)_2$
(3-hydroxyphloretin)

Fig. 9.4 Mechanisms of release of fungitoxins by hydrolysis or oxidation

principles of cabbage and other vegetable crucifers, is highly toxic to the mildew pathogen *Peronospora parasitica*. Evidence that release of isothiocyanate is causally connected with the control of mildew infection is based on two findings. First, in cultivated *Brassica oleracea*, there is a correlation between isothiocyanate content and disease resistance: thus allyl isothiocyanate content, measured in µg/g dry wt was found to be 630 in a resistant variety and between 450 and 21 in susceptible varieties. Second, in wild populations of cabbage, the highest proportion of resistant seedlings (up to 47%) occur in those populations with the highest levels of flavour volatiles. Since wild populations in general have much higher isothiocyanate contents than cultivars, it appears that selective breeding for milder flavoured *Brassica* vegetables has been a contributory factor to the general lack of resistance to powdery mildew in modern varieties.

Another convincing example of post-inhibitins having importance in disease resistance is that of the 1-tuliposides A and B. These two glucosides occur in young tulip bulbs and provide them with resistance to the pathogen *Fusarium oxysporum* during most of the growing season. The two glucosides are themselves only mildly antibiotic but they rearrange to the isomeric 6-tuliposides A and B, which are inert but which in turn undergo enzymic hydrolysis followed by cyclization to yield the highly fungitoxic tulipalins A and B (see Fig. 9.4 for relevant structures). The fungitoxicity of the latter pair of substances is thought to be related to their ability to complex with SH groups and to inhibit the enzymic activities of the attacking fungus (Beijersbergen and Lemmers, 1970). It is interesting, in passing, that the same substances have allergenic properties in man and tuliposide A and its reaction products are responsible for the skin disease caused by excessive handling of tulip bulbs. The contribution of tuliposides A and B to disease resistance may be fairly widespread in the Liliaceae, since these glucosides have been identified in 25% of some 200 species surveyed; although mainly present in *Tulipa*, they also occur in many *Alstroemeria* species (Slob *et al.*, 1975).

The role of phenolics as pre-infectional metabolites has already been discussed in a previous section (p. 201). It is possible that certain of these phenolics may also have a role as post-inhibitins. Thus, one general mechanism by which disease resistance is enhanced is by the oxidation of pre-existing 3,4-dihydroxyphenols, which may or may not be first released by hydrolytic cleavage of esters or glucosides. The *o*-quinones so formed (Fig. 9.4) appear to be highly toxic; moreover, they are capable of undergoing condensation with amino compounds, including amino acids, to give even more toxic products. This type of mechanism has been invoked to explain the resistance of apple varieties to their various fungal pathogens. The pre-existing compound is phloridzin, the β-glucoside of phloretin. After hydrolysis of phloridzin, the phloretin formed is first oxidized to 3-hydroxyphloretin and this then undergoes further oxidation, mediated by the enzyme phenolase, to quinone.

The processes by which these various steps occur is still not clear. Nevertheless, in resistant leaves, it appears that the fungitoxic *o*-quinone is formed only when the invading micro-organism damages cellular membranes, allowing the plant enzyme phenolase to oxidize the natural substrate. The product of this oxidation then arrests further fungal development. By contrast, in susceptible varieties, cellular damage is minimized, the potential of the leaves to form fungitoxic quinone is suppressed and the fungus is then able to invade the host tissues without let or hindrance (Sijpesteijn, 1969). Whether such a system actually provides disease resistance in apples is still debatable, since Hunter (1975) found that in the case of apple scab, *Venturia inaequalis,* neither phloridzin nor its simple breakdown products provided any degree of resistance. However, the related quinones were not directly tested, because of their high instability *in vivo.*

C. Post-Infectional Compounds: Phytoalexins

The Phytoalexin Concept

The phytoalexin concept of disease resistance has undoubtedly led to one of the major developments in physiological plant pathology of the last 15 years and it has probably stimulated more research into the mechanisms of disease resistance in plants than any other single idea. Today, the biochemical aspects of these antifungal agents are well known and only a summary is needed here. It should, however, be emphasized that physiological, ultrastructural and pathological aspects of phytoalexin synthesis are not yet fully documented and although it is widely accepted that phytoalexins have a place in disease resistance, many aspects of their production and metabolism *in vivo* are not yet understood. Before discussing the present state of the phytoalexin field, it is worth restating the main tenets of the theory, as postulated by Müller and Börger in 1941 from their studies of the reaction of potato varieties to virulent and avirulent strains of *Phytophthora.* These tenets are as follows:

(1) A phytoalexin is a compound which inhibits the development of the fungus in hypersensitive tissues and is formed or activated *only when* the host plants come in contact with the parasite.

(2) The defense reaction occurs only in living cells.

(3) The inhibitory agent is a discrete chemical substance, a product of the host cell.

(4) The phytoalexin is non-specific in its toxicity towards fungi; however, fungal species may be differentially sensitive to it.

(5) The basic response in both resistant and susceptible cells is the same, the basis of differentiation between resistant and susceptible hosts being the speed of formation of the phytoalexin.

(6) The defense reaction is confined to the tissue colonized by the fungus and its immediate neighbourhood.

(7) The resistant state is not inherited; it is developed after the fungus has attempted infection. The sensitivity of the host cell which determines the speed of the host reaction is specific and genotypically determined.

As already mentioned, belief in the phytoalexin theory was not vindicated until 20 years later when Cruickshank and Perrin (1960) crystallized and chemically characterized the first phytoalexin; this was pisatin, a pterocarpan derivative produced by pods of *Pisum sativum* inoculated with conidia of the

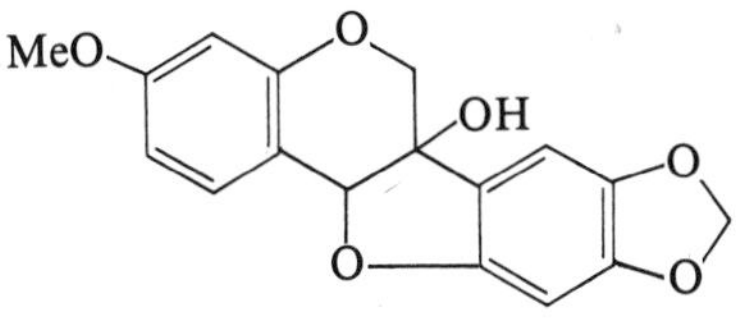

pisatin
(*Pisum sativum*, Leguminosae)

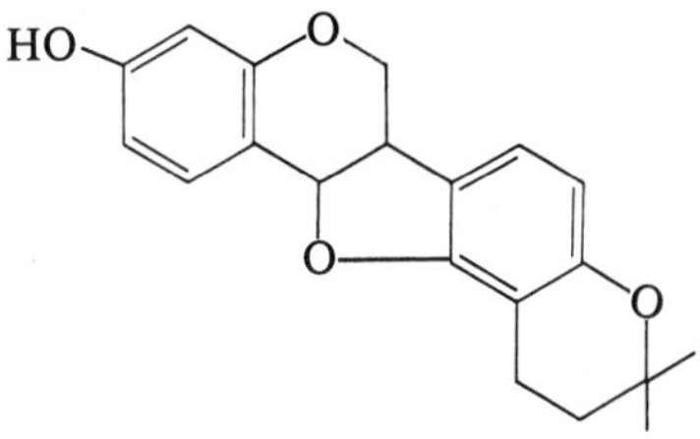

phaseollin
(*Phaseolus vulgaris*, Leguminosae)

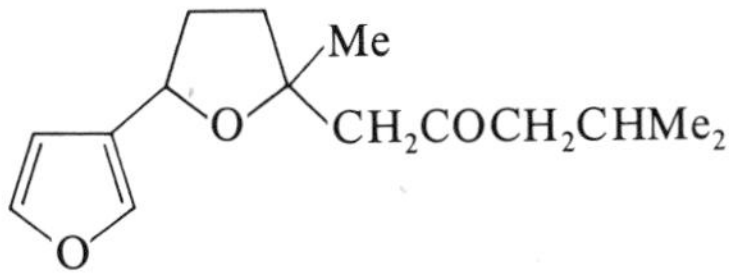

ipomeamarone
(*Ipomoea batatis*, Convolvulaceae)

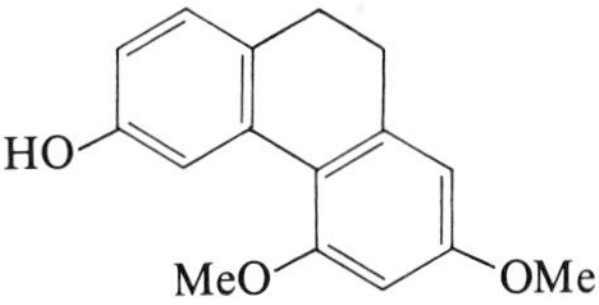

orchinol
(*Orchis militaris*, Orchidaceae)

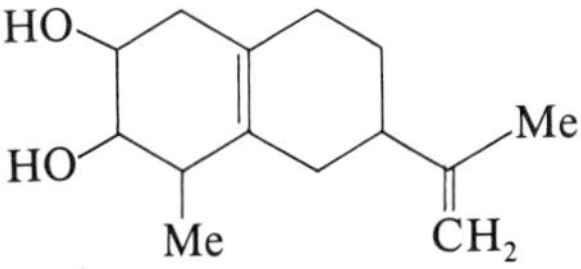

rishitin
(*Solanum tuberosum*, Solanaceae)

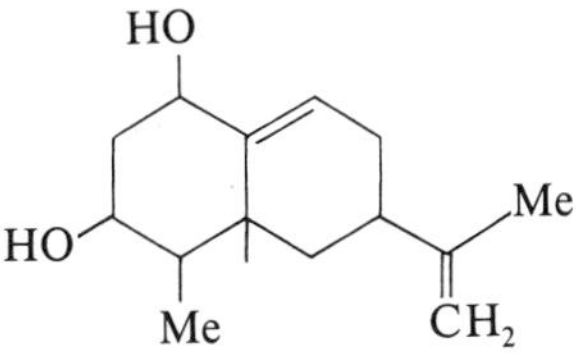

capsidiol
(*Capsicum frutescens*, Solanaceae)

$HOCH_2CHOHCH=CH(C{\equiv}C)_3CH=CHMe$

safynol
(*Carthamus tinctoria*, Compositae)

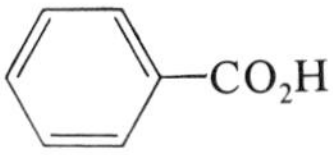

benzoic acid
(*Malus pumila*, Rosaceae)

Fig. 9.5 Structures of representative phytoalexins of higher plants

'brown rot fungus, *Monilinia fructicola*. Cruickshank and Perrin (1964) were able to show that pisatin fulfilled all the criteria required by Müller and Börger's theory and this substance remains one of the most fully investigated phytoalexins known today. Subsequent studies soon established that other legumes, particularly *Phaseolus vulgaris*, produced similar pterocarpans (e.g. phaseollin) on fungal inoculation. At the same time, reconsideration of compounds isolated from diseased plants in other families showed that phyto-alexin production is a feature of the Convolvulaceae (ipomeamarone from infected sweet potato) and of the Orchidaceae (orchinol from orchid tubers). Efforts were then directed towards identifying the compounds formed in response to microbial attack in many other crop plants and a range of chemical structures were found to fit the phytoalexin concept. In particular, several substances, among them the sesquiterpenoid rishitin, were charac-terized in the potato-blight interaction originally investigated by Müller and Börger. The chemical structures of a representative sample of phytoalexins known today are illustrated in Fig. 9.5.

Our knowledge of phytoalexins has increased considerably since the original hypothesis was proposed and although most known phytoalexins fit remark-ably well into the general scheme, some modifications of the tenets of the theory have to be considered in some instances. We now know that the interaction is more complex than originally envisaged, particularly since some fungi have the capacity to further metabolize and detoxify phytoalexins. Thus, the ability of a fungus to parasitize a particular plant is related at least in part to its ability to deal with the phytoalexins produced by the host. This further metabolism will be mentioned in a later section. First, however, some comments are required on factors inducing the phytoalexin response, on the structural variation among phytoalexins and on taxonomic and evolutionary aspects.

Factors Inducing the Phytoalexin Response

For a chemical substance to be regarded as a phytoalexin, its formation has to be induced experimentally in healthy plant tissue by inoculation or infection with micro-organisms. A simple procedure for testing the phytoalexin response of plants has been devised. This is the drop diffusate technique (Fig. 9.6), in which leaves are floated on water in light and droplets of a spore suspension of a non-pathogenic fungus are placed on the upper leaf surface (Higgins and Millar, 1968). A surface-active agent such as Tween-20 is added to prevent the droplets from spreading over the leaf surface. A second batch of leaves are set up at the same time, with aqueous Tween-20 droplets as a control. These are left for 48 hr and then the droplets are collected. In the case of a positive response, the droplets are found to contain high levels of the phytoalexin

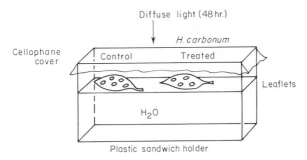

Fig. 9.6 Drop diffusate technique for phytoalexin induction

largely uncontaminated with other plant constituents. Thus, in a very simple way, it is possible to obtain a relatively pure phytoalexin sample, which can then be used for further investigation.

What happens in this leaf-droplet system is that the fungal spores start germinating in the droplets within 1–2 hr, and the resulting germ tubes then penetrate the host cells. As a consequence of this "trigger", the plant immediately responds by *de novo* synthesis of phytoalexin; such compounds, which are often detectable after several hours, reach maximum production at 48 to 72 hr. The phytoalexins are themselves synthesized within the leaf but much material is "pushed out" onto the leaf surface where the fungal invasion is occurring: hence, the accumulation of phytoalexin in the droplets. It has been argued (see Hargreaves *et al.*, 1976a) that the drop diffusate technique does not provide a complete picture of phytoalexin production, since certain substances may not diffuse from the leaf into the overlying droplets. However, tests have shown that for many species the same compounds are present in both the leaf and in the droplets, although there may be quantitative differences if more than one compound is produced.

In order to confirm phytoalexin synthesis, the droplet extracts must be tested for fungitoxicity. This can conveniently be done by TLC bioassay (see Fig. 9.7), in which the two extracts (phytoalexin solution and water control) are developed on a TLC plant in a suitable solvent. After drying, the plate is sprayed with a fungal spore suspension (e.g. of *Cladosporium herbarum*) and incubated for about 5 days at 25–30°. During this time, the fungus grows over the whole plate except where fungitoxic zones are present; these areas appear as white spots on a grey background. The TLC plate after development can also be sprayed with a range of diagnostic reagents (e.g. diazotised *p*-nitroaniline solution—a test for phenols) in order to determine to which chemical class the phytoalexin belongs. The final stage in the investigation is to identify the compounds present, using the standard procedures of organic chemistry.

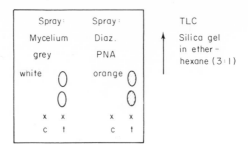

Fig. 9.7 Bioassay and detection of phytoalexins in control (c) and treated (t) droplets

While phytoalexins are formed reproducibly, most frequently and in the highest yield when plants are invaded with fungi, they are also formed on occasion when plants are subjected to bacterial or viral invasion (Deverall, 1972). However, they can also be formed under abiotic conditions, when plants are subjected to stress. Among such stress factors are UV irradiation, temperature shock, wounding and treatment with inorganic salts (e.g. aqueous mercuric chloride). It is even possible that phytoalexins occur in trace amounts in healthy tissue, although the evidence here is to some extent equivocal since a completely healthy unstressed plant is difficult to define precisely.

In conclusion, therefore, one has to accept the fact that phytoalexins are anti-microbial substances which can be produced in plants as part of a general repair and defense system and which are triggered off by a variety of agencies. In terms of disease resistance, it is not simply the ability to synthesize phytoalexin that is important, but the capacity to produce it in quantity, quickly enough in the right place and at the right time. This plants do when invaded by fungi and undoubtedly it is as antifungal agents that phytoalexins are most important from the ecological point of view.

Structural Variation Among Phytoalexins

Some of the structural variation encountered among the phytoalexins is illustrated in Fig. 9.5, which shows the typical phytoalexins produced by six plant families. It is clear from this that no simple relationship exists between chemical structure and fungitoxicity, since quite different structures can give high toxicity. The only general property that most, if not all, phytoalexins share is a degree of lipid solubility. Even the phenolic compounds (cf. maackiain, orchinol, phaseollin) have most of the polar hydroxyl groups masked by methylation or by methylenedioxy ring formation and are thus rendered lipid soluble. This property may be a necessary requirement for toxicity if the substance is going to interfere with, attack or block the membrane permeability of fungal cells.

Chemically, the simplest phytoalexin is benzoic acid, which has been implicated as a phytoalexin in the storage rot of apples, *Nectria galligena* (Swinburne, 1973). Most other phytoalexins are more complex, being isoflavanoid (pisatin, phaseollin etc.), terpenoid-derived (rishitin, ipomeamarone) or fatty acid derivatives (safynol, wyerone). Further details of most of these structures can be found in recent reviews, e.g. on sesquiterpenoid stress compounds of the Solanaceae (Stoessl *et al.*, 1976) and on the isoflavonoid fungitoxins of the Leguminosae (VanEtten and Pueppke, 1976; Harborne and Ingham, 1977).

The relationship between fungitoxicity and structure has been explored at the family level and some results are available with regard to the products of the Leguminosae (VanEtten, 1976; Harborne, 1977). It is apparent, for example, that the different classes of isoflavonoid fall into a series of increasing toxicity: isoflavones–isoflavanones–pterocarpans–isoflavans. Fungitoxicity is also dependent to a lesser extent on the nature and number of substituents in either aromatic ring. While almost all legumes that have been studied produce isoflavonoids, an apparently different class of phytoalexin, hydroxystilbenes, have been detected in *Arachis* and *Trifolium* (Ingham, 1976a). However, such

OESTROGENS

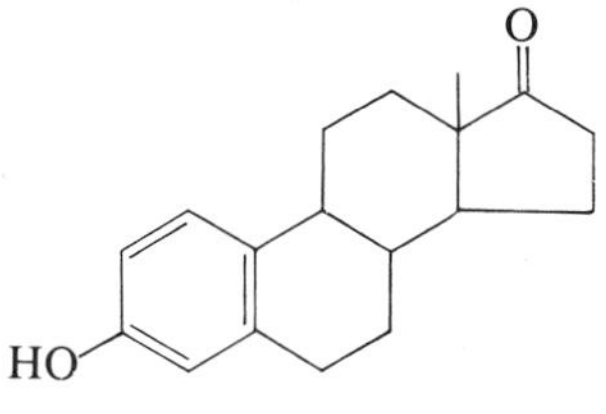

oestrone

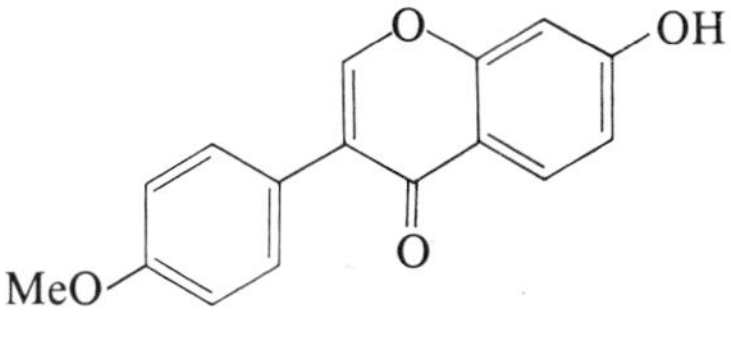

formononetin

FUNGITOXINS

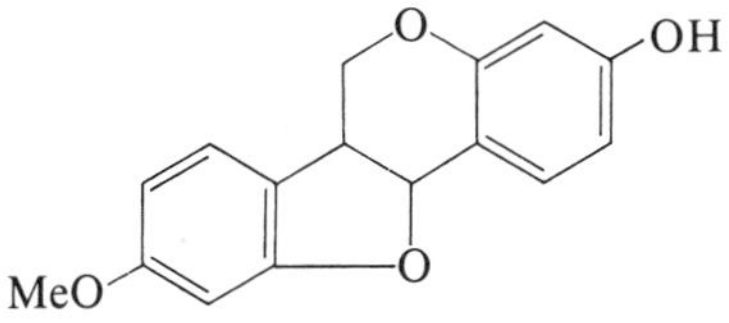

medicarpin

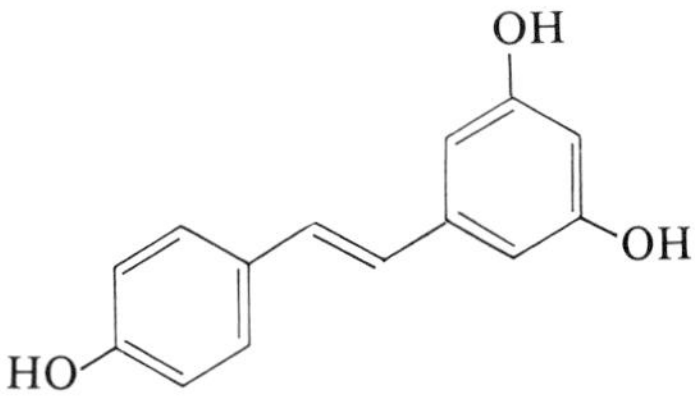

resveratrol

Fig. 9.8 Structural parallel between requirements for oestrogenic activity and fungitoxicity

Table 9.2 Types of phytoalexin produced in various plant families

Family	Phytoalexin type	Genera studied	Example[a]
Chenopodiaceae	Isoflavonoid	*Beta*	Betavulgarin from sugar beet *B. vulgaris*
Compositae	Polyacetylene	*Carthamus, Dahlia*	Safynol from safflower *C. tinctoria*
Convolvulaceae	Sesquiterpenoid furanolactone	*Ipomoea*	Ipomeamarone from sweet potato *I. batatus*
Euphorbiaceae	Diterpene	*Ricinus*	Casbene from castor bean *R. communis*
Leguminosae	Isoflavonoids[b]	Many	Pisatin from pea *Pisum sativum*
Malvaceae	Terpenoid polyphenol	*Gossypium*	Gossypol from cotton *G. barbadense*
Orchidaceae	Hydroxyphenanthrene	*Loroglossum, Orchis*	Orchinol from military orchid, *O. militaris*
Rosaceae	Benzoic acids	*Malus, Prunus*	Benzoic acid from apple *M. pumila*
Solanaceae	Oxygenated sesquiterpenes	*Capsicum, Datura, Lycopersicon, Nicotiana, Solanum*	Rishitin from potato *S. tuberosum*
Umbelliferae	Isocoumarins[c]	*Daucus*	6-Methoxymellein from carrot, *D. carota*
Vitaceae	Hydroxystilbene	*Vitis*	Resveratrol from grape vine, *V. vinifera*

[a] Literature references can be found in Ingham (1972).
[b] Other types occur rarely, e.g. acetylenes in *Vicia*, hydroxystilbenes in *Arachis* and *Trifolium* benzofurans in *Vigna* (see text).
[c] There is evidence that furanocoumarins act as phytoalexins in some Umbelliferae, e.g. xanthoxin in parsnip *Pastinaca sativa* and psoralen in celery *Petroselinum crispum*.

molecules (e.g. resveratrol), although biosynthetically distinct, are structurally very close to the isoflavonoid skeleton (Fig. 9.8). There is, indeed, a striking parallel here between fungitoxicity and oestrogenic activity. Thus legume iso-flavones are well known as weak oestrogens (see Chapter 4) and one of the most active synthetic oestrogens is the reduced hydroxystilbene, diethyl-stilboestrol. As mentioned above, both classes—isoflavonoid and stilbene—are also fungitoxic. This suggests that antifungal activity in legumes may be related to the production of a molecule which is a steroid "mimic" and can thus either interfere with the steroid nutrition of the fungus or more directly affect the membrane permeability of the fungal cell.

Taxonomic and Evolutionary Aspects

It is taxonomically significant that the type of phytoalexin induced on fungal infection is almost completely family specific; i.e. each plant family broadly produces its own type of phytoalexin molecule (Table 9.2). Furthermore, the type of compound produced is usually closely related to the secondary constituents that are most frequently accumulated as natural products in the given plant family. Thus, the Compositae produce polyacetylenes, the Solanaceae sesquiterpenoids, the Umbelliferae furanocoumarins and so on.

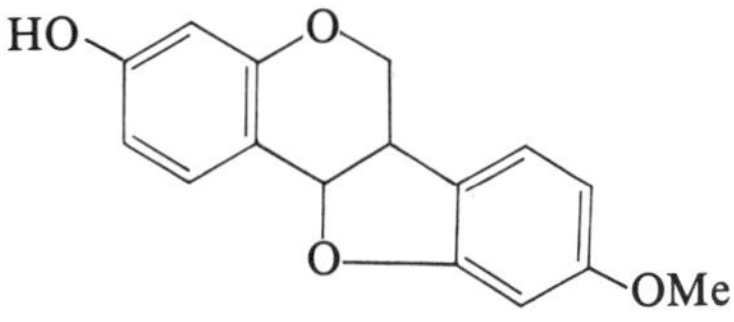

common type: pterocarpan
medicarpin (widespread)

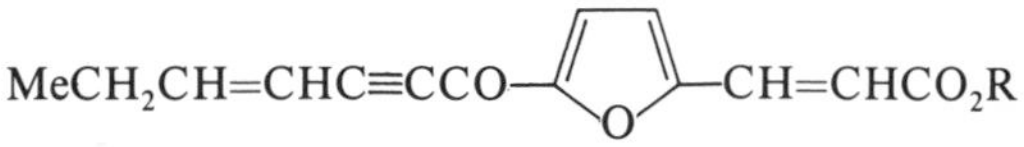

$MeCH_2CH=CHC\equiv CCO-\!\!\!\!\!\!\!\!-CH=CHCO_2R$

rare type: furanoacetylene
R = H, wyerone acid
R = Me, wyerone
R = Me, O at C_3–C_4, wyerone
epoxide (broad bean, *Vicia*)

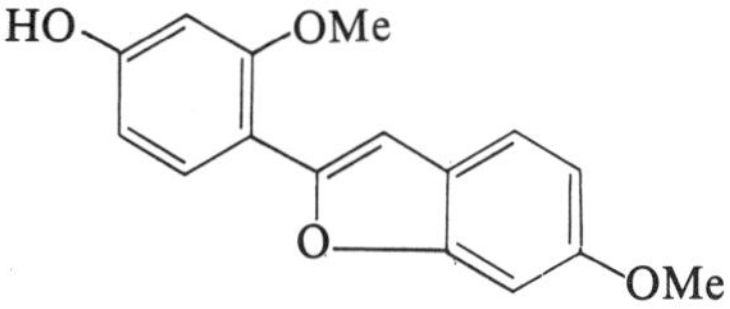

rare type: benzofuran
vignafuran (cowpea, *Vigna*)

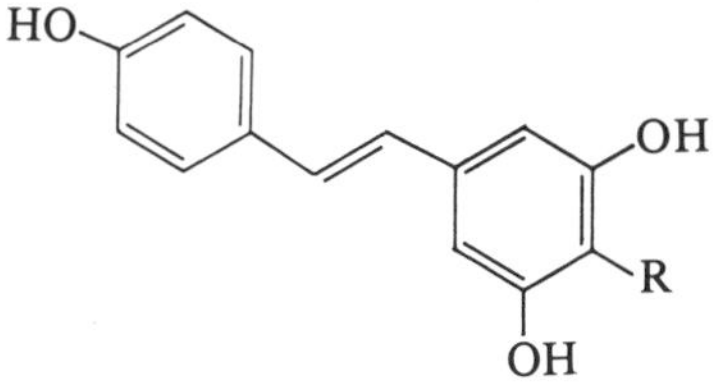

rare type: hydroxystilbene
R = H and R = isopentenyl (peanut, *Arachis*)

Fig. 9.9 Structural variation about legume phytoalexins

Table 9.3 Phytoalexin types produced in some characteristic legume genera

Tribe[a]	Genera studied	Presence/absence of			
		Isoflavone/Isoflavanone	Pterocarpan	Isoflavan	Other types
Podalyrieae	Baptisia	−	+	−	−
	Thermopsis	−	+	−	−
Cajaneae	Cajanus	+	−	−	−
Phaseoleae	Phaseolus	+	+	+	−
	Vigna	+	+	+	Benzofuran
Vicieae	Cicer	−	+	−	−
	Lathyrus	−	+	−	−
	Pisum	−	+	−	−
	Vicia	−	(+)	+	Acetylene
Trifolieae	Medicago	−	+	+	−
	Melilotus	−	+	−	−
	Trifolium	−	+	+	Stilbenes
	Trigonella	−	+	+	−
Loteae	Anthyllis	−	−	+	−
	Lotus	−	−	+	−
	Tetragonolobus	−	−	+	−
Hedysareae	Onobrychis	−	+	+	−
Stylosantheae	Arachis	−	−	−	Stilbenes

[a] Arranged in order according to Hutchinson (see Harborne et al., 1971).

The recent report (Johnson *et al.*, 1976) of betavulgarin (2′-hydroxy-5-methoxy-6,7-methylenedioxyisoflavone) as a phytoalexin in sugar-beet (Chenopodiaceae) is a little exceptional in that isoflavones have not as yet been encountered as natural products in this family.

The only family known at present to produce a variety of different phytoalexin types is the Leguminosae (see Fig. 9.9). The most anomalous case is that

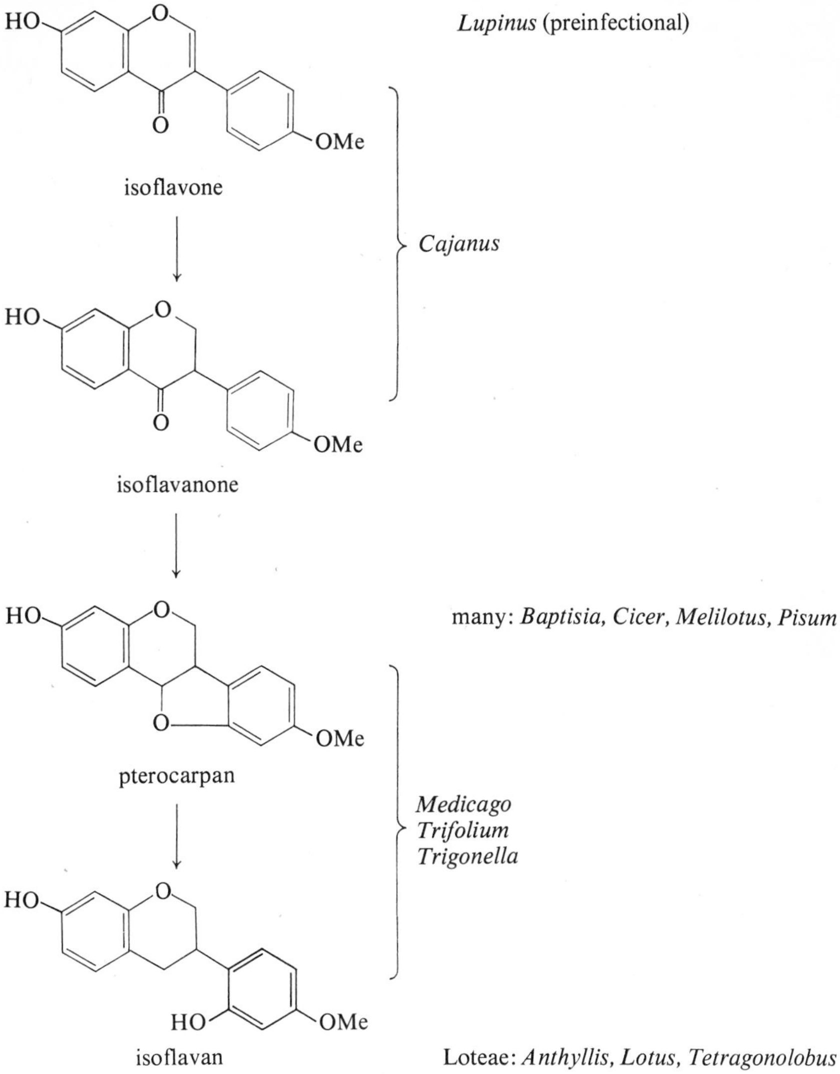

HO
O
O
OMe
isoflavone
Lupinus (preinfectional)
Cajanus
HO
O
O
OMe
isoflavanone
HO
O
O
OMe
pterocarpan
many: *Baptisia, Cicer, Melilotus, Pisum*
Medicago
Trifolium
Trigonella
HO
O
HO
OMe
isoflavan
Loteae: *Anthyllis, Lotus, Tetragonolobus*

Fig. 9.10 Phytalexin phyletic sequence

of the broad bean *Vicia faba*, which, when infected with *Botrytis cinerea*, synthesizes wyerone and two related furanoacetylenes (Fig. 9.9) (Hargreaves *et al.,* 1976b). Recent work by the same authors has shown that *V. faba* does actually produce trace amounts of the pterocarpan medicarpin as well, so that it is not completely anomalous in its response to fungal attack. Medicarpin could thus be regarded as a "primitive" response in the family as a whole, its place being largely superseded in this one genus *Vicia* by accumulation of furanoacetylene. Another new type of phytoalexin has recently been found in cowpea *Vigna unguiculata* leaves, namely the 2-arylbenzofuran, vignafuran (Preston *et al.,* 1975) but this structure is, in fact, closely related to that of the isoflavonoid phytoalexins and indeed is probably derived biosynthetically from a common intermediate.

Recent studies in the author's laboratory of phytoalexins in a range of legume genera have indicated that there is taxonomic value in inducing disease resistant factors in these plants. The compounds produced may be characteristic at the species, genus or tribal level. For example, at least six different patterns of phytoalexin response can be observed in the genus *Trigonella* and the patterns so revealed are correlated with morphological and with conventional chemical characters (Ingham and Harborne, 1976).

A summary of the present information available on the distribution of different phytoalexins in Leguminosae is given, according to tribal classification, Table 9.3. The results are clearly taxonomically significant in that different patterns can be observed in different tribes. Since the different structural types can be placed in an evolutionary series based both on biosynthesis and on increasing fungitoxicity (Fig. 9.10), the data shown in Table 9.3 are also of evolutionary interest. The results suggest that as plants co-evolve with these fungal parasites, they develop more and more effective phytoalexins to combat such invasion.

Further Metabolism of Phytoalexins

While plants are developing, by natural selection, more effective phytoalexins to ward off fungal attack, the fungi are themselves producing detoxification mechanisms which inactivate these antimicrobial agents. Certainly, there is increasing evidence that these compounds are further metabolized, principally by pathogenic fungi, to substances with decreased fungitoxicity. In the case of isoflavonoids, such detoxification appears to be an essential prerequisite for fungal pathogenicity in some interactions. It should be pointed out that non-pathogenic fungi may also have the enzymic machinery for detoxification.

A variety of mechanisms have been detected for detoxification. For isoflavonoids, two principal steps are hydroxylation of the nucleus and

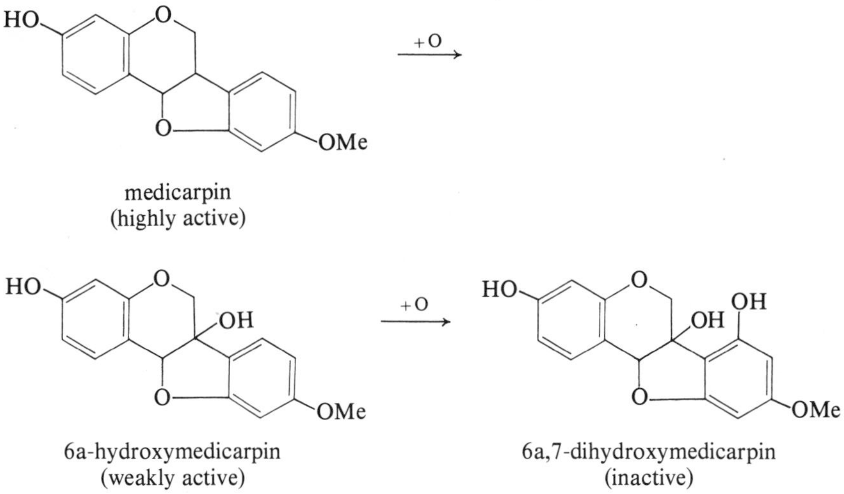

medicarpin
(highly active)

6a-hydroxymedicarpin
(weakly active)

6a,7-dihydroxymedicarpin
(inactive)

Fig. 9.11 Metabolism of medicarpin by *Botrytis* and *Colletotrichum*

demethylation of methoxyl groups; both processes at once reduce lipid solubility and increase water solubility. The products of such reactions are immediately more susceptible to oxidative cleavage of the aromatic rings and undoubtedly the ultimate fate of these phytoalexins is to be broken down by well described aromatic-cleavage pathways (Towers, 1964) to eventually yield CO_2. The first steps in the metabolism of medicarpin, the sweet clover phytoalexin, by *Botrytis cinerea*, have recently been worked out and are as shown in Fig. 9.11 (Ingham, 1976). Loss in fungitoxicity is quite dramatic: thus, medicarpin is highly active (ED_{50} 25 μg/ml against mycelial growth of *Helminthosporium carbonum*) while its fungus-derived hydroxylation production (6a-hydroxymedicarpin) has only weak antifungal properties (ED_{50} > 100 μg/ml). A second oxidation, which is carried out by *Colletotrichum coffeanum* but not by *Botrytis*, produces 6a,7-dihydroxymedicarpin (Fig. 9.11), which is virtually inactive as a fungitoxin.

For the fungus, the timing at which detoxifying enzymes are produced is clearly crucial to survival. While it is easy to demonstrate eventual turnover of many phytoalexins by fungi in culture, the important matter is whether turnover occurs *in vivo* at the time when the fungus first enters host cells. One can envisage a dynamic interaction occurring in biochemical terms between host and parasite before the ultimate outcome is decided—resistance or susceptibility. Our knowledge of these complexities is at present very limited and the understanding of the biochemistry of these interactions is an important goal for future research efforts.

III. PHYTOTOXINS IN PLANT DISEASE

A. The Pathotoxin Concept

All the chemicals discussed so far in this chapter have been higher plant products, either present as such in host tissue or induced by microbial attack. In a pathogenic situation, the invading microorganism is able to establish itself within the host and when this happens, it starts producing its own secondary constituents. It is these microbial substances which are often responsible for disease symptoms in the host and it is their deleterious effect on the growth and metabolism of the higher plant which eventually leads to death. Their production and fate is closely related to the susceptibility of higher plants to disease, once the biochemical barriers of resistance have been broken down. Their synthesis represents the aggressive force of the micro-organism. Thus pathotoxins, as these harmful compounds are called, are the expression of the virulence of the pathogen.

A number of pathotoxins have now been characterized in a variety of fungal and bacterial disease situations (Wood *et al.,* 1972). They can be either low molecular weight or high molecular weight compounds. Low molecular weight pathotoxins include those which have an effect on growth or cause wilting, i.e. the so-called wilting factors. High molecular weight compounds include the peptides which are causal agents in plant necrosis and also the enzymes which bring about tissue maceration and loss of cellular cohesion in the host plant. Both low and high molecular weight substances may be produced by the same organism. For example, Dutch elm disease, which is disseminated by a bark beetle of the genus *Scolytus,* is due to the fungus *Ceratocystis ulmi.* Its toxins, which cause necrotic lesions in the leaves as well as wilting, are of two types: a mixture of glycoproteins and also three low molecular weight phenolic metabolites (for structures, see Fig. 9.12) (Claydon *et al.,* 1974).

The simple hypothesis that a microbial toxin is directly responsible for the symptoms of a plant disease has only been demonstrated so far in a limited number of cases and our evidence that the vast majority of toxins are directly associated with particular diseases is still circumstantial. Among symptoms which can be directly attributed to toxin action are chlorosis, growth abnormalities, necrosis and wilting. Chlorosis, the destruction of the chloroplast and hence the loss of green colour in the leaf, may be due to the simple accumulation of ammonia in the tissues. For example, the phytotoxin of tobacco disease, i.e. the "wild fire toxin" of the bacterium *Pseudomonas tabaci,* is a small peptide which probably exerts its effect by interfering with the enzyme glutamine synthetase. This enzyme is a key one in nitrogen metabolism and if it is inhibited, the ammonia produced by reduction of nitrate cannot be coupled to glutamic acid and hence accumulates with disastrous consequences (Sinden and Durbin, 1968).

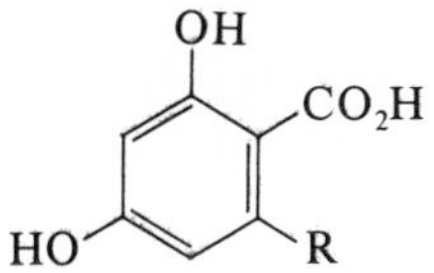

Ceratocystis toxins
R = CH_2COCH_3, $CHOHCOCH_3$
and $COCOCH_3$

(Dutch elm disease)

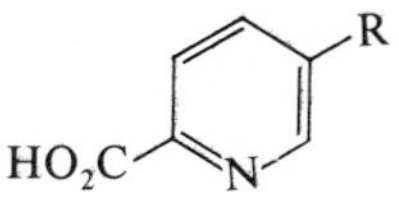

picolinic acid R = H
(*Pyricularia oryzae*, rice blast)
fusaric acid R = *n*-butyl
(*Fusarium oxysporum*, tomato wilt)

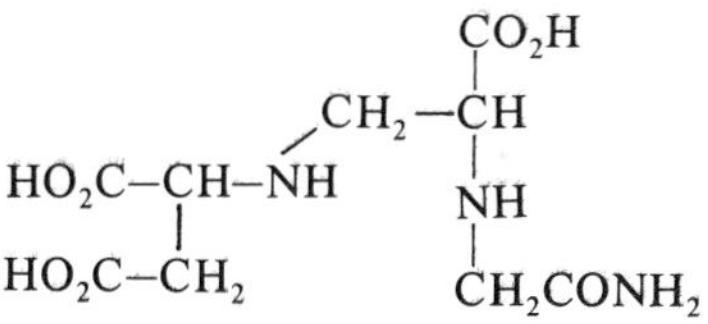

lycomarasmin
(tomato wilt)

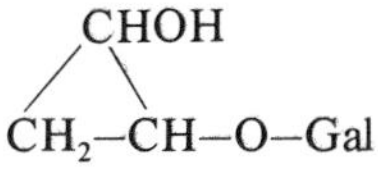

helminthosporoside
(sugar-cane eye spot)

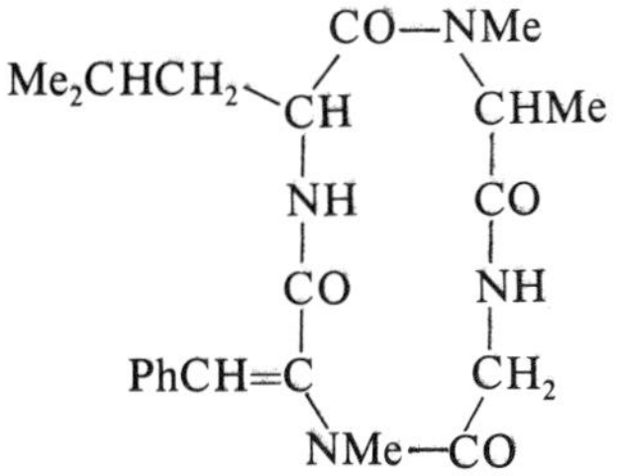

tentotoxin
(*Alternaria tenuis*, cotton chlorosis)

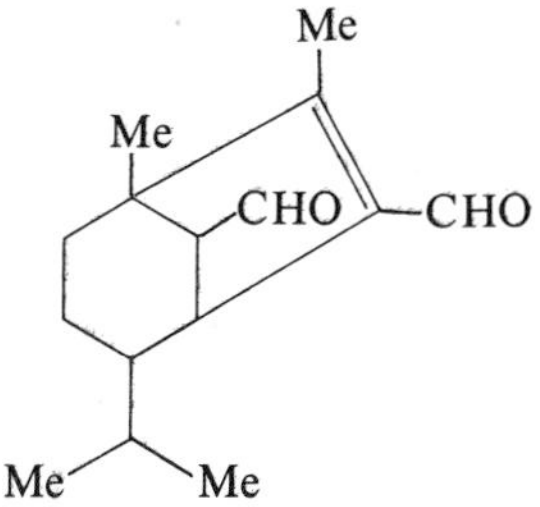

helmonthosporal
(*Helminthorium sativum*, cereal necrosis)

Fig. 9.12 Characteristic low molecular weight pathotoxins produced by fungal pathogens

Growth abnormalities are familiar symptoms of disease susceptibility and many are brought about by the synthesis of unusually high levels of one or other of the major growth hormones. The fungal disease of rice *Gibberella fujikuroi* causes elongation of the rice internodes, this being due to the gibberellins synthesized in large amount by the fungus once it is established in the rice plant. The discovery that this fungus has the ability to synthesize gibberellins provided an important breakthrough in plant physiology during the 1950s and led to the recognition of these compounds as higher plant hormones. Another example of hormonal synthesis is in the bacterial disease of pea plants *Corynebacterium fascians,* which causes fasciations due to the production by the bacterium of the cytokinin, 6-(γ,γ-dimethylallylamino)purine. These fasciations can be produced artificially by treating healthy plants with kinetin. Finally, auxin (indoleacetic acid) is produced by bacteria such as *Agrobacterium tumefaciens* and crown-gall tumours are a result of excessive localized auxin activity in plant tissues (Durbin, 1972).

Another common disease symptom is necrosis, which is characterized in leaf tissue by dark coloured lesions, dry in consistency and of a leathery or brittle texture. Such lesions are caused by complex biochemical changes in the tissue, but the primary effect may be a fairly simple one in terms of a blockage in primary metabolism. Fire blight, *Erwinia amylovora*, in apple shoots causes the evolution of ammonia, the toxic effects of which are expressed as necrosis in the twigs (Lovrekovich *et al.*, 1970).

Finally, wilting, the fourth symptom mentioned above, is usually considered to be due to the production by the invading organism of polysaccharide gums, which act by mechanical plugging of the xylem tissue thus directly restricting water uptake. There is evidence, however, that the mechanism of wilting may be more complex than this and in some cases may be the direct effect of a toxin in inducing water stress, e.g. by influencing the hormonal control of the stomatal apparatus of the leaf. Some of the agents responsible for causing wilting are considered in more detail in the following section.

B. Pyridine-Based Pathotoxins

Wilt diseases are commonly caused by a variety of bacteria which attack such plants as cotton, pea, banana and tomato. The symptoms are strikingly similar in all these host plants, with wilting of the leaves and shoots due to insufficient water flow through the xylem. Desiccation in the leaves can become acute and the disease often leads to the death of the plant. The consequences of wilting in trees are only too familiar to those who have witnessed during the last decade the demise of the Dutch elm in the United Kingdom, due to the phenomenal spread of a virulent strain of Dutch elm disease. The effects of wilting on crop plants can be just as dramatic. From the biochemical viewpoint, the most widely studied interaction is that of *Fusarium oxysporum* on the cultivated tomato.

Two different low molecular weight toxins have been found in *Fusarium* cultures and both have been implicated as wilting agents in the tomato. They are a small peptide lycomarasmin and a pyridine derivative, fusaric acid (5-*n*-butylpicolinic acid) (Fig. 9.12). The role of lycomarasmin in pathogenicity is still not entirely clear because although readily formed in culture, it has yet to be detected unequivocally in infected plants. This may be simply due to its great lability in solution. An interesting point regarding the mode of action of these pathotoxins is that both lycomarasmin and fusaric acid are metal chelators. The former has strong chelating properties and its translocation and activity may be related to the water-soluble complex it forms with iron. The activity of fusaric acid is also related to metal ion content, since its production, at least in culture, is dependent on the presence of zinc and unless sufficient is added, its synthesis is depressed.

The role of fusaric acid in causing wilting is reasonably well established. Thus it has been detected in plants after infection and is present in much higher concentrations in plants infected by virulent strains than those treated with avirulent strains. A given virulent strain of *Fusarium* produces up to 80 mg/l in *in vitro* culture and as much as 100 µg/l fresh wt fusaric acid has been found in badly infected tomato plants. As part of the co-evolution of *Fusarium* with the tomato, some varieties have developed the ability to resist attack. Such varieties apparently resist infection or the effects of infection because they are able to conjugate the fusaric acid with glycine, the resulting conjugate being inactive. This is not an all or nothing effect, since susceptible varieties are able to conjugate between 5–10% of the toxin in this way. However, the resistant varieties conjugate up to 25%, the greater efficiency in conjugating ability being apparently sufficient to avoid wilting.

Fusaric acid has been detected in other plants (cotton, flax and banana) besides tomato after inoculation with wilt pathogens and it seems to be fairly widely produced by *Fusarium* species. A comparison of fusaric acid with a range of synthetic pyridine derivatives has shown that the carboxyl group in the α-position to the nitrogen is essential for toxicity. The aliphatic side-chain in the β-position is also important, since its presence improves water permeability (Kern, 1972). It may be noted, however, that the side-chain is not necessary for toxicity *per se*, since the parent compound, picolinic acid, which lacks any β-substituent, causes necrosis in rice. Indeed, it is a major toxin of the agriculturally important disease "blast of rice" which is caused by the fungus *Pyricularia oryzae*. Picolinic acid is so highly toxic to rice plants that only 0·5 ng are needed to produce a lesion in the leaf following injection.

Picolinic acid, like fusaric, is a metal chelator and, in the rice blast disease, it acts largely by scavenging vital iron and copper ions from within the plant tissue; its toxic effects can be reversed by supplying these metal ions back to the plant. Picolinic acid is detoxified by the host plant by conversion to the methyl ester and the N-methyl ether and resistant rice varieties have been shown to have a greater capacity for detoxification than susceptible forms. The pathogenicity of *Pyricularia* in rice is partly due to the synthesis by the fungus of a second toxin, piricularin, $C_{18}H_{14}N_2O_3$, a compound still only partly characterized. It is interesting that this second pathotoxin is actually toxic to the conidia of the parasite and is capable of preventing germination of the spores at a concentration of 0·25 ppm. This inhibitory effect is circumvented *in vivo* by the fact that piricularin exists as a complex with protein, the complex being non-toxic to the fungus but still highly lethal to the host plant.

In addition to the toxic phenols produced in Dutch elm disease and the pyridine α-carboxylic acids of tomato wilt and blast of rice, a range of other low molecular weight toxins have been implicated as causative agents in plant disease. Among them are a number of cyclic peptides (e.g. tentotoxin of *Alternaria*), several naphthaquinones and many terpenoids, one of the simplest being helminthosporal from *Helminthosporium sativum* (see Fig. 9.12). The ability to cause damage in higher plants is not, however, restricted to relatively complex organic structures, since two very simple three-membered ring molecules have been reported as toxic agents, in different circumstances, in disease susceptibility. They are helminthosporoside and epoxysuccinic acid. Helminthosporoside, which probably has the structure 2-hydroxycyclopropyl α-galactoside (Fig. 9.12), is a selective toxin responsible for the eye spot symptom of sugar-cane infected by *Helminthosporium sacchari*. It produces characteristic reddish-brown stripes, called runners, when injected into susceptible sugar-cane leaves (Strobel, 1974). It is of special interest because of its selective mode of action: it apparently binds to a single protein in susceptible but not in resistant varieties. Resistant clones of sugar-cane contain a similar protein and binding will take place even here if the protein is first treated with detergent. The difference between resistance and susceptibility in this plant seems to be based, remarkably enough, on the availability or otherwise of a particular binding site on an individual protein of the host.

In complete contrast with helminthosporoside, epoxysuccinic acid is essentially non-selective in its toxic action. This substance was discovered to be a toxin quite indirectly when it was found that one of the standard Krebs' cycle acids, fumaric acid, accumulated in quantity in the *Rhizopus* infection on almond hulls. In this fungal disease of the fruits, the leaves of the tree *Prunus dulcis* are blighted and the twigs killed. That the fumaric acid appeared to be the causative agent was deduced from the isolation of high concentrations from blighted leaves and from the finding that the disease symptoms could be reproduced by applying fumaric acid to healthy trees. The idea that fumaric acid, a normal organic acid metabolite of plants, should produce disease symptoms in almond trees seems *a priori* unlikely, because under other circumstances the acid accumulates in higher plant tissues, particularly fruits, without any visible harmful effects. In fact, further investigation showed that fumaric acid was not the damaging toxin, but epoxysuccinic acid, formed from it by further metabolism was. The pathway of this metabolism is shown in Fig. 9.13.

The process by which epoxysuccinic acid acts as toxin appears to be as follows. The fungus acts primarily by synthesizing and causing the accumulation of fumaric acid in the host plant mesocarp. This acid is then translocated to leaves and twigs and it is only during further metabolism of the fumarate that the toxic intermediate is produced and accumulated in sufficient

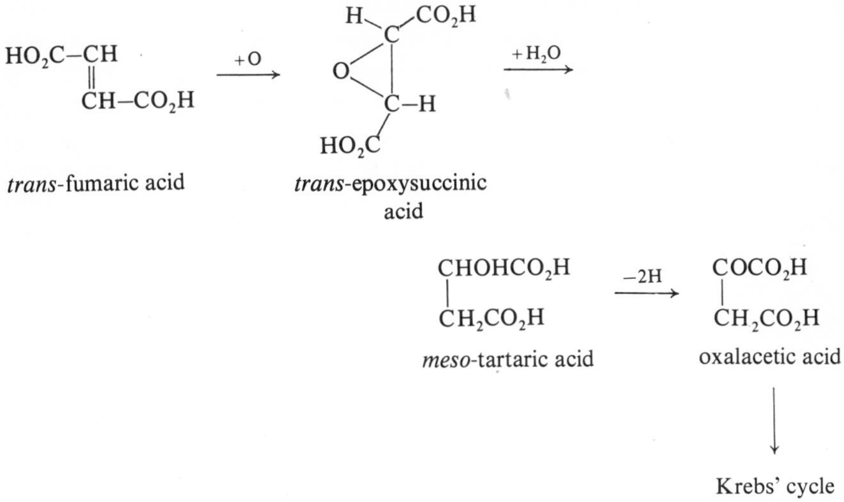

$$\underset{\substack{\| \\ CH-CO_2H}}{HO_2C-CH} \quad \xrightarrow{+O} \quad \underset{HO_2C}{\overset{H}{\underset{}{O}}} \overset{C}{\underset{C-H}{<}} \overset{CO_2H}{} \quad \xrightarrow{+H_2O}$$

trans-fumaric acid   trans-epoxysuccinic
                                    acid

$$\underset{CH_2CO_2H}{CHOHCO_2H} \quad \xrightarrow{-2H} \quad \underset{CH_2CO_2H}{COCO_2H}$$

meso-tartaric acid   oxalacetic acid

↓

Krebs' cycle

Fig. 9.13 Metabolism of fumaric acid, producing epoxysuccinic acid as a toxic intermediate

amount to produce the disease symptoms that are observed (Mirocha, 1972). The toxin is "turned over" by further oxidation to tartaric, which then enters the cycle via oxalacetate (Fig. 9.13). Disease in this instance is thus largely due to the fact that the host plant, when faced with exceptional amounts of a normal metabolite, develops a new modification of the respiratory pathway to deal with it and it is one of the intermediates in this "detoxification" pathway that actually causes tissue damage.

C. Macromolecular Toxins

While the structures of many of the simpler pathotoxins have been successfully elucidated by the sophisticated techniques of modern organic chemistry, chemical work on the high molecular weight toxins produced by bacteria and fungi has not progressed nearly so far. Problems in their characterization include the fact that they are often highly active at low concentration so that only small amounts may be produced in a given disease situation. Also, the toxins may be labile and lose their activity rapidly during the purification process. This is true of victorin, the selective pathotoxin of *Helminthosporium victoriae* which attacks oat plants.

The special interest of victorin is that it is the most potent and selective toxin known so far. Its potency and differential toxicity are illustrated by the fact that the crude culture filtrate of *H. victoriae* containing it has to be diluted down to one to ten million before it ceases showing a disease symptom in a susceptible oat plant. By contrast, a dilution of 1 : 25 is the limit where a symptom can be induced in a resistant variety. The selectivity of victorin, which is the dilution end-point for susceptible plants over that for resistant plants, is thus 400,000. Other similar high molecular weight toxins have been isolated from diseased tissues of maize, sorghum and peas and these have selectivities of between 25 and 300. Victorin is a unique molecule in showing such a striking differential toxicity in cereal plants. From the chemical viewpoint, the available information indicates that it is a polypeptide and has several active forms, one of which has an isoelectric point at pH 10 (Luke and Gracen, 1972). Its toxicity seems to be related in the initial stages of infection to a disruption of cell permeability (Wheeler and Luke, 1963). Its striking biological potency should stimulate further work on its chemical structure.

No account of the biochemical effects of pathogenic micro-organisms on higher plants would be complete without at least a mention of the role of microbial enzymes on the disruption and destruction of host tissues following infection. This subject—the degradation of higher plant cell walls by parasites—has been extensively investigated by R. K. S. Wood and his students, among others, and much information is available in Wood (1967) and in later reviews (Wood *et al.*, 1972; Friend and Threlfall, 1976). The degradative enzymes have been particularly studied in soft rots of storage tissues such as potatoes, carrots and citrus fruits. Organisms responsible include *Botrytis cinerea, Rhizoctonia solani, Sclerotinia fructigena* and various *Aspergillus* and *Penicillium* species.

In brief then, these enzymes produced by the attacking organism cause loss of coherence in the invaded tissues. As a result, the cells are separated, a process called maceration, and the naked protoplasts released soon die. The effects can be seen in any rotting fruit or vegetable where the rotted tissue loses all its resistance to mechanical damage. The enzymes implicated are the cellulases, hemicellulases and various pectic enzymes (pectinesterases, poly-galacturonases, *trans*-eliminases, etc.). The pectinases are especially destructive since they break down the linkages between the cellulose microfibrils and the components of the cell wall matrix. The cellulose and other components (including glycoprotein) so released are then further broken down by cellulases, hemicellulases and proteases. The activities of these various enzymes are determined by the pH of the tissue and the presence of calcium ions.

It is clear from these experiments that the pathogenic fungi have highly effective enzymes for destroying plant tissues, once they become well established in the host plant. The materials released are ultimately used by the fungal parasite in the maintenance of its intermediary metabolism.

IV. CONCLUSION

In the interaction between higher plants and micro-organisms leading to disease, there is evidence of co-evolution in both the resistance mechanisms developed by the higher plants and also in the various ways that the virulent micro-organism can damage the host. This is summarized in Table 9.4. In the case of disease resistance, there are at least three mechanisms: (1) accumulation of a fungitoxic compound at the surface of the plant where invasion is most likely, especially on the upper leaf surface: (2) after infective stimulation, the release of toxin already present in the tissue in bound form: and (3) *de novo* synthesis of tailor-made fungitoxins, the phytoalexins. Similarly, in disease susceptibility, micro-organisms employ a variety of approaches to destroy their host. These are: (a) pathotoxin production; (b) over production of a growth hormone; (c) interference with primary metabolism; and (d) synthesis of hydrolytic enzymes which destroy the coherence of the organism.

These interactions are dynamic in that possibilities for changing the balance in favour of one or other party are always present. The micro-organism can evolve by developing phytoalexin detoxification mechanisms. Similarly, higher plants can retaliate to invading parasites by degrading or conjugating the pathotoxins formed in their tissues.

In any interaction that has been investigated closely, considerable chemical

Table 9.4 Summary of biochemical mechanisms of disease resistance and susceptibility in plants

	Higher plant	Micro-organism
Resistance (hypersensitive reaction)	1. Pre-infectional toxin 2. Post-infectional toxin formed from pre-existing substrate 3. Post-infectional toxin formed *de novo* (phytoalexin)	Invasion arrested or toxin metabolized to harmless products
Susceptibility (disease symptoms)	Biodegraded or conjugated	1. Pathotoxins (low MW or peptides) 2. Growth hormone synthesis 3. Primary metabolite accumulation 4. Enzyme degradation

complexity has become apparent. Thus, recent investigations of the broad bean–*Botrytis* interaction indicate that at least seven different phytoalexins are formed (Hargreaves *et al.,* 1976a). Again, in the pea–*Fusarium solani* interaction, some phytoalexins are formed immediately after infection; others are produced several days after the primary infection (Pueppke and VanEtten, 1976). Further, in the potato–*Phytophthora infestans* interaction, recent research (Friend, 1976) indicates that defense through phytoalexin synthesis is less important than defense through the esterification of cell wall poly-saccharide by phenolic acids. Similar chemical complexity exists among the pathotoxins of fungi and bacteria. In Dutch elm disease, a range of toxins (see p. 220) are produced by the invading fungus. In most other cases examined, two or more compounds often of widely differing structures have been implicated in pathogenicity.

There is, of course, considerable biological complexity in plant disease and physiological factors can be immensely important in determining whether the plant suffers infection and in determining the severity of the attack. As Wheeler (1975) puts it: "pathogenesis can be viewed as a battle between a plant and a pathogen which is refereed by the environment". Of many environmental factors, temperature and humidity are undoubtedly particularly important. A further complexity may be introduced by the presence of other micro-organisms into the system. These may be present either in the soil or in the aerial regions (the phyllospere) around the plant. They may be beneficial to the plant and antagonistic to the micro-organism. For example, damage to tomato plants caused by the fungus *Sclerotium rolfsii* is alleviated if a second fungus *Trichoderma harzianum* is added to the soil. Biological control is thus established by the second fungus overgrowing and killing the first (Wells *et al.,* 1972).

In spite of the many biological factors which may often be decisive in determining resistance or susceptibility, it is still true that the actual weapons of the fight are biochemical in nature. Further studies of the biochemistry of phytoalexins and pathotoxins can only enrich our present imperfect understan-ding of resistance mechanisms in higher plants. Potentially, there are enormous practical benefits to be gained by applying the results so gained to crop protection. Phytoalexins, for example, are antifungal by definition and they could be applied as fungicidal chemicals to disease control. Preliminary experiments with the sesquiterpenoid capsidiol, the phytoalexin of peppers, have shown that, when sprayed on in solution at concentrations of 5×10^{-4} M, it will control late blight (*Phytophthora*) attack on tomatoes (Ward *et al.,* 1975).

Since phytoalexin production is a fairly general resistance mechanism, these substances offer interesting possibilities for cross protection of crop plants. Thus the phytoalexin of one plant (in the above case, pepper) might be much more effective in controlling a disease of a second plant (e.g. tomato) than the pathogens it normally encounters. Finally, synthetic analogues of phytoalexins might be developed fruitfully to produce fungicidal agents which are persistent and are not as readily biodegradable as the natural molecules.

BIBLIOGRAPHY

Books and Review Articles

Cruickshank, I. A. M. and Perrin, D. R. (1964). Pathological function of phenolic compounds in plants. In: Harborne, J. B. (ed.), "Biochemistry of Phenolic Compounds", pp. 511–544. Academic Press, London.

Deverall, B. J. (1972). Phytoalexins. In: Harborne, J. B. (ed.), "Phytochemical Ecology", pp. 217–234. Academic Press, London.

Durbin, R. D. (1972). Bacterial phytotoxins. In: Wood, R. K. S., Ballio, A. and Graniti, A. (eds.), "Phytotoxins in Plant Diseases", pp. 19–33. Academic Press, London.

Friend, J. and Threlfall, D. R. (eds.) (1976). "Biochemical Aspects of Plant–Parasite Relationships", 354 pp. Academic Press, London.

Harborne, J. B. (1977). Chemosystematics and coevolution. *Pure Appl. Chem.* (in press).

Harborne, J. B. and Ingham, J. L. (1977). Higher plant–fungi coevolution: phytoalexins. In: Harborne, J. B. (ed.), "Biochemical Aspects of Plant and Animal Coevolution" (in preparation).

Harborne, J. B., Boulter, D. and Turner, B. L. (eds.) (1971). "Chemotaxonomy of the Leguminosae", pp. 275–277. Academic Press, London.

Heitefuss, R. and Williams, P. H. (eds.) (1976). "Physiological Plant Pathology", Vol. 4 in the New Series Encyclopedia of Plant Physiology, 890 pp. Springer-Verlag, Berlin.

Hillis, W. E. (ed.) (1962). "Wood extractives." Academic Press, New York.

Ingham, J. L. (1972). Phytoalexins and other natural products as factors in plant disease resistance. *Botan. Rev.* **38**, 343–424.

Ingham, J. L. (1973). Disease resistance in plants: the concept of pre-infectional and post-infectional resistance. *Phytopath. Z.* **78**, 314–335.

McClure, J. W. (1975). Physiology and function of flavonoids. In: Harborne, J. B., Mabry, T. J. and H. (eds.), "The Flavonoids", pp. 970–1055. Chapman and Hall, London.

Mirocha, C. J. (1972). Phytotoxins and metabolism. In: Wood, R. K. S., Ballio, A. and Graniti, A. (eds.), "Phytotoxins in Plant Diseases", pp. 191–209. Academic Press, London.

Stoessl, A., Stothers, J. B. and Ward, E. W. B. (1976). Sesquiterpenoid stress compounds of the Solanaceae. *Phytochemistry* **15**, 855–872.

Swinburne, T. R. (1973). The resistance of immature Bramley's seedling apples to rotting by *Nectria galligena*. In: Byrde, R. J. W. and Cutting, C. V. (eds.), "Fungal Pathogenicity and the Plants Response", pp. 365–382. Academic Press, London.

Strobel, G. A. (1974). Phytotoxins produced by plant parasites. *Ann. Rev. Plant Physiol.* **25**, 541–566.

VanEtten, H. D. and Pueppke, S. G. (1976). Isoflavonoid phytoalexins. In: Friend, J. and Threlfall, D. R., "Biochemical Aspects of Plant–Parasite Relationships", pp. 239–290. Academic Press, London.

Wheeler, H. (1975). "Plant Pathogenesis", 106 pp. Springer-Verlag, Berlin.
Wood, R. K. S. (1967). "Physiological Plant Pathology", 570 pp. Blackwell Scientific Pub.; Oxford.
Wood, R. K. S., Ballio, A. and Graniti, A. (eds.) (1972). "Phytotoxins in Plant Diseases", 530 pp. Academic Press, London.

Literature References

Beijersbergen, J. C. M. and Lemmers, C. B. G. (1970). *Acta Bot. Neerl.* **19**, 114.
Burkhardt, H. J., Maizel, J. V. and Mitchell, H. K. (1964). *Biochemistry* **3**, 426–431.
Claydon, N., Grove, J. F. and Hosken, M. (1974). *Phytochemistry* **13**, 2567–2572.
Cruickshank, I. A. M. and Perrin, D. R. (1960). *Nature* **187**, 799–800.
Friend, J. (1976). In: Friend, J. and Threlfall, D. R., "Biochemical Aspects of Plant–Parasite Relationships", pp. 291–304. Academic Press, London.
Greathouse, G. A. and Watkins, G. M. (1938). *Amer. J. Bot.* **25**, 743–748.
Greenaway, W. and Whatley, F. R. (1976). In: Smith, H. (ed.), "Commentaries in Plant Science", pp. 249–262. Pergamon Press, Oxford.
Greenhalgh, J. R. and Mitchell, N. D. (1976). *New Phytol.* **77**, 391–398.
Harborne, J. B., Ingham, J. L., King, L. and Payne, M. (1976). *Phytochemistry* **15**, 1485–1488.
Hargreaves, J. A., Mansfield, J. W. and Coxon, K. R. (1976a). *Nature* **262**, 318–319.
Hargreaves, J. A., Mansfield, J. W., Coxon, D. T. and Price, K. R. (1976b). *Phytochemistry* **15**, 1119–1121.
Higgins, V. J. and Millar, R. L. (1968). *Phytopathology* **58**, 1377–1383.
Hughes, J. C. and Swain, T. (1960). *Phytopathology* **50**, 398–400.
Hulme, A. C. and Edney, K. L. (1960). In: Pridham, J. B. (ed.), "Phenolics in Plants in Health and Disease", pp. 87–94. Pergamon Press, Oxford.
Hunter, L. D. (1975). *Phytochemistry* **14**, 1519–1522.
Hunter, L. D., Kirkham, D. S. and Hignett, R. C. (1968). *J. Gen. Microbiol.* **53**, 61–67.
Ingham, J. L. (1976a). *Phytochemistry* **15**, 1791–1793.
Ingham, J. L. (1976b). *Phytochemistry* **15**, 1489–1496.
Ingham, J. L. and Harborne, J. B. (1976). *Nature* **260**, 241–243.
Johnson, G., Maag, D. D., Johnson, D. K. and Thomas, R. D. (1976). *Physiol. Plant Path.* **8**, 225–230.
Jurd, L., Corse, J., King, A. D., Bayne, H. and Mihara, K. (1971). *Phytochemistry* **10**, 2971–2974.
Kern, H. (1972). In: Wood, R. K. S., Ballio, A. and Graniti, A. (eds.), "Phytotoxins in Plant Disease", pp. 35–48. Academic Press, London.
Kirkham, D. S. and Hunter, L. D. (1964). *Nature (Lond.)* **201**, 638.
Lovrekovich, L., Lovrekovich, H. and Goodman, R. N. (1970). *Can. J. Bot.* **48**, 999–1000.
Luke, H. H. and Gracen, V. E. (1972). In: Kadis, S., Ciegler, A. and Ajl, S. J. (eds.), "Microbial Toxins", Vol. 8, pp. 139–168. Academic Press, London.
Lüning, H. U. and Schlösser, E. (1976). *Z. Pflanzenkrankheiten & Pflanzenschutz* **83**, 317–327.
Millar, R. L. and Higgins, V. J. (1970). *Phytopathology* **60**, 104–110.
Müller, K. O. and Börger, H. (1941). *Arb. biol. Abt. (Ansl.-Reichstanst.), Berl.* **23**, 189–231.

Mulvena, D., Webb, E. C. and Zerner, B. (1969). *Phytochemistry* **8**, 393–395.

Offord, H. R. (1940). *Bull. U.S. Bur. Ent.* E-518.

Piatelli, M. and Impellizzeri, G. (1971). *Phytochemistry* **10**, 2657–2660.

Preston, N. W., Chamberlain, K. and Skipp, R. A. (1975). *Phytochemistry* **14**, 1843–1844.

Pueppke, S. G. and VanEtten, H. D. (1976). *Physiological Plant Pathology* **8**, 51–61.

Scheffer, T. C. and Cowling, E. B. (1966). *Ann. Rev. Phytopath.* **4**, 147–170.

Sijpesteign, A. K. (1969). *Meded. Landbouwhogesch (Gent)* **34**, 379–391.

Sinden, S. L. and Durbin, R. D. (1968). *Nature* **219**, 379–380.

Slob, A., Jekel, B., Jong, B. and Schlatmann, E. (1975). *Phytochemistry* **14**, 1997–2006.

Stoessl, A. (1967). *Canad. J. Chem.* **45**, 1745–1760.

Towers, G. H. N. (1964). In: Harborne, J. B. (ed.), "Biochemistry of Phenolic Compounds", pp. 249–294. Academic Press, London.

Turner, E. M. C. (1960). *Nature* **186**, 325–326.

VanEtten, H. D. (1976). *Phytochemistry* **15**, 655–659.

Walker, J. C. and Stahmann, M. A. (1955). *Ann. Rev. Plant Physiol.* **6**, 351–366.

Ward, H. M. (1905). *Ann. Bot.* **19**, 1–54.

Ward, E. W. B., Unwin, C. H. and Stoessl, A. (1975). *Phytopathology* **65**, 168–169.

Wells, H. D., Bell, D. K. and Jaworski, C. A. (1972). *Phytopathology* **62**, 442–447.

Wheeler, H. and Luke, H. H. (1963). *Ann. Rev. Microbiol.* **17**, 223–242.

SUBJECT INDEX

A

Abrin, 65
Abscisic acid, 13
3-Acetyl-6-methoxybenzaldehyde, 183
Acid phosphatases in grass roots, 16
Aflatoxin B$_1$, 67
Alarm pheromones, 161
Alcohol dehydrogenase induction, 10
Alkaloids,
    and aphid feeding, 116
    as defense agents, 172
    as feeding deterrents, 94, 122, 136
    as pigments, 37
    as toxins, 61
    distribution in plants, 3
    distribution in animals, 170
cis-7-Alkenol acetate, 157
Allelopathic effects on vegetation, 186
Allyl isothiocyanate, 114, 206
Amines and plant odours, 46
Amino acids, non-protein, 3, 61
Amino acids, protein,
    and analogues, 61
    and aphid feeding, 115
    in nectars, 53
Androstanetriol, 85
Androstenedione, 85
5-α-Androst-16-en-3-one, 163
Anosmia in humans, 131
Ant and non-ant Acacias, 74
Anthocyanidins of flowers, 34
Arbutin, 23
Aristolochic acid, 172
Association between warning coloration
    and plant toxins, 77
Atropine, 64
Aureusidin, 37
Avenacin, 200
Azadirachtin, 124
Azetidine 2-carboxylic acid, 61

B

Benzoic acid, 209
Berberine, 200
Betaine, 19
Betaxanthins, 38
α-Bisabolol, 45
Boar odour, 164
Bornyl acetate, 157
exo-Brevicomin, 99
Bufotalin, 170

C

δ-Cadinene, 50
Calotropin, 76
Calvin photosynthetic cycle, 6
Camphene, 187
Camphor, 187
Canavanine, 61
Cantharidin, 167
Capsaicin, 144
Capsidiol, 209, 228
Cardenolides,
    coevolutionary role, 75
    of milkweed, 76
    toxic effects of, 66
Carnegeine, 95
β-Carotene, 36
Carotenoids in flowers, 36
Catalpol, 116
Catechin 7-xyloside, 113
Catechol, 200
Ceratocystis toxins, 221
Characteristic odours and chemicals that
    represent them, 132
Chemical mimicry and bitterness, 105
Chlorogenic acid, 204
Cholesterol, 91
Choline, 19
Cicutoxin, 67

233

INDEX OF PLANT NAMES

238

INDEX OF ANIMAL SPECIES